'My life belongs to the whole community
and as long as I live it is my privilege
to do for it whatsoever I can.
I want to be thoroughly used up when I die,
for the harder I work, the more I live.
I rejoice in life for its own sake.
Life is no "brief candle" to me. It is
a sort of splendid torch which I have got hold of
for the moment; and I want to make it burn
as brightly as possible
before handing it on to future generations.'

BERNARD SHAW, at Brighton, 1907

September 11, 1977-February 28, 1978

Humanities Research Center   The University of Texas at Austin

SHAW: An Exhibit

A CATALOG BY DAN H. LAURENCE
FOR AN EXHIBIT SELECTED AND PREPARED WITH LOIS B. GARCIA

In memory of Lew David Feldman
who filled with treasure
the house that Harry and Warren built

Foreword

Bernard Shaw claimed to be a man of fifteen distinct reputations, and actually enumerated them for a biographer: a critic of art, a critic of music, a critic of literature, a critic of the drama, a novelist, a dramatist, an economist, a funny man, a streetcorner agitator, a Shelleyan atheist, a Fabian Socialist, a vegetarian, a humanitarian, a preacher, and a philosopher. In each of these manifestations the didact was at work, for Shaw, all his long life (1856–1950), stood firm in the belief that man, gifted by his creator with reasoning ability and with conscience, had an obligation to work for the public good and for an improved humanity. He was, in Thomas Mann's phrase, 'mankind's friend', wielding unceasingly 'the shining sword of his word and wit against the most appalling power threatening the triumph of the [human] experiment—stupidity.'

To achieve his social goals ('I am a Socialist', he proclaimed in 1907, 'because I have learnt . . . that freedom without law is impossible; and I have become a religious agitator because I have observed that men without religion have no courage'), Shaw determinedly propelled himself into the limelight by resorting to self-advertisement ('a modest man is such a nuisance'), the jingling of the bells of the jester's cap, and outrageously provocative utterances. An incorrigible and inveterate actor, he strove deliberately to be controversial and abrasive, to make his audiences 'thoroughly uncomfortable'. Conversion, he argued, is not possible without an initial aggressive act of shock: 'you cannot have an advance in morality until you shake the prevailing sense of right and wrong sufficiently to compel a readjustment.'

As a dramatist dedicated to the proposition that intellect is the greatest of the passions, Shaw directed his efforts to those playgoers who, in the words of the critic of the London *Times* after the first performance of *Man and Superman,* 'do not leave their brains along with their wraps in the cloak room.' Theater to Shaw was more than just an entertainment. He saw it as part of the common spiritual heritage of man, detecting in it a fundamental unity with Church, each offering 'communion' in its own terms to its congregation. Theater, he maintained, 'is really a weekday church': a good play 'is essentially identical with a church service as a combination of artistic ritual, profession of faith, and sermon.' Carrying this a step further, he declared that only through an identification of the artist's purpose with the purpose of the universe is the artist made great.

Despite occasional frustration and momentary self-doubt, Shaw's unshakable idealism, his ironic detachment and rationality sustained him through ninetyfour years of life, though they not infrequently reduced his opponents to mouth-frothing, gibbering loons. Essentially an optimist, motivated by the same spirit as Carlyle's 'Everlasting Yea', Shaw confronted life with insatiable curiosity: he was interested in everything, he said, because everything was interesting.

For three-quarters of a century Shaw offered audiences a unique distillation of wisdom, combining logic, wit, conscience, courage, and liveliness of intellect, on a range of subjects so wide that he must be accounted the closest equivalent to Renaissance man the modern world has yet seen.

The present exhibit, conceivably the largest single-author display ever mounted, has been designed to reveal with simple clarity and objectivity as many as possible of the myriad facets of Shaw and the diversity of his often-still-controversial interests, drawing upon representative examples of the Shaw materials in the Humanities Research Center collections: shorthand and longhand manuscripts, multiple stages of corrected typescripts, rough proofs and revised rehearsal copies of plays, directors' prompt copies, set sketches, rehearsal notes, theatre programs, photographs, presentation copies, texts of lectures, correspondence (selected from more than 4000 pieces of Shaw correspondence with performers, publishers and printers, politicians, friends, and the general public), transcriptions of shorthand diaries, working notebooks, accounts books, draft contracts, licences for performance, royalty statements, press cuttings, and a wealth of miscellanea, including his wife's household accounts and his mother's spirit drawings. And this, it must be stressed, is a mere sampling. The *undisplayed* Shaw materials, every bit as valuable and intriguing, occupy more than seven drawers of card entries in the HRC catalogs.

'A great artist', Shaw once said, 'is not a lump of genius to be gaped at, but a combination to be analyzed.' The Shaw holdings in the HRC make this accomplishment feasible.

Dan H. Laurence

Shaw had strong opinions about typographical style. As his own publisher he insisted upon a clean page, free of extraneous apostrophes and endstops, which he called 'uncouth bacilli'. He also required that extraneous vowels (like the 'u' in 'humour' and the final 'e' in 'Shakespeare') be deleted, and that words be spelled ('advertize' and 'wernt') as they are pronounced. Occasionally he clung idiosyncratically to historic spelling (notably 'shew' for 'show').

To increase the reader's consciousness of Shaw's dicta in printing, this catalog has been styled throughout to conform with Shaw's views. The sole departure is the retention of quotation marks and italics for manuscript and book titles, as their absence would, in an exhibit catalog, create bibliographical chaos. All direct quotations have, of course, been reproduced *literatim* and *seriatim*.

An asterisk preceding an entry number in the catalog indicates that the item, if a manuscript or book, is displayed in an individual case; if a photograph, poster, or art work, it is hung in the Leeds Gallery.

D.H.L.

Shaw: An Exhibit

EARLY YEARS

1 To John Araben, a Belfast scholar. Typewritten letter, 1 November 1944. Shaw responds to a request for biographical information concerning Dr Henry R. Parker, headmaster of the Wesleyan Connexional School, which Shaw had attended briefly as 'a dayboy' in 1867–68.

> It was the cheapest of the Dublin Protestant schools of any social pretensions, and could not afford to give adequate attention to the number of dayboys and boarders it took on. . . . There was really no teaching. Latin and Greek were the only subjects that were taken seriously: history, geography, arithmetic and Euclid, were in the curriculum; but education meant Caesar, Virgil, and Homer. . . . Such discipline and study as there was, were learnt and enforced at home; for we were all snobbishly respectable, and would not speak to one unfortunate outcast whose father was a pawnbroker.

2 To Noreys Connell ('Conal O'Riordan'), Irish author. Autograph postcard, 13 July 1910, and typewritten letter, 16 July 1910. Shaw discusses plays in which the XV century Irish rebel Jack Cade figures, and recalls that as a boy in Dublin he had a toytheatre play about Cade, 'for which I cut out scenes & characters. . . .'

> I also got those scenes and characters at that very shop opposite the Queen's Theatre, kept in tremendous order by a maîtresse femme whom I still remember well enough to put into a play if occasion should arise.

3 To Lucinda Elizabeth Shaw, mother of Bernard Shaw. Autograph letter, 24 February (misdated 24 October) 1875, from Dublin; bound with autograph letter, 24 February 1875, to Shaw's sister Lucinda Frances, known theatrically as Lucy Carr Shaw. Mrs Shaw, who had deserted her husband in 1873, was in London, where she had attempted to coerce Lucy into participating in an amateur operatic project. Shaw's precocious letter to his mother (one of the three earliest Shaw letters that survive) reveals a remarkable degree of selfpossession and urbanity for a nineteen-year-old.

> My respected parent
> I write to tell you that you may as well drop all your dignity with Lucy. You are basely betrayed. . . . I told her everything you said about her. . . . I told her all! All! ALL! I trust you may not catch it on her return to the maternal bosom. I trust you have not caught it already. I trust that no profane language rises involuntarily to your lips as you peruse these words. I know that you will love me as you never did before for my straightforward conduct. I feel that even now you are wishing you could kiss me. . . . I laugh as I picture the dismay, the rage, the elevation of your back, with which you will greet this. I give you warning that there is no use in trying to crush me. . . . If you are anxious to know what I said to Lucy, I have no doubt she will shew you my letters and you are quite welcome to shew her this. Meanwhile I have the honor to remain, dear mother, your affectionate & dutiful son
>
> GBShaw

4 To C. Uniacke Townshend, Shaw's Dublin employer. Autograph copy of a letter, 29 February 1876; transcribed in a small pocket notebook, dated 1875 on the upper cover, containing notes, accounts, and addresses relating to Shaw's Dublin activities in 1875–76. He had been employed in a landagents' office since his withdrawal from school in 1871, at the age of fifteen. Having decided now to follow his mother and sister to London, Shaw gave his employer a month's notice of his intention to quit the agency.

> My reason is, that I object to receive a salary for which I give no adequate value. Not having enough to do, it follows that the little I have is not well done. . . . Under these circumstances I prefer to discontinue my services. . . .

5 *General Regulations respecting Open Competitive Examinations for Situations in the Civil Service.* Dated in Shaw's autograph 6th November 1876 (which may have been the date of a scheduled examination). Shaw prepared for the examination by enrolling in a cram course conducted by E.W. John, whose prospectus (identified and dated in Shaw's hand on the reverse) is also displayed. After a short period of boredom Shaw withdrew from the course. He never took the examination.

6 Cabinet photograph of Shaw at 23, by Window & Grove, London, 4 July 1879.

(Copy letter to C.U. Townshend)   61 Harcourt St
29 Feb. 1876

Dear Sir, I beg to give you notice, that at the end of next month, I shall leave your office.

My reason is, that I object to receive a salary for which I give no adequate value. Not having enough to do, it follows that the little I do is not well done. When I ceased to act as Cashier I anticipated this, and have since become satisfied that I was right.

Under these circumstances I prefer to discontinue my services & remain very truly yrs

C. Uniacke Townshend Esq
1 Harcourt St.

4

---

7 To Arnold White, manager and secretary of the Edison Telephone Company, London. Draft letter, 5 October 1879. Introduced by a relative to White, Shaw drew up a conspectus of his employment record to date, including his work as a ghostwriting musical critic for the *Hornet*, a satiric weekly, in 1876–77.

> [A] friend of mine who was musical critic to a weekly paper, offered me the emoluments of the post if I would discharge its duties. I threw up my studies [for the civil service], and set to work to reform the musical profession. At the end of a year my friend was one of the most unpopular men in London, the paper was getting into difficulties, and complications were arising from the proprietor's doubts as to a critic who was . . . capable of being in two places at the same time.

8 Pocket sketchbook, dated 2 September 1878 on the inner cover, containing drawings by Shaw. It also contains a list of rights of way obtained for the Edison Telephone Company in 1879.

9 To the manager of the Way-Leave Department of the Edison Telephone Company (a Mr Dauglish). Draft letter, 31 December 1879. WITH: Shaw's hand-signed business card (dated on the reverse in his autograph: 'From 14th November 1879 to 5th July 1880'), and a report of way-leave consents, dated 17 February 1880. Shaw had undertaken to work on a commission basis, his job being to persuade property owners to permit the stringing of telephone lines across their rooftops. In the first six weeks he earned half a crown! His letter of resignation led to a revised financial agreement guaranteeing him a basic salary of £48 per annum. Several weeks later he was promoted to the post of department head at an increased salary plus commission. By June 1880 Shaw was chafing to return to creative writing, and withdrew from the commercial world to work on his second autobiographical novel, *The Irrational Knot*.

10 Job-hunting letters, 1880–83.

(a) To John Messent, Briton Medical Association. Autograph draft, 5 August 1880.

(b) To 'E.H.', staff member of a 'Daily Liberal Paper.' Autograph draft, 24 September 1880.

(c) To 'H.B.', staff member of a 'Liberal Paper'. Autograph draft, 24 September 1880.

(d) To C. Payne, staff member of a Brixton newspaper. Shorthand draft, 20 August 1882, with transcription.

(e) To unidentified correspondent seeking a shorthand clerk. Shorthand draft, 20 August 1882, with transcription.

(f) To 'H.C.B.', seeking a private secretary. Shorthand draft, 21 August 1883, with transcription.

Although Shaw, prodded by his family, dutifully scanned the classified columns of the newspapers and responded to a number of advertisements over the succeeding years, his efforts to find employment were only sporadic and halfhearted. It is unlikely that he anticipated a favorable response from 'H.C.B.' upon receipt of a letter informing him:

I am willing to act as Private Secretary for £105 a year, am 27, have not had a University education, have had 5 years experience of business (dating from 1871), and some literary practice. I am no mathematician nor linguist, nor have I ever acted as Secretary; but as far as I can judge from the terms in your advertisement, you might find my application worth considering if the more promising ones come to nothing.

11 *The Voice*. Draft fragment of an introduction to a work Shaw was ghostwriting for the voice teacher George John (Vandeleur) Lee, with whom the Shaws had been closely involved in Ireland. The book was not completed. The fragment consists of three pages, undated (probably 1881), in a small pocket notebook, labelled 'Waste Book', containing numerous other notes, addresses, and a drawing. Additional notes for *The Voice* survive in a pocket notebook for 1882–83 which Shaw used primarily for recording doggerel compositions. (See No. 564.)

12 Program of an amateur operatic performance 'in aid of the fund for the relief of the distressed ladies of Ireland', London, 1 July 1882. The performance was conceived and conducted in his home by Vandeleur Lee. Shaw served as stage manager (and rehearsal pianist) for Lee on this and a number of other occasions.

13 From Alice Lockett. Six letters, dated 11 September 1883 through 15 January 1884, in shorthand copies made by Shaw in a small pocket notebook, on the first page of which he has noted in shorthand: 'Returned the originals of these letters to the writer 12/4/84.' Shaw met Alice Mary Lockett, a student nurse, in the summer of 1881, and instantly fell in love. For more than three years he carried on a stormy romance with Alice. Temperamentally, however, they were incompatible, and succeeded only in bruising each other's sensitive egos. Alice and her family survive as characters in two of Shaw's novels, *Love*

Among the Artists and *An Unsocial Socialist*, which he was unable to sell to publishers at the time of their composition.

15th January 1884

Heavens! What a stupid letter! . . . I laugh at your sentimental speeches, and attribute them all to temporary insanity. . . . George Shaw, I consider you an object to be pitied —but the truth is, I might just as well speak to a stone. Nothing affects you: you are a machine, and perfectly incapable of feeling of any kind whatever. Now your book has failed—for which I am truly sorry for your sake, although it is perhaps better for other people. I suppose you mean to begin another and be another year dependent on your mother. Why on earth don't you work?

14 *Un Petit Drame*. Autograph manuscript, 7 October 1884. 3 pages on 2 leaves. Written as an exercise for Mrs Pakenham Beatty, with whom Shaw was studying French. The playlet is largely autobiographical, dealing with the Beatty family, their physician, and mutual friends, as well as Shaw himself, dubbed by the Beattys 'old man Shaw'.

15 Diaries 1885–97. In January 1885 Shaw commenced to keep a record of his activities, noting mostly in shorthand his appointments, lectures, writings, finances, sexual involvements, food habits, and other matters of interest in his daily activities, to which he added annual summations. The diaries were bequeathed to the library of the London School of Economics. In the 1950s a retired American scholar Dr Stanley Rypins, himself a Fabian, ventured to transcribe and annotate the full texts of the diaries. When, after several years, he completed his painstaking and laborious task, he was denied permission by the Shaw Estate to publish the work. The unpublished transcription of the diary texts, invaluable to scholars, was acquired by the Humanities Research Center.

29 October 1885. Went to Psychical [Research Society] in the evening. Podmore suggested I should sleep at a haunted house [in Wandsworth]. I agreed. . . . Slept there. Terrific nightmare.

Notes, 1886. This page I am writing up on the 26th December 1887, having in my inveterate laziness and procrastination put it off for a whole year. . . . *Habits*: The same as last year, except that I made a stand against late rising by using an alarm clock and actually succeeding in getting up regularly at 8 every morning until the end of the year when the clock broke and I began immediately to relapse. I got a new clock, but did not quite regain my punctuality, which by and by, made me so sleepy in the afternoon that I got into the habit of taking a nap in the [British] Museum over my books.

13 May 1886. JP [Jane Patterson, Shaw's lover] called here in the morning distracted about my letters. There was a scene and much pathetic petting and kissing, after which she went away comparatively happy.

15 May 1886. After tea went to JP's. . . . Slight scene in consequence of my refusing to budge from our new platonic relations.

16 Photograph of Jane Patterson. From a color transparency of a portrait by Robert Anning Bell. 'Jenny' Patterson, who became Shaw's lover in 1885, was a passionate 'womanly woman', some fifteen years his senior, who placidly made carpet slippers for Shaw when he pleased her and furiously shied crockery at him when he didnt. Their tempestuous relationship survived for more than seven years. When, however, her jealousy caused her to create an embarrassing scene in the presence of another of Shaw's inamoratas in 1893 (see No. 198), Shaw refused to see her again.

17 Report to the Hampstead Historic Society on readings in Marx's *Capital*. Autograph manuscript, 11 March 1885. 8 pp. Report on readings in Proudhon's *What is Property?* Autograph manuscript, 21 January 1886. 10 pp. Under the influence of the American economist Henry George, whom he heard speak in September 1882, Shaw plunged heavily into economic studies. These led him briefly into the camp of H.M. Hyndman's Social Democratic Federation, but eventually (on 5 September 1884) into membership in the recently founded Fabian Society. In 1885 he joined an economic circle and the Hampstead Historic for further study.

*18 Poster for the copyright performance of Edward Rose's play *Odd: To Say the Least of It!* Novelty Theatre, London, 6 November 1886. Shaw, costumed and bewigged, made his first appearance as an actor in this performance, in the role of Chubb Dumpleton.

19 Scenario 'For Play'. Autograph manuscript, with a few shorthand notes, 29 June 1889. 6 pp. Written in a small pocket notebook (containing brief unrelated notes on a seventh page). This was an outline for a play *The Cassone*, which was begun on 28 August 1889 and abandoned, unfinished, late in 1890. The outline and the drafted fragments were published in the Bodley Head Bernard Shaw *Collected Plays with their Prefaces*, Vol. 7 (1974).

20 Florence Farr: Portrait sketch of Shaw, in pastel chalks (ca. 1912). Miss Farr was an actress with whom Shaw became intimately related in the early 1890s. In the portrait he is depicted as she first knew him, with fair hair and red beard. She presented the portrait to her nephew before departing for Ceylon, where she died in 1917.

21 To Pakenham Beatty, a poet who had been one of Shaw's close friends and sparring partners (they were both devotees of prizefighting) since the early 1880s. Autograph lettercard, 17 September 1895. WITH: Membership certificate No. 621 of the Cyclists' Touring Club, 1896. Shaw had learned to ride a bicycle while on holiday at Beachy Head in April 1895. His first major mishap occurred on 12 September of that year when he collided on a hill in Monmouth with a cycle ridden by Bertrand Russell.

> If you hear rumors of my death, contradict them. I have had a most awful bicycle smash—the quintessence of ten railway collisions—brother of Earl Russell . . . dashed into at full speed flying down a hill—£3.10.0 damage to machine —got up within the prescribed ten seconds, but had subsequently to admit knock-out—Russell bereft of his knickerbockers but otherwise unhurt. . . .

22 To Robert Williamson, press officer of the annual bicycle show, London. Autograph letter, 3 October 1948, on reverse of Williamson's typewritten letter of 27 September. Shaw responds to a request for his views on cycling.

> To learn biking try to stand a penny on its edge. Impossible when the penny is stationary, easy when it is rolling. Once convinced of this, rush the machine and jump on. Jump off or fall off when it stops. Keep on at this until you *suddenly* find that you can balance. Do not expect to improve with practice. You wont. The change from hopeless failure to complete success is instan[tan]eous and miraculous.

23 Accounts Books 1898–1928 (2 volumes) and tax account records 1885–1900. Shaw meticulously recorded his professional income from all sources, and chronicled at the back of the first volume his gross income for the years 1885–1917. The entries over the years are in a number of hands, including those of Shaw, Charlotte Shaw, and several secretaries: Georgina Gillmore, Ann M. Elder, Mabel McConnell, Blanche Patch, and Beatrice Caldwell.

EARLY WORK

24 *A Practical System of Moral Education for Females*. Autograph manuscript, with revisions, January–February 1878. 30 pp., with subject index by Shaw on reverse of title leaf. Published posthumously as *My Dear Dorothea* (1956), illustrated by Clare Winsten, with a note by Stephen Winsten. The work was modelled after Lady Chesterfield's letters to her little daughter, 'Being a code of manners and morals for the nursery', which Shaw had read in 1877.

25 *Christian Names*. An essay, described by Shaw as 'serio-comic', published in *One and All*, 11 October 1879. Shaw received a payment of fifteen shillings for the unsigned piece.

26 *Exhausted Arts*. Autograph manuscript, 13 June 1880. 9 pp., with extensive revisions added in 1881–82. A shorthand note by Shaw on the reverse of the last leaf indicates that the essay was written 'in some haste' while working for the Edison Telephone Company. In 1882 he sent it to the editor of the *Pall Mall Gazette*, from whom he was seeking journalistic employment, and who had asked for a short middle article. 'He immediately washed his hands of me.' Unpublished.

27 *Open Air Meetings*. Autograph manuscript, undated (ca. 1884). 10 pp. Unpublished.

> Do you like to take your lectures lying down? Here you may gratify your fancy. The green sward is the natural couch of man. . . . There is room for you in this circle of listeners, flat on their backs, with their feet converging towards one of Mr. Henry George's disciples, who is content if his most stirring appeals to them to 'nationalize' the land succeed in eliciting a lazy ''Ear, 'ear, guv'nor' from some supine proletaire.

28 *Immaturity* (1879). Published in 1930. Second page proofs, datestamped 31 October 1928, with proofs of preface, datestamped 8 February 1929. Corrected and revised.

29 *Immaturity*. Typewritten manuscript, with minor revision. 1 p. Final leaf of preface, drafted at Ayot St Lawrence, Summer 1921. Autograph note at foot: 'This is the last page of the preface to Immaturity. The rest is torn up. Kept to fix the date. Not printed until 1928 for publication in 1929' [*sic*].

30 *The Irrational Knot* (1880). Serialized in *Our Corner*, April 1885 to February 1887. The parts are bound in one volume with those of *Love Among the Artists* from the same journal. Shaw's own copy, bound for him in 1899 by Zaehnsdorf in brown full morocco with gilt dentelles and marbled endpapers. Four of Shaw's five novels made their first appearances in the Socialist journals *To-day* and *Our Corner* between 1884 and 1888. The last novel, *An Unsocial Socialist*, appeared earliest, in March 1884.

31 *Love Among the Artists* (1881). Autograph manuscript fragment of Book II, Chapter 2. 2 pp. Most of this manuscript was inadvertently disposed of to the dustman when Shaw's mother moved from Fitzroy Square in 1907. Only 62 pages are known to have survived; most of these are in the Burgunder Collection at Cornell University and the Berg Collection of the New York Public Library.

32 *Cashel Byron's Profession* (1882). Published as a book in 1886. This was Shaw's first work to attain book publication.

33 *An Unsocial Socialist* (1883). Published as a book in 1887. The earliest issue contains an error on the title page, identifying Shaw as 'Author of "The Confessions of Byron Cashel's Profession".' This was later corrected by insertion of a cancel title. Shaw, in the displayed copy, has underlined the error and written: 'This ridiculous blunder is supposed to confer special desirability on the book. To me it is an excellent reason for pitching it into the fire.' The volume contains an inscription by its original owner, John Ward, dated March 1890: 'I think this is the most comical novel I have ever read. It is original "instructive" and interesting, in truth a deep satir [*sic*] upon modern society.'

34 Drafts of letters to publishers. From 1879 to 1884 Shaw stolidly posted off copies of the manuscripts of his novels, as they reached completion, to all the principal British publishers of fiction, and an occasional American one with London offices, with complete lack of success.

(a) To W. Blackwood & Sons, 22 September 1880, concerning *Immaturity*.

(b) To Chatto & Windus, 26 June 1881, concerning *The Irrational Knot*.

(c) To W. Blackwood & Sons, 20 June 1883, concerning *Love Among the Artists*; shorthand, with transcription.

(d) To R. Bentley & Son, 29 May 1883, concerning *Cashel Byron's Profession*; shorthand, with transcription. On the same leaf with this are shorthand drafts of letters to Bentley and to Joshua Hatton, editor of *Colburn's New Monthly Magazine*, both dated 15 April 1883.

35 From George Radford, a solicitor, to his brother Ernest, a poet, 9 August 1884, concerning payment to Shaw of £4.14.6 (five guineas, less commission) for a screed attacking patent medicines. It was Shaw's largest remuneration in ten years of writing.

36 *Index and Glossary to Thomas Lodge's Works.* Glasgow: Hunterian Club, 1888. Shaw accepted an invitation in January 1884 to provide an index and glossary to a new edition of Lodge's works, for a fee of five guineas. It proved to be a gruelling project, with each of the 19 separate parts of the edition independently paginated. Shaw slaved industriously for several months, but his interest eventually palled. As the work interfered with his numerous Socialist commitments he tended increasingly to procrastinate. In July 1885, when there still remained about 200 words to gloss, he managed to transfer the illpaid assignment to other hands, receiving payment proportionately for the work he had completed. His name, which had appeared on the proof sheets, was removed from the title page, however, and his scholarship went uncredited.

37 Prospectus of a Fabian Society course of seven lectures on 'Socialism in Contemporary Life', the last of which is a lecture by Shaw on Ibsen on 18 July 1890. On the reverse is a typewritten letter of 16 April 1890 from Shaw to the French Socialist-journalist Jules Magny. WITH: *The Quintessence of Ibsenism* (1891), which grew out of the lecture. It was the first book on Ibsen written in the English language.

38 Insert leaf, in Shaw's autograph, for the chapter 'The Technical Novelty of Ibsen's Plays', in the 1913 edition of *The Quintessence of Ibsenism*, 'Now completed to the Death of Ibsen.'

> When England wept over the deaths of little Nell and Paul Dombey, the strong soul of Ruskin was moved to scorn: to novelists who were at a loss to make their books sell he offered the formula: when in doubt, kill a child. But Ibsen did not kill little Eyolf to manufacture pathos. The surest way to achieve a thoroughly bad performance of Little Eyolf is to conceive it as a sentimental tale of a drowned darling.

39 *Widowers' Houses* (1893). No. 1 in the Independent Theatre Series of Plays, edited by J.T. Grein. This was Shaw's first published play. A revised version was subsequently included in *Plays Pleasant and Unpleasant* (1898).

40 Draft agreement with the publisher Grant Richards for the publication of *Plays Pleasant and Unpleasant*. Typewritten manuscript, heavily revised, with one page in Shaw's autograph, dated 20 May 1897. 4 pp. An autograph note by Shaw, on a small card attached to the agreement, explains its history.

41 Discarded scraps from the prefaces to *Plays Pleasant and Unpleasant*. 14 pp. The ever-resourceful writer subsequently incorporated one of the fragments into his 13 November 1897 *Saturday Review* criticism of J.M. Barrie's play *The Little Minister*.

42 *Plays Pleasant and Unpleasant* (1898), in two volumes. Vol. 1 contains a presentation inscription 'From the Author to Florence Blanche Louka Farr Easter 1898'. Miss Farr had created the rôles of Blanche in *Widowers' Houses* and Louka in *Arms and the Man*. WITH: Advertising flyer, drafted by Shaw for the publisher.

43 *The Perfect Wagnerite* (1898). First edition, with a presentation inscription to Dickens's daughter Kate Perugini, dated Xmas 1898 on the halftitle.

> to Mrs Kate
> Who has had to wait
> But who is not
> At all forgot
> this copy of his book is presented with fi-
> Delity by
> her humble servant
> G.B.S.

43

44 Record of travel and living expenses for a journey to Bayreuth, July–August 1889, with a sketch of the Bayreuth Festival stage. In a small pocket notebook, which also contains notes on points raised during discussions following a considerable number of Shaw's lectures, and jottings on Edward German's incidental music for Richard Mansfield's production of Shakespear's *Richard III*, used in a music review in the *Star*.

45   To Henry Arthur Jones, one of Britain's two most popular contemporary playwrights (the other being Arthur W. Pinero). Autograph letter, 8 January 1899. Shaw discusses *The Perfect Wagnerite*.

> It is all very well to swim about in Wagner, without bothering as to his meaning; but the best established truth in the world is that no man produces a work of art of the very first order except under the pressure of strong conviction & definite meaning as to the constitution of the world.

The HRC possesses 36 pieces of Shaw correspondence (1894–1926) to Jones.

46   Programs of Bayreuth Festival performances of Wagner, 1908, with Shaw's autograph comments, sent to the theatre manager J.E. Vedrenne, on *Siegfried* (27 July), *Lohengrin* (31 July), and *Parsifal* (1 August). Not displayed: *Das Rheingold* (25 July).

JOURNALISM

47   To T.P. O'Connor, editor and publisher of the *Star*. Autograph letter, 9 February 1888. Shaw had been hired by O'Connor's deputy, H.W. Massingham, as a political writer for the just-founded newspaper, but his views clashed violently with those of O'Connor. After three weeks' employment Shaw submitted his resignation.

> Dear Chief
>   This is my resignation. I am not worth my salt to the Star; and you will be more at your ease without having constantly to suppress my articles . . . though what is to become of you . . . when you have no one to guide you through the mists of sentimental Utopianism is more than I can foresee. The special Providence that protects children be your safeguard!

48   To T.P. O'Connor. Autograph letter, 5 February 1890. Shaw continued, after his resignation, to contribute to the *Star* on a freelance basis. In February 1889 he was appointed musical critic, at which time he created his now famous alter ego 'Corno di Bassetto.' One year later he threatened to retire from critical journalism when O'Connor declined to increase his salary. He did not, however, withdraw until May 1890, by which time he had concluded arrangements to transfer his services to the *World*.

> Reviewing is hell. . . . Nothing so fatal to an artist as a regular income.

49   From W.E. Henley, poet and editor of the *Scots Observer*. Autograph letter, 4 July 1890. A response to Shaw's decision not to contribute any further musical articles after Henley, an anti-Wagnerite, had tampered with his text of a Wagnerian article.

> I really don't see why because I don't worship Richard the Bleater & you do, you should not write me an Arthur Sullivan & a Rubinstein. . . . I should be grateful—yea, heartily grateful—to you if you'd take back your no, & fall in. If you will, perhaps I'll ask you for some politics.

50   Musical criticisms in the *World*, signed 'G.B.S.', 1 November 1893 to 8 August 1894. Mounted and bound. Opened to display Shaw's column for 20 December 1893, commencing: 'Like all intelligent people, I greatly dislike Christmas.'

51   *The Christian Wagnerite*. Galley of a review of David Irvine's *'Parsifal' and Wagner's Christianity*, published in the *Morning Leader*, 27 May 1899, signed 'Corno di Bassetto'.

52   [Visit to the Holbein Madonna at Darmstadt.] Draft of a humorous travel essay written in the character of 'Corno di Bassetto', July 1894 (misdated 1889 by Shaw, on inner front cover, in his later years). Unpublished. 9 pp., in a small pocket notebook, with brief notes on Bayreuth in German at the front and back.

> It is just the sort of afternoon to spend in a second class foreign town—too sultry to make even the lightest macintosh bearable, and raining like mad every ten minutes. . . . Baedeker suggested going to the top of a facsimile of the Duke of York's column, for the sake of the view. I should have expected more sense from Baedeker on a wet day.

53   Theatre criticisms in the *Saturday Review*, signed 'G.B.S.', 26 January 1895 to 23 April 1898. Mounted and bound. Opened to display a 23 February 1895 review of Oscar Wilde's *The Importance of Being Earnest*.

> I cannot say that I greatly cared for 'The Importance of Being Earnest.' It amused me, of course; but unless comedy touches me as well as amuses me, it leaves me with a sense of having wasted my evening. I go to the theatre to be moved to laughter, not to be tickled or bustled into it. . . .

54 To Jim Connell, political journalist and Socialist. Autograph letter, 22 May 1896. Shaw, only two years away from his retirement as an active journalist, expresses his views on journalism.

> We are all—our generation, I mean—at the age at which every journalist who has not become an editor or become highly skilled in some very special line of journalistic work, realises that the sooner he gets out of it the better for himself.

55 Institute of Journalists nomination form, filled out by Shaw, signed by H.W. Massingham, then assistant editor of the *Daily Chronicle*. 16 March 1894. Shaw retained his membership in the Institute until his death 56 years later.

CHARLOTTE SHAW

Charlotte Frances Payne-Townshend, an attractive, intelligent, serious-minded Irish 'millionairess', met Shaw at the home of Beatrice and Sidney Webb on 29 January 1896. He was instantly attracted to the lady with the light green eyes; by August of that year he had informed the actress Ellen Terry 'I am going to refresh my heart by falling in love with her . . . but, mind, only with her, not with the million. . . .' Nothing decisive occurred, however, until Shaw was incapacitated by a leg injury in the spring of 1898, when, he told a friend, 'I proposed to make her my widow.' They were married in a London registry office on 1 June 1898, when Shaw was approaching his fortysecond birthday and Charlotte was just a year younger.

56 Three postcards from Shaw concerning his honeymoon. To Grant Richards, his publisher, 19 June 1898. To Mrs Henry Arthur Jones, wife of the playwright, 20 June 1898. To Sally Fairchild, American friend of Ellen Terry, 24 June 1898:

> Oh, yes, I dare say! Plenty of good luck! On the 9th May I underwent an operation on my left foot. On the 1st June the lady who was nursing me carried me into a registrar's office & married me. On Friday last week I fell downstairs and broke my left arm. What do you think of that for a career?

57 Large silver pocket watch, with winder key. This was Charlotte's wedding gift to Shaw. Engraved on the reverse is the inscription: 'G.B.S. 1898'.

58 *Meditations.* Two volumes containing autograph and typewritten transcriptions of materials on the Yoga Sutras, the Bhagavad Gita, Pythagorean philosophy, etc. The first volume is bound in pale tan linen, labelled *Meditations* on the upper cover and spine. The second is bound in brown leather, decorated with black rules; unlabelled. Charlotte, who had been intrigued by Eastern philosophy since she visited India in 1892–93, made a close study of various religious and philosophical disciplines, recording her thoughts and copying passages from her readings into a series of bound quarto books which she kept near her bedside and which she carried with her on her travels. She proselytized by making gifts of pocket-sized copies of philosophical works to people she met and liked. In her late years she became an ardent disciple of the Russian philosopher P.D. Ouspensky, whose work is quoted in the *Meditations* volumes.

59 T. Spicer-Simpson: Medallion of Charlotte Shaw, in bronze. Charlotte and GBS each commissioned a medallion from the sculptor in 1921. It was quite a coup for Spicer-Simpson to have obtained Charlotte's consent to pose, for she had a lifelong aversion to the making and the diffusion of portraits of herself. It was, she admitted, a superstition bordering on mania.

59

60 List of suggestions for the casting of *Captain Brassbound's Conversion*. Autograph manuscript, in Charlotte Shaw's hand, labelled 'copy' and dated 11 August 1905. Charlotte performed secretarial duties for Shaw whenever a professional secretary was inaccessible. On this occasion they were vacationing in Derry, during Shaw's first visit to Ireland since his departure in 1876 at the age of twenty.

61 Works edited by Charlotte Shaw:

(a) *Rent and Value*. Fabian Tract No. 142 (1909), adapted from Shaw's 'The Economic Basis of Socialism' (*Fabian Essays in Socialism*, 1889).

(b) *The National Insurance Bill: A Criticism* (Fabian Women's Group, 1911), with a preface by Mrs Bernard Shaw.

(c) *The Wisdom of Bernard Shaw* (New York, 1913), chosen by Charlotte F. Shaw. A British edition (1912) was titled *Selected Passages from the Works of Bernard Shaw*.

62 'Notes on the Preface'. Autograph note from Shaw to Charlotte, undated (1914), 1 p. Charlotte had asked Shaw to read her preface to the first separate edition of Brieux's *Damaged Goods*. Under the heading 'General Remarks' he informs her: 'The preface is quite brilliant GBS.' With: Eugène Brieux, *Damaged Goods* (London, 1914), with a foreword by Mrs Bernard Shaw.

63 Charlotte Shaw to T.E. Lawrence ('Lawrence of Arabia'). Autograph correspondence card, 'Monday morning' (no date, ca. October 1924). The Shaws had virtually adopted Lawrence, who soon took their name for his own. Both Charlotte and GBS read the 'Oxford' proofs of his *Seven Pillars of Wisdom* and gave him valuable critical advice.

> GBS has taken to the proofs like a duck to water & is working at them as if they were his own! . . . We both feel the first chapter is not quite right.

64 T.E. Lawrence, *Seven Pillars of Wisdom*. Inscribed in Shaw's hand: 'Proof of the first 7 chapters of The Seven Pillars (final subscription edition) sent to Mrs Bernard Shaw by Lawrence. . . .'

65 Charlotte Shaw to William Maxwell, Shaw's printer, of the Edinburgh firm of R. & R. Clark, Ltd. Autograph letters of 25 May and 13 July 1931. Autograph postcard of 24 November 1934. For several years Charlotte undertook much of the editing and proofing of the enormous edition of Shaw's collected works, in both the 'limited' and 'standard' editions. She also served as liaison between Ayot and Edinburgh, keeping close tabs on the manuscripts and proofs, the correspondence, the indexing, and the invoices.

66 Photograph (by Cay's Photo Service Agency) of Shaw, Commander C.K. Newton (a representative of the South African visitors' bureau), and Charlotte (invariably unobtrusive in the background) at Cape Town dock, 11 January 1932.

67 To Blanche Patch. Autograph letter, 14 February 1932. Shaw informs her, from Knysna, Cape Province, that he has had 'a mishap' while driving a rented automobile, in which Charlotte was 'badly knocked about'. Although he optimistically assumed they would be able to sail for England by the following week, Charlotte was so severely sprained and bruised that they were obliged to remain in seclusion for more than a month. During this time Shaw occupied himself by writing *The Adventures of the Black Girl in Her Search for God*.

The HRC possesses 175 pieces of Shaw's correspondence (1920–50) to Blanche Patch.

68 To Harley Granville Barker, actor, director, playwright, and Shakespearean scholar. Autograph postcard, 14 September 1943. Although he and Charlotte had not seen or communicated with Barker for more than twentyfive years, Shaw was moved to inform him personally of Charlotte's death, remembering the deep affection they had once shared.

> Charlotte died last Sunday, the 12th September, at half past two in the morning. She had not forgotten you. . . . It was a blessedly happy ending; but you could not have believed that I should be so deeply moved. You will not, I know, mind my writing this to you. She was 86. I am 87. G.B.S.

The HRC possesses over 200 pieces of Shaw correspondence (1900–43) to Barker and his first wife, Lillah McCarthy.

69 To William Maxwell. Autograph postcards, 22 and 25 November 1943. Shaw requests that he print a postcard bearing Charlotte's likeness, from a photograph taken by Shaw, with an inscription beneath it to read IN MEMORY OF | MRS BERNARD SHAW | 1857–1943   A few days later he has second thoughts about the inscription.

> Somehow I dont feel happy about the words 'In memory of' on that Xmas card. It makes a tombstone of it, and wont look so well as the name with the two dates under it (they tell the whole story) and nothing else.

70 Photograph of Charlotte Shaw taken by her husband, ca. 1935. It was this portrait which Shaw sent to William Maxwell for reproduction.

71 Notes by Charlotte Shaw for her last will and testament; undated. Autograph manuscript, 3 pages on 2 leaves. At her death she left the income from her £150,000 estate as a life interest to Shaw. After his demise the bulk of the Estate—some £94,000—was to be placed in Irish trusts administered by the National City Bank of Dublin, the money to be used 'in its uncontrolled discretion': (a) To make grants to foundations or institutions having as their object the bringing of masterpieces of fine art within the reach of the Irish people; (b) To teach self-control, elocution, oratory and deportment, the arts of personal contact and social intercourse, and the other arts of public, private, professional and business life to Irish men and women; and (c) To establish a chair or readership at an Irish university to give instruction in those subjects.

72 From E.W. Wykes, a solicitor of Lawrence, Graham & Co., to Shaw. Typewritten letter, 12 September 1946. Shaw had considered relinquishing the income from Charlotte's estate, releasing it immediately to the Irish Trusts. Wykes informs him that, in the event he decides to do so, the matter would first have to be brought before the courts to determine whether or not Charlotte's legacies were valid charitable bequests. Although the action would be instituted by the Irish bank to which the funds would be entrusted, Shaw would have to be a party to the action. Rather than face the ordeal and publicity that might ensue, Shaw opted to retain the income until his death. The test action was not taken until December 1951, a year after Shaw's death, at which time Charlotte's bequests were upheld.

73 Fragment of an invoice for storage, at Golders Green Crematorium, of the urn containing Charlotte's ashes, indicating payment through 21 July 1946. In accordance with Shaw's testamentary instructions, his own body was cremated after his death on 2 November 1950 and the ashes 'inseparably mixed' with Charlotte's. The Public Trustee, as Shaw's executor, arranged then for the ashes to be scattered without ceremony in the garden at Ayot.

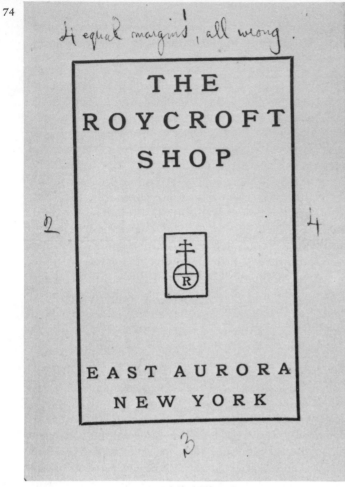

4 equal margins, all wrong.

THE
ROYCROFT
SHOP

⊕

EAST AURORA
NEW YORK

B O O K S

AND BOOKS, those miraculous memories of high thoughts and golden moods, those magical shells tremulous with the secrets of the ocean of life, those love-letters that pass from hand to hand of a thousand lovers that never meet, those honeycombs of dreams, those orchards of knowledge, those still-beating hearts of the noble dead, those mysterious signals that beckon along the darksome pathways of the past, voices through which the myriad lispings of the earth find perfect speech, oracles through which its mysteries call like voices in moonlit woods, prisms of beauty, urns stored with all the sweets of all the summers of time, immortal nightingales that sing for ever to the rose of life: Books, Bibles—ah me! what have ye become today!

RICHARD LE GALLIENNE

4 different types and a rule. Type spaced so as to make a perfect delta of rivers.

PUBLISHING

74 *On Going to Church* (1896). An unauthorized edition by the Roycroft Press, East Aurora, N.Y. WITH: A leaflet advertisement for the Roycroft Press, on which Shaw has penned some disdainful comments, after tracing more than a dozen 'rivers' of white spacing in a specimen passage: 'Type spaced so as to make a perfect delta of rivers.' Shaw loathed these grotesque parodies of William Morris's Kelmscott Press productions, and took every opportunity to castigate the 'Roycroft idiots' for their 'dirty felt end papers, sham Kelmscott capitals, [and] leaf ornaments in quad sauce. . . .'

*75 *Tutte le Opere di Dante Alighieri.* Ashendene Press, 1909. One of 105 copies printed on paper; bound in oak boards with brown morocco back and clasps. Although Shaw had no collector's instinct, he admired finely printed press books and subscribed for a number of them. In 1949 he gathered together those which remained in his possession, provided biographical or critical inscriptions on their flyleaves, and consigned them to Sotheby's for auction. This volume was purchased for £110 by the Antarctic explorer Apsley Cherry-Garrard, one of Shaw's neighbors at Ayot.

> Dante's verbal music fascinates me like that of Shakespear. I am under no illusion as to Italian being a beautiful language . . . but as Dante wrote it it sings irresistibly even when what it says is no longer credible.

76 *Plays Pleasant and Unpleasant.* Heavily revised proofs of the preface to *Plays Unpleasant*, date-stamped 1 February 1898. 14 pp. WITH: Mock statement of account, in Shaw's autograph, sent to Grant Richards upon receipt of a publisher's statement deducting printers' charges from the author's royalties for excessive proof corrections; dated 30 September 1898.

77 To Grant Richards. Autograph letter, 5 December 1898. Shaw has just received an advance copy of *The Perfect Wagnerite*. (The copy on display is inscribed by Shaw's sister Lucy to her friend Janey Drysdale.)

> The binding exhibits a hellish misconception of my suggestion. The holland should come right up to the back, leaving no margin of blue; and the blue should not be glistening ribbed sticky silk, but a kindred material to the holland, and really blue in color, which this adulterated horror is not. The paper is miserable, and the folding & binding of the most commercially unconscientious kind. . . . Why, oh why, didnt you send me a case before deciding?

The HRC possesses 134 pieces of Shaw correspondence (1893–1947) to Richards.

78 From Grant Richards. Typewritten letter, 24 May 1899, responding to Shaw's renewed criticism of Richards's publishing methods and his failure to advertize sufficiently.

> If I followed my first inclination I should say to you: 'Manufacture the books yourself: get Longmans to sell them, and be damned to you! . . . It is my business to make my books look well, and occasionally I satisfy myself with them, so that your superintendence of the production was entirely unnecessary. . . . As I labour under the necessity of attempting to make each book pay for itself I did not go on spending money on advertising 'The Perfect Wagnerite' when it was perfectly obvious that money so spent would not return in a proportionate increase in circulation. . . . I have noticed that authors with even more sense than you have, when the public show this indifference, visit it on the head of their publisher.

79 To Grant Richards. Typewritten letter, 21 June 1903, and autograph letter, 30 March 1904. Shaw decided, in face of the meagre sale of his books by Richards, that he must abandon the conventional royalty system and control his own publishing destiny by assuming the rôle of publisher. Accordingly, he contracted with Constable & Co. to serve as his agent, selling his new play *Man and Superman* on a commission basis. The agreement lasted for 47 years, until Shaw's death. 'I now look forward', he wrote to Richards, 'to a frantic competitive struggle between the two firms as to which can sell most copies.' The competition did not last for long, as Richards's firm went into bankruptcy 18 months later. WITH: *Man and Superman* (London, 1903), containing a presentation inscription on the half title:

> read, for the first time in its life,
> to H.G. Wells and Jane, his wife,
> by G. Bernard Shaw.

80 *Man and Superman*: Statement of American sales through 31 December 1908 by the publishing firm of Brentano in New York. Brentano had profitably marketed unauthorized editions of Shaw's novels at the turn of the century. When his American publisher, Herbert S. Stone of Chicago, went bankrupt, Shaw followed comic opera tradition by legitimatizing the pirates, inviting them to be his authorized American publisher.

81 To Holbrook Jackson, editor and publisher. Autograph letter, 12 November 1907. Shaw had written a polemic attacking Max Nordau's book *Degeneration* in 1895; it appeared as 'A Degenerate's View of Nordau' in *Liberty* (Boston). When his German translator encouraged him to revise it for publication in the German press in 1907, Shaw arranged for the New Age Press, of which Jackson was a director, to issue a small edition of the essay, which he proposed to call *The Sanity of Art: an Exposure of Some Current Nonsense about Artists Being Degenerates*. The final 's' vanished by the time the book was published.

The HRC possesses 23 pieces of Shaw correspondence (1907–25) to Jackson.

82 [Business Maxims for Playwrights.] Autograph manuscript, in pencil; undated. 4 pp. The Society of Authors was one of Shaw's most dedicated interests. He was elected to its Council of Management in February 1905 and joined its Dramatic Sub-Committee early in 1906, serving on both until late in 1915, when his wartime unpopularity after the publication of *Common Sense About the War* led him to withdraw for the sake of amity within the Society. He continued to serve without formality until his death. WITH: Autograph correspondence card to G. Herbert Thring, Secretary of the Society, 18 August 1914, enclosing a four-page leaflet *The War Emergency . . . Memorandum of Suggestions* issued by the Fabian Society to its local committees to encourage hard-headed, realistic economics and protection against the loss of prewar Trade Union gains.

> I wish we could put something in The Author on the lines of the DONTS in the enclosed document, p 3. Otherwise our people & their wives, being romantic, will plunge into all sorts of foolery under the impression that they are being patriotic.

83 To Arthur W. Pinero. Autograph letter, 24 November 1908. Shaw, as usual, is intriguing to strengthen the working quality of a committee by eliminating its drones, who in this instance include W. Somerset Maugham, William Archer, and Edith Nesbit Bland.

> I should put down Mrs Bland . . . but we should have an agitation for Votes for Women unless there were at least one petticoat on the committee, and rightly so; for you never get to the lowest depths of literary sweating & theatrical blackmailing unless you have a woman to help.

The HRC possesses 38 pieces of Shaw correspondence (1906–30) to Pinero.

84 To William Maxwell and R. & R. Clark, Ltd. Autograph compliments card, 19 August 1933; five autograph postcards, 10 February 1929, 13 November 1930, 9 June 1934, 8 May 1940, and 10 October 1948; four specimen titles for *Saint Joan* and *The Apple Cart* in the collected edition (1930), with Shaw's comments written on three of them. Shaw's dealings with his printers necessitated a steady stream of correspondence as he painstakingly attended to all the details of publishing, including the study of specimen typeset (he was reluctantly convinced by Maxwell in 1930 to switch from Caslon handset to Fournier linotype after weighing a considerable number of alternatives); corrections of author's errors and typos; and a flow of proofs as his manuscripts descended on the Edinburgh firm section by section, fresh from his pen.

> A schoolboy writes to me pointing out a hideous mistake in the Too True volume on p. 155 in the cross head. Seventh commandment (adultery) should be sixth commandment (kill). What is Edinburgh coming to when they dont know even the numbers of the commandments? Mend the plate instantly, and blush.

> The I.W.G. [*Intelligent Woman's Guide to Socialism*] paper is what I should like: the old edition of the plays is too thick and woolly. Is there rag enough in it to make it reasonably permanent?

> Nobody buys the Fourniers: I live on films now.

The HRC possesses 65 pieces of Shaw correspondence (1912–50) to Maxwell and 207 pieces (1915–49) to R. & R. Clark, Ltd.

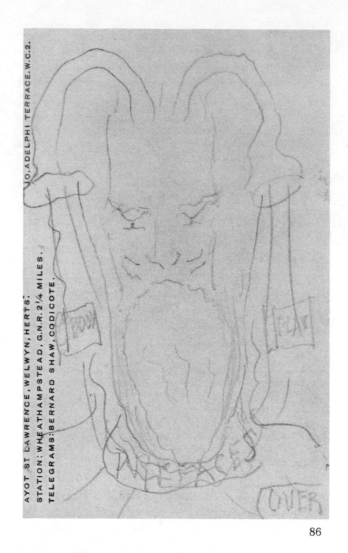

86

85 To William Maxwell. Autograph note, 4 March 1937, accompanying a specimen title page for the Limited Editions Club edition of Dickens's *Great Expectations*, designed by Maxwell and illustrated by Gordon Ross, with an introduction by Shaw. 'The title page of this is impossible', Shaw informed Maxwell after receiving the proofs, arguing on the proof of the title: 'The boy in the drawing is a David Copperfield boy, not a blacksmith's apprentice.' WITH: Drawing by Shaw, dated 3 March 1937 and captioned: 'This is the young blacksmith wishing he were not a common boy and fit to marry Estella. Excuse his muscles.' Maxwell added a memorandum at the foot of the title: 'This page arose out of Shaw's idea that [John] Farleigh should do the title page. We got G.B.S. to abandon the notion.'

84

86 To John Farleigh. Typewritten letter, 6 December 1933. Shaw encourages Farleigh to design a title page for an omnibus volume of his collected prefaces: 'the pictorial, monumental masonic, cornucopian style with muses and torches and emblems round a fearfully impressive portrait is what occurred to me.' He enclosed a correspondence card on which he had drawn in pencil two suggested designs. One of these sketches is a self-portrait, with books pouring out of downturned horns growing from Shaw's head like cornucopias, his mouth yawning cavernously wide, and a collar round his neck lettered PREFACES. WITH: Farleigh's preliminary sketch and his final drawing for the wood-engraved title design.

87 To Dodd, Mead & Co., Shaw's American publishers from 1932 until the present day. Typewritten manuscript, consisting of an unsigned draft of a letter (identified in Blanche Patch's hand), undated (ca. 1950). Edward Dodd had been bedevilling Shaw for some years to publish a collection of his private correspondence. 'Put it out of your head', Shaw wrote to him in 1949. 'There are billions of them, and I am adding to them every day.' When Dodd pressed him again the following year, Shaw replied testily:

> Dear Dodds, Mead, Uncle Tom Cobbley and all,
>
> Since all I can say fails to convince you that a selected collection of my letters will be the work of a lifetime and is now commercially impossible, let me now say finally, flatly, positively, pigheadedly, irrevocably, and inexorably that I will not let you attempt it, and that letters from you containing any mention of it will be hurled in the basket with the most profane oaths I can command.
>
> If you come in the fall to continue the discussion I will set all the dogs in Ayot Saint Lawrence on you. You will be welcome only with the subject barred.

PHOTOGRAPHY

Although Shaw did not become a practising photographer until 1898, he was one of the first critics in England to recognize the importance of photography as an art form. Photography, says Shaw's protagonist Sidney Trefusis in Chapter XII of *An Unsocial Socialist*, written in 1883, is 'the only art that interests me. . . .' And he lectures to his guests on the superiority of the photograph to most contemporary art. Once photography is 'perfected in its recently discovered power of reproducing colour as well as form', it will do away with nine-tenths of 'painting as we understand it at present . . . the remaining tenth only holding its own against [photographs] by dint of extraordinary excellence!'

88 Written interview: replies to questions by Helmut Gernsheim on 12 small slips, 19 September 1949.

> I always wanted to draw and paint. I had no literary ambition: I aspired to be a Michael Angelo, not a Shakespear. But I could not draw well enough to satisfy myself; and the instruction I could get was worse than useless. So when dry plates and push buttons came into the market I bought a box camera and began pushing the button. This was in 1898.

89 Kodak camera of the type used by Shaw between 1898 and 1905. From the Mark Muller Collection.

90 Selfportrait, with Charlotte Shaw, photographed through a mirror with a Kodak box camera, ca. 1899. Reproduction.

91 Photographs by Shaw of Beatrice Webb (ca. 1900) and Harley Granville Barker (ca. 1904, in The Old House, Harmer Green). Reproductions.

92 Catalog, 1902, of the tenth annual exhibition of the Photographic Salon. Shaw's notes on the upper cover (and within the catalog), for his review-articles in the 9 and 16 October issues of the *Amateur Photographer*, were written in the Henry Sweet system of shorthand which he was studying at the moment and which he very briefly substituted for his accustomed Pitman system.

93 To Frederick H. Evans, photographer and former bookseller. Autograph postcard, 28 November 1902. Shaw discusses his complex methods of developing film.

> I am a real scientific timing developist. . . . However, I confess that I generally develop the whole roll without separating the exposures, & put up with the resultant variations for the sake of the simplicity of the operation.

The HRC possesses 33 pieces of Shaw correspondence (1895–1922) to Evans.

94 Catalog, 1906, of an exhibition of the work of Alvin Langdon Coburn, young American photographer, sponsored by the Royal Photographic Society, with a preface by Shaw.

95 To Nora Charrington Martin, teenage daughter of the actress Janet Achurch. Autograph letter, 21 September 1907.

> I grieve to say that all our best photographs—12 of them—were blanks, as I forgot to draw the slide before we exposed them.

96 *Colour Photography and Other Recent Developments of the Camera. The Studio*: Special Summer Number, 1908. Plate No. 93, 'A Landscape', reproduced from Shaw's autochrome (a Lumière transparent color 'positive'), shares company with work by such photographic giants as Coburn, Alfred Stieglitz, Robert Demachy, Baron De Meyer, and Gertrude Käsebier. 'The reader', says Dixon Scott in his introduction, 'is looking at . . . the grey church tower [of Ayot's XIV century church ruins] rising up among the autumn leafage, the slant of cloudless sky ascending sharply behind; and he finds that his sensation is almost precisely that which he gets when he looks at a piece of nature through the wrong end of a telescope —the effect of a sharpened and acidulated nature, a nature curiously tense and glittering, almost metallic.'

97 Photographs by Shaw of Ayot St Lawrence: (1) Shaw's Corner, viewed from the south side; (2) The Dell at Shaw's Corner; (3) XIV century church ruins, whose history Shaw has recorded on the reverse in a pencilled note.

98 Photograph (by Alfred Eisenstaedt) of Shaw posed with Leica camera on his Whitehall Court terrace, London, in 1932. At the end of the second world war Shaw acquired a Minipax camera, which served him until his death.

FORGERIES

A number of forged Shaw letters and manuscripts were passed off to credulous dealers in 1929–31 as genuine autographs by a journalist, Lewis Wynne, with whom Shaw had recently become acquainted. Although Shaw's attention was soon drawn to the documents by a dealer who questioned their authenticity and identified the forger to him, he made no public outcry and did nothing privately to hinder the perpetrator, being contemptuous of the growing practice of autograph collecting. He sat back, instead, and quietly enjoyed the amusing spectacle of greedy collectors snapping up the spurious materials at enormous cost.

The forgeries were not even reasonable facsimiles of Shaw's hand, yet they passed muster because their contents rang true—as well they might since Wynne craftily concocted them out of authentic Shavian utterances in Fabian tracts, play prefaces, and letters to editors, rearranging the texts just sufficiently to create an impression that they were direct responses to journalistic queries. The forgeries ceased only when, in 1931, Wynne was arrested, tried, and found guilty of unrelated charges of theft and sentenced to a prison term.

The letters and manuscripts which Wynne had sold to dealers in London eventually found their way into virtually every significant Shaw collection in the United States, and still turn up occasionally in the market. As recently as 1973 one of the forgeries was offered as genuine in a Charles Hamilton auction catalog—reproduced in facsimile!

99 Lewis Wynne, 'G.B.S.' Autograph draft, incomplete, with Shaw's extensive revisions; undated (September 1929). 2 pp. The fragment was returned to Wynne by Shaw's secretary Blanche Patch on 4 October 1929 with the information that Shaw had been interrupted in the midst of correcting it by 'an overwhelming amount of business that simply had to be attended to', and that she had retrieved it from a pile of neglected manuscripts.

100 To Lewis Wynne. Autograph letter, 25 May 1930. WITH: Amended galleys of Wynne's article, 'G.B.S. A Personal Sketch.'

> I have . . . struck out a terrible statement about my helping struggling youngsters in literature. . . . You can do me no greater injury than to suggest that I am a good mark for people who want to borrow money or have their works read and recommended.

101 Forged autograph letters and manuscripts by Lewis Wynne.

(a) *The League of Nations.* 8 pp. Full text of Fabian Tract No. 226 (1929). Displayed with a copy of the original tract.

I really cannot keep on doing this kind of thing. Your letters are getting to be a weekly nuisance and already my complaisance in this respect has led me to violate a pious resolution. I give you the passage you ask for from the preface to "Fanny's First Play" in the hope that you will sell it and help to reduce the absurdly high market price of my autograph letters.

"Mere morality, or the substitution of custom for conscience was once accounted a shameful thing: people talked of right and wrong, of honor and dishonour, of sin and grace, of salvation and damnation, not of morality and immorality. The word morality, if we met it in the Bible, would surprise us as much as the word telephone or motor car. Nowadays we do not seem to know that there is any other test of conduct except morality, and the result is that the young had better have their souls awakened by disgrace, capture by the police, and a month's hard labour, than drift along from their cradles to their graves doing what other people do for no other reason than that other people do it, and knowing nothing of good or evil, or courage and cowardice, or indeed anything but how to keep hunger and concupiscence and fashionable dressing within the bounds of good taste except when their excesses can be concealed. Is it any wonder that I am driven to offer to young people in our suburbs the desperate advice: Do something that will get you into trouble? But please do not suppose that I defend a state of things which makes such advice the best that can be given under the circumstances, or that I do not know how difficult it is to find a way of getting into trouble that will combine loss of respectability with integrity of self-respect and a reasonable consideration for other people's feelings and interests on every point except their dread of losing their own respectability. But when there's a will there's a way. I hate to see dead people walking about; it is unnatural; and our respectable middle class people are all as dead as mutton. But of the mouth of Mrs. Knox I have delivered on them the judgment of her God."

(b)   Letter to L. Gaston, dated April 1929. 3 pp. Consists of an abridged text of *The League of Nations* tract with a note at the end: 'Quote from this but do not reproduce in full without my permission—which you will not obtain.'

(c)   Letter to F. Anstey, dated October 1924. 2 pp. An extract from Fabian Tract No. 41, *The Fabian Society: What it has Done; & How it has Done it* (1892).

(d)   Statement on the agitation for a National Theatre, dated November 1929. 2 pp. The text is from a letter to Israel Gollancz, read at the National Theatre Conference, London, 25 November 1929.

(e)   Statement on wealth and poverty, for an unidentified journalist, undated. 1 p. An extract from 'The Basis of Socialism: Economic', in *Fabian Essays in Socialism* (1889).

(f)   Statement on the revolutionaries of the Commune, for an unidentified journalist, undated. 1 p. 'You may quote all this if you like—but in your article *only*.' An extract from the preface to the 1908 edition of *Fabian Essays in Socialism*.

(g)   A note to an unidentified correspondent, dated August 1929. 1 p. Shaw allegedly supplies a footnote for his correspondent's incomplete transcription of Fabian Tract No. 5, *The Impossibilities of Anarchism* (1893). 'Quote by all means, but please quote accurately.'

(h)   Statement for Lewis Wynne, undated. 1 p. An extract from Fabian Tract No. 107, *Socialism for Millionaires* (1901).

(i)   Transcription of an extract from the preface to *Fanny's First Play*, undated, for unidentified correspondent, preceded by a spurious comment. 1 p.

> I really cannot keep on doing this kind of thing. Your letters are getting to be a weekly nuisance and already my complaisance in this respect has led me to violate a pious resolution. I give you the passage you ask for . . . in the hope that you will sell it and help to reduce the absurdly high market price of my autograph letters.

FABIAN SOCIALISM

102   *Fabian Tracts.* Shaw drafted his first tract for the Society in 1884, the year in which he became a member, and his last in 1929. During this period of fortyfive years he was the author of sixteen tracts and, as chairman of the Publications Committee for nearly twenty years, edited and revised (often quite extensively) at least two dozen others. Fabian Tracts written entirely by Shaw include:

(a)   No. 2 *A Manifesto* (1884). Inscribed on cover: 'This was the first tract I wrote for the Fabian Society before I induced [Sidney] Webb to join.' Undated.

(b)   No. 3 *To Provident Landlords and Capitalists* (1885). Inscribed on cover: 'This tract also I wrote for the Society before it was transformed by the accession at my instance of Webb and [Sydney] Olivier.' Undated.

(c)   No. 13 *What Socialism Is* (1890). Inscribed on cover: 'This attempt of mine to define Socialism is pretty crude, as anyone can see by comparing it with the Intelligent Woman's Guide written nearly forty years later; but it was the best I could do then.' 24 August 1929.

(d)   No. 40 *Fabian Election Manifesto* (1892).

(e)   No. 41 *The Fabian Society: Its Early History* (1892; revised and reprinted 1909). Inscribed on cover: 'This is a little scrap of autobiography, which you can glance at some day when you feel curious about my young lionhood; but it will be easier to tear it up.' Undated.

(f)   No. 43 (called 'Fabian Leaflet No. 43') *Vote! Vote! Vote!* (1892).

(g)   No. 45 *The Impossibilities of Anarchism* (1893).

(h)   No. 49 *A Plan of Campaign for Labor* (1894).

(i)   No. 70 *Report on Fabian Policy* (1896).

(j)   No. 93 *Women as Councillors* (1900).

(k)   No. 107 *Socialism for Millionaires* (1901).

(l)   No. 116 *Fabianism and the Fiscal Question* (1904).

(m)   No. 146 *Socialism and Superior Brains* (1909).

103   *Anarchism versus State Socialism.* Revolutionary Reprints, No. 1 (1896). First published in the *Anarchist*, March 1885. An unauthorized reprint of the essay in the Boston Socialist weekly, *Liberty*, 11 April 1885, marked the first appearance of a Shaw work in America. Across the face of the pamphlet Shaw has written a history of the piece, explaining that it was written for an anarchist friend [Charlotte Wilson], and that his own views on the subject appear in Fabian Tract No. 45, *The Impossibilities of Anarchism* (1893).

104 *Socialism and the Family.* Autograph manuscript, unpublished. 12 pp. Read to the Fabian Society on 1 October 1886. A pencilled note in the Society's minute book reads: 'This was one of Shaw's most outrageous performances.' The note is in Shaw's hand. WITH: Photograph of Shaw, from an original by Frederick Hollyer, London, November 1886.

105 To the Secretary of the Socialist League. Autograph draft of a resolution for a proposed debate between Shaw and Charles Bradlaugh, wellknown secularist and social political reformer. On the reverse is a shorthand draft of a letter, 25 [24] February 1887, outlining the conditions Shaw sought to impose. The David and Goliath tournament foundered when Bradlaugh declined to accede to the arbitrary conditions with which Shaw attempted to hedge him.

106 *Fabian Essays in Socialism* (1889). A collection of essays by Shaw, Sydney Olivier, Sidney Webb, Annie Besant, William Clarke, Graham Wallas, and Hubert Bland. Shaw took charge of production of the book from first to last: he edited and revised the texts, wrote the preface, compiled the index, supervised the designing of the cover, arranged for the blocks, chose the paper, selected the type, and drafted the handbill announcement. *Fabian Essays* was destined to become the first Fabian 'best-seller', running to many editions in England and the United States, and remaining in print to the present day.

107 To Jim Connell. Autograph letter, 1 January 1889. Shaw rejects Connell's appeal to the Fabians for Shaw to stand for Parliament from Deptford.

> If I could pay my own expenses I should not be so particular about the risk of defeat; but it is impossible for me to throw away other men's money, time and votes in order to figure as a candidate.

108 *The Fabian Society.* Large broadside, reprinted from the *Scottish Leader*, where it appeared unsigned on 4 September 1890. A brief history of the Society, written by Shaw.

105

109 To Jules Magny. Autograph letter, 12 September 1890. Shaw informs him that he is about to embark on a lecture tour, giving 13 lectures in 13 days. The valediction to the letter reads:

> Eh bien!
> Par exemple!
> Sacrebleu!
> Mille millions!
> Vive la Révolution!
> Sentiments les plus distingués!

The HRC possesses 15 pieces of Shaw correspondence (1889–1901) to Magny.

110 To B. Guinandeau, a member of the editorial staff of the French newspaper *La Justice*. Autograph draft, in French, of a letter accompanying Shaw's responses to a series of questions on British Socialism, 12 August 1892.

> Cher Citoyen
> Voilà mes réponses à votre catéchisme. Il faut avoir de l'indulgence pour mon style brittanique: j'ai fait de mon mieux pour m'expliquer au moins intelligiblement.

111 To Amy Lawrence, a student at Girton College who fell under Shaw's spell and joined the Fabian Society in 1893. Autograph lettercard, 26 October 1892. Shaw gives Miss Lawrence a lesson in economics.

[Handwritten:] Can you give me any wrinkles for working this election? I think Walfayon got me on the list on the understanding that I kept three carriages & could command three hundred more. I have written a letter to every woman on the register — about 650 all told — urging

29 FITZROY SQUARE, W.
27 October 1900.

Please do not be misled by the recent newspaper paragraphs stating that I have been elected to the new Borough Council of St. Pancras (Ward 7) without a contest. There is a full list of twelve candidates in the field for the six seats ; and the return of a Fabian is very far from being a foregone conclusion. I shall need all the help I can get for bringing up voters next Thursday, and for canvassing in the meantime.

The Committee Room is at 6 FRANCIS STREET, TOTTENHAM COURT ROAD. The Election Agent, Mr. THORNTON RUTTER, will give volunteer canvassers plenty to do. Nearest railway stations, Tottenham Court Road on the twopenny tube, and Gower Street on the Metropolitan. Carriages wanted for Thursday. G. BERNARD SHAW.

[Handwritten:] the importance of returning me as their champion &c. The result seems fairly safe; but I want to do all I can to keep up my character as an active candidate — being really an utter fainéant.

PRINTED & PUBLISHED BY G. STANDRING, FINSBURY ST.

112 *Manifesto of English Socialists* (1 May 1893). In January 1893 a Joint Committee of Socialist Bodies was formed by the Fabian Society, the Social Democratic Federation, and the Hammersmith Socialist Society. Shaw, H.M. Hyndman, and William Morris, representing the three bodies, undertook to draft a joint manifesto, published on May Day. As might have been foreseen, the Fabians and the S.D.F. could not agree on a defined policy, and in July the Fabian Society withdrew its delegates. Half a century later, on 3 January 1944, Shaw inscribed his recollections of the publication in red ink at the top of the first page of a copy of the Manifesto.

> Every attempt to bring the Manifesto down to tin tacks failed: Hyndman would not accept Shaw's amendments nor Shaw Hyndman's. They had to patch up a string of pious generalities which committed them to nothing and only cloaked their differences. . . . I have never considered the result worth the penny charged for it.

113 Cyclostyled electioneering letter to constituents in the Borough of St Pancras, signed by Shaw, 31 October 1900, concerning the need for improvement in the quality of official staff appointments. After a defeat in 1894 Shaw was elected to the St Pancras Vestry (which shortly thereafter was reorganized as a Borough) in 1897. He was now running (successfully) for re-election. Shaw's campaign literature included a printed postcard of 27 October 1900, warning that his re-election was far from certain, and calling on Fabian friends to assist him as canvassers and to provide carriages 'for bringing up voters' to the polls. This card was addressed, with an autograph note, to Mrs R.C. Phillimore, wife of a fellow councillor.

114 *Transvaal War Meeting*. Cyclostyled Fabian notice of a 'Suggested Modification of [S.G.] Hobson's Resolution', drafted by Shaw. 2 pp. Autograph note, in pencil, to the theatre manager Frederick Whelen, 17 November 1899, on the second page. This document marked the start of a highly emotional conflict within the Society between Imperialists and anti-Imperialists, leading to the publication of *Fabianism and the Empire* and the resignations of a number of influential members.

115 *Fabianism and the Empire: A Manifesto by the Fabian Society. Edited by Bernard Shaw* (1900). The Fabians, at the start of the Transvaal war, determined to issue a tract on Imperialism. At the annual meeting in May 1900 a resolution was passed asking the Society to prepare and submit to the membership 'a constructive criticism from the Socialist standpoint of the actions and programmes of the various political parties.' The assignment inevitably fell to Shaw, who drafted the controversial text, examined and reconciled 134 amended proofs of the 20,000 word document that had been submitted by post to members, and patiently resolved all the differences that arose during a three-hour heated members' meeting in September to discuss the views propounded in the document. 'Shaw has accomplished many difficult feats', noted Edward R. Pease, the Society's secretary, in his *History of the Fabian Society* (1916), 'but none of them, in my opinion, excels that of drafting for the Society and carrying through the manifesto. . . .'

116 Election address (February 1904), drafted by Shaw, who had agreed to contest, as a Progressive candidate, a seat from South St Pancras on the London County Council. His running mate, Sir William Nevill Geary, was a virtual nonentity who knew little about practical politics. It therefore devolved upon Shaw to run the campaign almost singlehanded. He formed a women's committee, comprised of Beatrice Webb, Lady Stanley, and Mrs R.C. Phillimore (in the chair), to organize and run ladies' meetings, hitherto unheard-of in local politics. Printed letter, 13 February 1904. He distributed cyclostyled letters to Laborites (2 March), offering to promote legislation to protect shop assistants; to licensed victuallers (20 February), assuring them that, in spite of his own teetotallism, he would work in their interest by supporting the Council's present temperance policy; to police officers (3 March), promising to 'steadily support the full civil rights of the Force, and resist all

attempts to impose discipline of the military type on it'; to shop merchants (13 February), indicating that, like them, he favored electric trams past their doors rather than tube trains under the streets. Despite all his frantic efforts Shaw limped in a poor third, losing to two Moderates. He never again sought public office.

117 To Frederick H. Evans. Autograph postcard, 30 January 1904, seeking a photograph for reproduction on the cover of his election address.

> The negative of yours which was reproduced in The World's Work is the only one of all the series which has any sign of a collar in it: hence its pre-eminent fitness for election purposes.

118 To Emery Walker and Sydney Cockerell, partners in a printing and engraving firm. Autograph letter, on campaign stationery, 23 February 1904. Shaw, who has been calling on all of his friends to support his efforts, provides a list of printers and engravers who are on the voters' register in South St Pancras.

> If you happen to know them, will you write to them asking them to vote for those old & tried friends of the artistic classes, Shaw & Geary.

The HRC possesses 34 pieces of Shaw correspondence (1889–1932) to Walker and 62 pieces (1899–1950) to Cockerell.

119 *Report of the Special Committee . . . to consider measures for increasing the scope, influence, income, and activity of the Society. Together with the Executive Committee's Report and resolutions thereon.* November 1906. H.G. Wells, whom Shaw had proposed for membership in the Fabian Society in 1903, unexpectedly rebelled against its Old Guard with a controversial lecture 'Faults of the Fabian' on 9 February 1906, which triggered a reform movement within the Society, headed by Wells. To appease him the Executive agreed to endorse his call for the appointment of a special committee to 'consider what means should be taken to increase the scope, influence, income and activity of the Society. . . .' In November the Society published a report of the special committee, drafted by Wells, with the reply of the Executive, drafted by Shaw. Wells, ever impatient, chose to gamble on complete success or failure by an attempt to force the

THE INTERNATIONAL
SOCIALIST BUREAU. .

(BRITISH SECTION)

DRAFT MANIFESTO

Submitted to the Section by

BERNARD SHAW.

Another surprise! Only the other day I told somebody that I had always maintained that the war would last 30 years and peter out from exhaustion in a stalemate.* And now this document, which I had completely forgotten, proves that in August 1915, a year after the fighting began, I forecast the end quite accurately.

I wonder what happened to this proposal. My mind is a blank concerning it.

G. Bernard Shaw

4th Nov. 1929.

3rd September, 1915.

* It seemed impossible that Capitalism could have made such a mess of its job that the Central Empires were as incapable of supporting themselves from their own resources as the British Islands,

acceptance of his report by the membership. At a special meeting on 14 December, for which Edward Pease circulated an 'emergency whip' postcard urging attendance and warning that the amendment 'involves the whole future of the Society', the shrewd and skilled Shaw had no difficulty out-manœuvering Wells, who gave the Fabians little trouble thereafter. He resigned from the Society in 1908.

120 Souvenir of a mass meeting of Socialists in Trafalgar Square, 25 July 1909, to protest the official reception of the Tsar of Russia. Shaw is listed as one of the speakers, representing the Fabian Society. The souvenir is printed on a paper serviette.

121 To Edward R. Pease. Autograph postcard, 26 October 1911. Shaw declines to stand as a Fabian candidate for a Labor seat in Parliament until he sees evidence that the Labor Party will support him.

> As a matter of fact I am quite sure that I am not wanted— why should I be?—and the F.S. should have the sense to see that, & not expose itself & me to a rebuff.

The HRC possesses 82 pieces of Shaw correspondence (1893–1924) to Pease.

122 *Draft Manifesto*, written by Shaw and submitted to the British Section of the International Socialist Bureau, 3 September 1915. The pamphlet, printed and distributed at Shaw's own expense, was a reply to the manifesto of the German Social Democratic Party issued on 23 June of the same year. Inscribed by Shaw on the cover, 4 November 1929:

> Only the other day I told somebody that I had always maintained that the war would last 30 years and peter out from exhaustion in a stalemate. And now this document, which I had completely forgotten, proves that in August 1915, a year after the fighting began, I forecast the end quite accurately.

123 *Fabianism and the War*. Duplicated typewritten manuscript, with corrections. 9 pp. Accompanied by a duplicated typewritten 'official' letter from Shaw to Edward R. Pease, 1 January 1917, headed PROPOSED MANIFESTO ON REPUBLICANISM and labelled CONFIDENTIAL. 2 pp. WITH: Typewritten draft, containing autograph revisions and inserted sectional captions in red ink, dated 1 January 1917. 13 pp. Also displayed is Pease's typewritten (carbon) reply for the Executive Committee, 16 January 1917, indicating that the committee was not particularly

happy about the proposal, although it attempted to show a co-operative spirit.

The manifesto declared for 'a republican solution of the territorial problems raised by the war', as Shaw noted in a diary he had commenced that day (1 January). It was only a leg-pull of the Fabian Executive, he informed H.G. Wells; he had no hope of stirring up anything but 'an unquiet recalcitrance.'

LECTURES

124 To Pattie Moye, a member of the managing committee of the Zetetical Society, London, founded in 1878 'to furnish opportunities for the unrestricted discussion of Social, Political, and Philosophical subjects.' Draft letter, 18 December 1881, on the last page of which is a brief syllabus of Shaw's proposed lecture. WITH: Zetetical Society program of its 1881–82 lecture schedule. Shaw tells Mrs Moye he is prepared to deliver a paper entitled 'On what is called "The Sacredness of Human Life", and its bearing on the question of Capital Punishment.' It was his first platform appearance, on 8 February 1882.

125 *Report of the Proceedings of the Industrial Remuneration Conference* (1885). The volume contains a report, drafted by Shaw, of his speech on 30 January 1885 in a discussion on Land Nationalization.

126 *That Realism is the Goal of Fiction*. Unpublished paper, delivered before the Blackheath Essay and Debating Society on 18 January 1888. Autograph manuscript, dated 13–14 January. 14 pp. WITH: Printed announcement card.

> Dickens was an Unrealist when he, in the most literal sense, made fun of Tony Weller instead of making a man of him. We find him later on, when he had become one of the greatest of the Realists, taking his characters with tragic seriousness. The fun of Mr. Weller is the poorest of chaff in comparison with the subtle ironies and rich absurdities of Mr. Dorrit, or of Pip in 'Great Expectations': yet we are not always sure which side of the mouth to laugh at them with; for they are taken seriously, and are very real. Yet there are people who believe that Pickwick is the best book Dickens ever wrote, and that his four last books—his great works—are dull.

127 To Janet Achurch. Autograph letter, 17 June 1889. Shaw sends two books to Miss Achurch, whose

Dear Sir,

This is all I can think of on the subject at present. As it is Sunday afternoon I am writing at the disadvantage of having my sister on the one hand & my mother on the other. Miss Shaw, who is a Roman Catholic on Sabbath evenings, and a Protestant (when she is up in time) in the morning, is playing the pianoforte. Meanwhile Mrs Shaw reads, and remonstrates at intervals with her daughter, who is neglecting an important appointment, now half-an-hour overdue. These remonstrances provoke retorts, and end in brief domestic storms which sweep over Mr Shaw, and fill his soul with malice. So perhaps you will excuse me if I am not quite clear. If there is any point on which you are doubtful please let me know, and I will do my best to elucidate it, even though you will expend ingenuity to yourself if you suppose that your own intelligence can be in any way indebted to any warped humor. To be strong in argument one must have faith in it, whereas, to my mind, it is less means of dictating truths of reasoning ourselves for pretending to believe what we know in our hearts to be nonsense. With which profound remark, and an apology for the length of this letter, I am, dear Mr Moye

Yours faithfully,

Mr Moye
3 Southwick St
Hyde Park
W.

124

G. B. S.

131

acquaintance he has just made, and informs her that he was able to attend her performance in *A Doll's House* only because of an indisposition.

> Kindly consider that for years past every Sunday evening of mine has been spent on some more or less squalid platform, lecturing, lecturing, lecturing, and lecturing. At the end of last month I caught a chill for the first time in my life. It ended in a bad throat: I nevertheless had to orate four times in the following week. That settled me. I had to stop positively for a fortnight, and so I got last Sunday free.

The HRC possesses 93 pieces of Shaw correspondence (1889–1912) to Janet Achurch and 161 pieces (1890–1924) to her husband Charles Charrington.

128   *The Legal Eight Hours Question: A Two Nights' Public Debate between Mr. G.W. Foote and Mr. George Bernard Shaw* (1891). A verbatim report, revised and corrected by the disputants. Foote was a secularist writer and editor, who later became head of the National Secular Society. It was Shaw's first major debate.

129   To Edward R. Pease. Autograph postcard, 4 February 1895. Shaw's lecture schedule is so crowded that he is obliged to put off Leeds. WITH: Autograph postcard to Pease, 25 September 1893, listing Shaw's principal lectures for November, to be inserted in *Fabian News*.

> A glance at my diary would convince you that I am hopelessly overdone—no less than ten evenings this month are already booked for public orations alone, without counting theatrical & private-public engagements.

130   Flyers and announcement cards of Shaw lectures:

(a)   Fabian Society: 'The Illusions which Blind us to Socialism', 4 November 1887.

(b)   Peace Demonstration in Hyde Park, Sunday, 26 July 1896 (Shaw's fortieth birthday).

(c)   National Anti-Sweating League: 'The Social Principles of the Minimum Wage', 6 June 1907. H.G. Wells in the chair.

(d)   Irish Dominion League: 'An Irish Dominion' (undated; probably 1920).

131   William Rothenstein: Sketch of Shaw lecturing. Ink, on a correspondence card, 5½″ by 3½″. Undated.

132   To Clarence H. Norman, court stenographer and Socialist journalist. Autograph postcard, 3 March 1908, with a printed message announcing 'I have given up lecturing on Sundays. Formerly I hardly did anything else on that day. Now I am compelled to keep my weekends for rest.' An autograph note from Shaw concerns the Congo political situation.

The HRC possesses 28 pieces of Shaw correspondence (1907–47) to Norman.

133   Printed lectures: *Art in Education* (1911). *The Case for Equality* (1913). *Foundation Oration* (University of London, 1920). Dozens of Shaw's lectures were published, often without his knowledge or consent, and with garbled and corrupt texts. Most of these were obscure, fragile pamphlets, published in limited quantity, which have become exceedingly scarce. This copy of *Art in Education* is the only one known to survive, and only five copies of the *Foundation Oration* have been noted.

134   To Clarence H. Norman. Autograph postcard, 27 October 1913. Shaw asks him to make a verbatim report of his address at the City Temple. Disturbed by the inaccurate newspaper reports of his lectures, Shaw took to commissioning professional transcriptions at his own expense, which he then frequently offered for sale to the press syndicates, editing and polishing them in the process.

> If I manage to spit out anything good on the spur of the moment I may be able later on to do some business with it in America.

135   *The Redistribution of Income*. Draft syllabus for a Fabian Society series of six lectures, October-December 1914. Typewritten manuscript, revised by Shaw (and corrected in an unidentified hand). 3 pp., plus an autograph layout for the syllabus cover. WITH: Autograph draft, 13 pp., and incomplete typewritten transcription (corrected by Shaw's secretary Ann M. Elder), 30 pp., of the first lecture. Admission ticket for the third lecture, in the Kingsway Hall, London, 11 November 1914. The success of the lectures led to an annual series, with Shaw as star attraction, which kept the Fabian Society solvent for the next twenty years.

*136 *Spoken English and Broken English.* Recorded in the autumn of 1927 for the Linguaphone Institute. Issued on two 12″ shellac records in a cardboard case, with a pamphlet containing the text. In keeping with his lifelong custom of accepting no payment for his lectures, Shaw declined a fee. The Institute shewed its gratitude by presenting him with a set of the records in a specially designed brown morocco case with leather pockets and a gilt-edged paper board inset on hinges with four inlaid photographs of Shaw and the Institute's staff during the recording session. On the front of the case is a gilt-stamped inscription in uniform capitals: 'TO | BERNARD SHAW | AN APPRECIATION | THE LINGUAPHONE INSTITUTE | LONDON'. 13¾″ by 14⅜″, in a slip case.

137 *Do We Agree? A Debate between G.K. Chesterton and Bernard Shaw with Hilaire Belloc in the chair* (1928). A publisher's note on page 5 indicates that 'this account of a public discussion between Mr. Chesterton and Mr. Shaw is something less than a verbatim report. But with some assistance from the debaters it has been possible to save enough from oblivion to justify publication.' It was the second time the three men had shared the platform in a debate. On the earlier occasion (November 1911) Belloc had taken the chair for a Shaw-Chesterton free-for-all on the Shaw resolution 'that a Democrat who is not also a Socialist is no gentleman.'

138 'Notes for speech proposing Prof. Einstein's health. . . .' Typewritten (carbon) manuscript, corrected in an unidentified hand, 28 October 1930. Shaw's toast was offered at a dinner honoring Albert Einstein, sponsored by the Jewish societies Ort-Oze, at the Savoy Hotel, London; it was broadcast to the United States by shortwave relay. Most of the material in Shaw's rather prolix speech anticipated his play *In Good King Charles's Golden Days* (1939), and may well have inspired it.

139 Corrected proof of syllabus for a Fabian Society lecture, 'In Praise of Guy Fawkes', passed for press on 24 July 1932. WITH: Typewritten manuscript, revised, of syllabus for a Fabian Society lecture, 'The Impossibilities of Freedom', delivered 26 November 1925. 3 pp.

140 *The Future of Political Science in America* (1933). Revised text of a lecture delivered before the Academy of Political Science in the Metropolitan Opera House, New York, 11 April 1933. The work was published in England under the title *The Political Madhouse in America and Nearer Home.* This was Shaw's only lecture in America, and his last formal appearance on the platform. It was carried coast to coast by the National Broadcasting Company, giving Shaw the largest listening audience he had ever had.

*141 Four photographs of Shaw aboard the Empress of Britain in New York harbor, 11 April 1933. (*New York Journal-American* photographic archive, Photography Collection.) Shaw is seen with visiting dignitaries, preparing for a press conference, posing for photographers. Behind Shaw in the second photograph and in the background in the fourth is Archibald Henderson, his authorized biographer.

142 Printed postcard message to be sent to program chairmen who solicit lecture appearances. 'Mr. Bernard Shaw has long since been obliged by advancing years to retire from . . . the platform.' He continued, however, to make frequent informal speeches even in his eighties and nineties. By the time of his death Shaw had addressed more than two thousand audiences.

CENSORSHIP

British dramatists had been subjected to the oppressive yoke of a censorship statute since 1737, their freedom of expression circumscribed by the frequently perverse caprices and the despotism of the Lord Chamberlain's reader of plays. Paradoxically, the censorship actually debauched the stage by fostering immorality at the expense of earnest drama. Instead of prohibiting vice as a stage subject it encouraged the presentation of vice as attractive. Plays which dealt frivolously and even lasciviously with such controversial subjects as seduction, promiscuity, adultery, and prostitution received licences so long as the subjects were presented 'agreeably', or so long as their practitioners suffered retributive justice by the end of the evening, wheras the sober dramas of 'stern, public-spirited and intellectually honest writers' were inexorably suppressed. Enraged by the circumstance that a dedicated dramatist had perforce to submit to the whim of an irresponsible reader from whose decision there was no possible appeal, Shaw fought implacably for a freedom for the theatre comparable to that which was accorded the press.

143 *The Censorship of the Stage in England* (1899). Typewritten manuscript, corrected and revised. 20 pp. Shaw describes for American readers how British censorship works, and points up its absurdities and inequities by examining the scandalousness of some of the plays passed by the censor. The article was submitted to the *North American Review* on the understanding that it would either be published in its entirety or be returned. Despite the editor's pledge, the text was bowdlerized when published in August 1899.

144 To Robert W. Welch, London representative of the *New York Times*. Autograph postcard, 27 September 1905. Shaw, responding earlier to a report that his play *Man and Superman* had been suppressed by Arthur E. Bostwick, an official of the New York Public Library, labelled the action 'Comstockery', a term he coined to denote the bluenose activities of Americans like Anthony Comstock, secretary of the New York Society for the Suppression of Vice, who endeavored to restrain as obscene all outspoken literary expression. When Welch apparently remonstrated, Shaw wrote again, from Ireland.

> I am sorry to say that every time I scratch an American I *do* find a Comstocker. Comstock is a thoroughly representative man. Bostwick also is not 'one man': he is the representative of the citizens of New York. When the 'appreciative Americans' say it is not their fault, all they mean is that they are mugwumps. You make your institutions & you must stand the blame they bring you.

145 *The Author's Apology from Mrs Warren's Profession* (1905). When, at the instigation of Anthony Comstock, the New York police closed Arnold Daly's production of *Mrs Warren's Profession* after its first performance on 30 October 1905, charging the principals involved with 'disorderly conduct', Shaw's New York publishers used the opportunity to issue a special edition of the preface he had written for the 1902 British edition of the play (see No. 210). It also contained an introduction 'The Tyranny of Police and Press' by the journalist John Corbin of the New York *Sun*, in which he castigated the behavior of the local press.

> Before the production of the play all of the sensational papers, and some that pretend not to be sensational, used column upon column of their most prominent space to create an unwarranted expectation of something lewd, and after it used those same columns to falsify what actually happened. The denunciations of the play were hysterical and hypocritical in proportion as the papers were yellow and foul. . . . In such a mess of calculated sensationalism and venal hypocrisy it is not strange that the real purport of the play should have escaped notice. . . . That our press, at once the freest in the world and the one that most vilely abuses its freedom, should become an engine to crush the freedom of the stage is grotesquely comic.

When in 1906 the Court of Special Sessions in New York rejected the charges and ruled that Shaw's play was not in violation of the penal code, the editor of the New York *World* cabled to Shaw: 'What's your opinion American morals now?' He replied: 'Strange country where the press is blind and the eyes of justice open'.

146 *The Censorship of Plays.* Three galley proofs, corrected and revised, of a letter to the editor of the *Nation* (London), published 16 November 1907. WITH: Pamphlet, *The Censorship of Plays . . . The Case for Abolition* (1908), containing a reprint of Shaw's letter.

> [Y]ou want a man [as censor] who will undertake to know, better than Tolstoy or Ibsen or George Meredith or Dickens or Carlyle or Ruskin or Shakespeare or Shelley, what moral truths the world needs to be reminded of—how far the pity and horror of tragedy dare be carried—on what institutions the antiseptic derision of comedy may be allowed to play without destroying anything really vital in them.
>   Now it is clear without argument that no man who was not a born fool would pretend for the moment to be capable of such a task; and the reason that some censors have talked as if they were capable of it is that some censors have been born fools. The Prime Minister would be as much horrified at having such godlike powers attributed to him as Paul and Barnabas were at Lystra when the people sacrificed to them.

147 A note concerning a deputation of playwrights to the Prime Minister to protest dramatic censorship. Typewritten manuscript, revised. 1 p. Published (unsigned) in the *New Age*, 21 November 1907. Due to the illness of the Prime Minister, Sir Henry Campbell-Bannerman, the deputation was received by his deputy, Herbert Gladstone. Shaw, to avoid being an irritant, declined to be a member of the deputation.

148 *Blanco Posnet Banned by the Censor: Statement by Mr. Bernard Shaw.* A broadside printed and distributed by Shaw to the press on 22 May 1909 after learning that his play *The Shewing-up of Blanco Posnet* had been denied a licence by the examiner of plays. He questions the rationale by which the 'simple cupidities and concupiscences' of *The Merry Widow* are sanctioned on the British stage while his own highly moral and edifying drama of the struggle of a man with God is declared 'not morally fit' for performance.

> I shall allow the play to be performed in America and throughout Europe. I shall publish it. . . . So England will have its Merry Widow; and the other countries will have their Blanco Posnet. It is not for me to say which will have the best of that bargain in the long run.

149 Lady Gregory to Sir James B. Dougherty, Undersecretary to the Lord Lieutenant of Ireland. Autograph draft, 20 August [1909], written at the foot of page 2 of an undated (ca. 19 August) typewritten transcription of a letter from Dougherty. Upon learning that Shaw had offered his play to W.B. Yeats and Lady Gregory, the directors of Dublin's Abbey Theatre, which was outside the jurisdiction of the Lord Chamberlain's censor, Dougherty committed the impropriety of threatening, in the Viceroy's name, to revoke the Abbey's patent if *Blanco Posnet* were performed there. Although Yeats and Lady Gregory publicly announced their defiance of the threat, the draft of Lady Gregory's letter to Dougherty indicates that sufficient concessions were made, through alterations in the text, to convince the Lord Lieutenant that further interference would be inexpedient. The play was performed as scheduled on 25 August 1909. Although Shaw was in Ireland, he did not attend.

150 To Ben Iden Payne, general manager of the Gaiety Theatre, Manchester. Autograph (carbon) letter, 12 September 1909. Iden Payne had applied to the censor, G.A. Redford, after the production of *Blanco Posnet* in Dublin, asking him to reconsider his refusal of a licence. Redford rejected the script, noting that the passages he had originally objected to were still present, but intimating he was ready to cooperate if 'you are prepared to comply with the Lord Chamberlain's requirements, which it appears to me would be very easy. . . .'

What [Redford] means is, 'If your blasphemous blackguard of an author will only be reasonable, and turn his play into a coarse and worthless melodrama, and thereby confess that I was right about him, he can have his license without any trouble.' It is useless to reason with a man who is in this state of mind; and it is brutal to argue with him about a play which he simply does not understand. . . . He even means to be kind to me in the way in which a police court missionary is kind to a pickpocket; and the only difficulty in the matter is that, as it happens, I am not a pickpocket.

See Nos. 341–344 for additional material relating to the *Blanco Posnet* controversy.

151 *Statement of the Evidence in chief of Bernard Shaw before the Joint-Committee on Stage Plays.* . . . The dramatists' prolonged agitation against the censorship led in 1909 to the appointment of a parliamentary committee of inquiry of both houses, under the chairmanship of the Rt. Hon. Herbert Samuel. The moment Shaw learned of the formation of the committee he began to draft a statement to present in evidence. The completed text, printed at his own expense, ran to 11,000 words. He distributed copies to all of the members of the Joint Select Committee prior to its first meeting on 29 July.

152 From Gilbert Murray, Greek scholar, translator of Euripides. Typewritten letter (with typed initials), 18 July 1909. Murray discusses the censorship of *The Shewing-up of Blanco Posnet.*

> I consider the censoring . . . to be the act of a man with no moral sense at all—and precious little intellect either. But somehow I can not get into the proper crusading spirit. . . . Do send me your Areopagitica. I fully see that the high and general line is the right one to take, if only I could rise to it.

153 To 'Colleagues' in the Dramatists' Club. Typewritten draft, corrected, dated 28 July 1909, with a cyclostyled, signed typewritten letter of the same date, and a list of 82 names of recipients of the letter, including Barrie, Wells, Kipling, Conan Doyle, Galsworthy, Lady Gregory, Maugham, Barker, and Beerbohm. A similar letter was issued to members of the Society of Authors. Accompanying each letter was a copy of Shaw's printed *Statement* for the Joint Select Committee on censorship.

154 *Imaginary Statement by a British Matron.* Shorthand manuscript, undated (July 1909). 4 pp. *Model*

BLANCO POSNET BANNED BY THE CENSOR.

STATEMENT BY MR. BERNARD SHAW.

I have no information to add to that which is already public property. The decision whether a play is morally fit to be performed or not, rests with the King absolutely; and I am not in the King's confidence. To write a play too vile for public performance even at the very indulgent standard applied to our London theatres is as grave an offence as a man can commit, short of downright felony: in fact, it is much worse than most felonies. To announce it for production at a theatre of high reputation is almost as bad. I presume the King would not hold up Mr. Tree and myself before Europe and America as guilty of this disgraceful conduct unless he had the most entire confidence in his own judgment or that of his advisers. The injury—not to mention the insult—to us is very considerable; but the disgrace will depend on the extent to which the public shares the King's faith in this matter. It would be affectation for me to pretend to share it. I shall allow the play to be performed in America and throughout Europe. I shall publish it. I should not do that if I shared the King's opinion of it. I have far more at stake than anyone else concerned; for I should be ruined if I lost the confidence of the public in my honor and conscience as a playwright, as I have no following among vicious or thoughtless people. But I naturally regret that Mr. Tree, the first of our successful West-End managers to step into the gap left by the retirement of Messrs. Vedrenne and Barker from what may be called National Theatre work with his Afternoon Theatre, should find that he has only exposed himself to what is virtually a rebuke for misconduct from the very quarter in which he might have expected the most enlightened support. The effect on the future of the theatre will be seen later on. Young men are at this moment writing plays for the repertory theatres of Mr. Frohman and Mr. Herbert Trench. They cannot afford, as I accidentally can, to lose the price of months of arduous labor and be blacklisted by managers as dangerous. This reminder to them that there is safety in The Merry Widow and the utmost danger in plays of the kind I write, will inevitably act as a lesson to them which will seem gratifying and hopeful only to those who not only enjoy The Merry Widow—I enjoy it myself greatly for the matter of that—but who think that it presents a complete, satisfactory, and edifying view of human motive and destiny.

I repeat that I do not know why the play has been declared unfit to exist. It is a very simple and even crude melodrama, with absolutely no sexual interest whatever. It represents a little community of violent, cruel, sensual, ignorant, blasphemous, bloodthirsty backwoodsmen, whose conception of manliness is mere brute pugnacity, and whose favorite sport is lynching. Into this welter of crude newspaperized savagery there suddenly comes a force—not mentioned in The Merry Widow—to which they give the name of God, the slightest regard for which they make it a point of honor to despise as mere weakness of character. That force nevertheless, at the crisis which is the subject of the drama, makes them do its will and not their own in a manner very amazing to themselves, and, I should hope, not altogether unedifying to the spectators. I am given to understand that the introduction of this force into my play as a substitute for the simple cupidities and concupiscences of The Merry Widow is the feature that renders the play unfit for performance. It was precisely the feature which made the play worth writing to me. What is called the struggle of a man with God is the most dramatic of all conflicts: in fact, the only one that makes really good drama. But our royal rule is that conflict with God cannot be permitted on the stage. Except when the name of God is taken altogether in vain, by way of swearing, the Divine Antagonist must be spoken of, even by the most hardened and savage outlaws, with the decorum and devotional respect observed by our Bishops. Handel's Messiah, for instance, is unfit for performance in the theatre because the chorus bursts into fierce derision of divinity. They shoot out their lips and wag their heads, reviling, taunting, saying "Let Him deliver him if He delight in him." (I have noticed, by the way, that this chorus is very commonly sung in England as if it were a hymn.) Well, my hero had to shoot out his lip and wag his head. He went to his salvation as St. Paul did, kicking against the pricks, and not at all as Mr. Pecksniff went to his damnation. And that, I understand, is why the King will not allow him to be exhibited on the stage in England. He could have been seduced by the Merry Widow with impunity. So England will have its Merry Widow; and the other countries will have their Blanco Posnet. It is not for me to say which will have the best of that bargain in the long run.

great |

Proof for a Cultured Peer and *Model Proof for a Spiritual Peer.* Shorthand manuscript, undated (July 1909). 6 pp. With transcriptions. Drafts of humorous models for the presentation of testimony, prepared by Shaw for the guidance of cooperative witnesses coming before the Joint Select Committee. In addition, Shaw supplied informational circulars to scheduled witnesses, and planted unsigned articles and news notes in the publications of sympathetic editors.

155 From Herbert Samuel, chairman of the Joint Select Committee. Typewritten letter, 3 August 1909. He indicates to Shaw that the rejection of the printed statement was based on fear of a proliferation of such statements, in which case 'we should be inflicting upon the public a very ponderous volume,—ponderous physically if not intellectually. . . .' The committee published its report in November 1909, after fifteen meetings, together with a full transcript of the proceedings, which filled a mammoth blue book. Though it incorporated in its report many of the dramatists' suggestions for 'preventing the abuse as an instrument of censorship of the power of licensing theatres', it did not recommend the abolition of the Examiner of Plays. The censorship persisted in England until more than a decade after Shaw's death, but his unyielding resistance to it and his powerful philippics helped to bring about its demise.

156 To A.E. Filmer, theatrical manager. Autograph postcard, 23 November 1922. Shaw discusses the appointment of the new Lord Chamberlain (Lord Sandhurst) and the possibility of a licence at this time for public performance of the long-banned *Mrs Warren's Profession.*

> I should not, however, plead the precedent of [Shelley's] The Cenci, as nothing makes St James's so nervous as the fear that every concession it makes will bring a host of further demands on its tolerance.

157 *Censorship as a Police Duty.* An address to the Chief Constables' Association, 8 June 1928. Published in the *Reports of the Special General Conference* (1928).

> Years and years ago it was asked how are we to get rid of the censorship of the Lord Chamberlain, and I said, 'You will have to abolish the Monarchy first.'

158 Radio talk on film censorship, broadcast by Shaw on the B.B.C., 20 January 1935. Typewritten manuscript, extensively revised; undated. 2 pp. Shaw agrees with the Prime Minister, Ramsay MacDonald, that 'censorships are the very devil' and deplores the method of censorship employed by the government, 'which is that of handing the job over to some frail and erring mortal man, and making him omnipotent on the assumption that his official status will make him infallible and omniscient. . . .' At the foot of the second page Shaw has scribbled: 'This contains 488 counted . . . words, and can be delivered *allegro con brio* by the author in three and a half minutes.'

AGITATIONS

159 *Letter from Mr. G. Bernard Shaw, read at a Public Meeting of the Ratepayers of St. Pancras, on the 17th March, 1899 . . . to call attention to the insanitary condition of the parish.* Printed leaflet. Shaw was still recuperating from an infected foot which had incapacitated him for nearly a year.

> I regret to say that the state of my health after eighteen years residence in St. Pancras does not permit of my attending your meeting.

160 To Charles Gane, Honorary Secretary of the National Anti-Vaccination League. Printed broadside letter, 22 February 1906. Shaw, unable to attend the annual meeting of the League, sends a message to be read at the meeting. Shaw's contention during this period was that vaccination, as then officially practised, was 'really nothing short of attempted murder.' Far from being a crank on the subject, Shaw was well versed in the procedures used in vaccination and aware of the appallingly high death statistics related to faulty inoculations. For four years he served on the Public Health Committee of the St Pancras Borough Council, working intimately with the borough's medical officer, Dr John F. Sykes. He inspected tenements, sweatshops, hospitals, and workhouses; studied all the latest health statistics from other boroughs and abroad; and carried on a two-year battle in the press between 1902 and 1904 to awaken Londoners to the truth about the health conditions in their residential neighborhoods. In a debate by the United Law Society in 1901 he proposed a resolution 'That it is desirable . . . that a careful re-examination of the evidence should be made by a body of statistical and actuarial experts, from which body medical men should be rigorously excluded.'

161 *Almroth Wright.* The second of two companion essays (the first was on the physician Edward Jenner, discoverer of vaccination). Typewritten manuscript, with revisions, 4 February 1923. 15 pp. WITH: Three galley proofs, containing corrections partly by Shaw and partly copied in by Charlotte Shaw, and an insertion of 13 typewritten lines, revised, affixed to the third galley. Sir Almroth Wright, the famed bacteriologist and physician, who provided Shaw with the theme for *The Doctor's Dilemma* (1906), was the prototype for Sir Colenso Ridgeon in the play.

162 *What is to be done with the Doctors?* Typewritten (carbon) manuscript; undated. 87 pp. Published in the *English Review*, December 1917–March 1918. Asked by a Manchester newspaper to contribute to a series entitled 'Have We Lost Faith?' Shaw replied tersely: 'Certainly not; but we have transferred it from God to the General Medical Council.' The medical fraternity, Shaw insisted, were engaged in a conspiracy to exploit popular credulity and human suffering, and to hide their own shortcomings. He insisted that the doctor's responsibility was to save life, not to risk it, and he urged the government to bring the medical profession under effective public control by treating every death as 'a probable murder.' As a Socialist Shaw advocated a state medical service, available to the poor as readily as to the rich, staffed by 'doctors whom we can believe in, and whose prosperity shall depend not on the nation's sickness but its health.'

163 From William Archer, critic and playwright, informing Shaw that he faces imminent surgery. Typewritten letter, 17 December 1924. Shaw has written beneath the letter: 'He died—killed by the operation—on the 27th December.' It was Archer who had obtained for Shaw his first steady journalistic employment in 1885 and had encouraged him to write his first play. Despite strong differences of opinion on many subjects, they had been steadfast friends for forty years. The news of Archer's death, said Shaw in a memoir in 1927, 'threw me into a transport of fury.

. . . I am unfashionable enough to hold that an operation which does not justify itself by its promised results should always be the subject of a stringent inquest; for I have never been able to regard a death caused by an operation as a natural death. My rage may have been unjust to the surgeons; but it carried me over my first sense of bereavement. . . . I still feel that when he went he took a piece of me with him.'

164 *The Test of Character.* A buff card, 6¼″ by 5″, circulated as propaganda by the London & Provincial Anti-Vivisection Society (ca. 1908), consisting of an extract from a lecture by Shaw to the Society on 30 May 1900 (with quotations from other anti-vivisectionists on the reverse side). It was in the 1900 lecture that Shaw charged the vivisector with being 'the dynamitard of science', an expression which became a battle cry for anti-vivisectionists the world over.

You do not settle whether an experiment is justified or not by merely shewing that it is of some use. . . . Yet the doctors seem to think utility a sufficient justification of vivisectional experiments which do not always stop at animals, and, let me add, logically, should not stop at animals; for surely, if

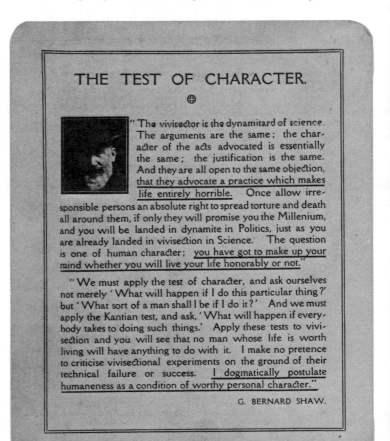

THE TEST OF CHARACTER.

" The vivisector is the dynamitard of science. The arguments are the same; the character of the acts advocated is essentially the same; the justification is the same. And they are all open to the same objection, that they advocate a practice which makes life entirely horrible. Once allow irresponsible persons an absolute right to spread torture and death all around them, if only they will promise you the Millenium, and you will be landed in dynamite in Politics, just as you are already landed in vivisection in Science. The question is one of human character; you have got to make up your mind whether you will live your life honorably or not."

" We must apply the test of character, and ask ourselves not merely ' What will happen if I do this particular thing?' but ' What sort of a man shall I be if I do it?' And we must apply the Kantian test, and ask, ' What will happen if everybody takes to doing such things.' Apply these tests to vivisection and you will see that no man whose life is worth living will have anything to do with it. I make no pretence to criticise vivisectional experiments on the ground of their technical failure or success. I dogmatically postulate humaneness as a condition of worthy personal character."

G. BERNARD SHAW.

Published by the London & Provincial Anti-Vivisection Society, 22a Regent St., S.W.

a doctor believes that vivisectional experiments on animals are justified by what they teach him, then, since he knows that these experiments must necessarily be less instructive than experiments on human beings, he must be a coward if he does not sacrifice one or two comparatively valueless human beings in order to find out a little more accurately what he is trying to discover. You see, you cannot bring a question of this kind to a utilitarian test at all. If you once begin that particular line of argument you will find yourself landed in horrors of which you have no conception.

165 *Shaw on Vivisection* (1949). Compiled and edited nominally by G.H. Bowker for the National Anti-Vivisection Society, with most of the preparation done by Shaw, assisted by Dr F.E. Loewenstein. Typewritten manuscript, with revisions and additions in Shaw's hand, 1947–48. First published in London, 1949. Also displayed is the first American edition (Chicago, 1951) with a dramatic cover design by Eric Wenstrand. Shaw had published his first pronouncement against vivisection in a book review in the *Pall Mall Gazette* in December 1887: 'The question is really one of the acknowledgment of a moral relation between man and beast. Deny such relations, and men may clearly be as cruel to animals as they please. Admit it, and you still have a right to make a horse work for its living, but not to torture it.' His last statement on the subject was an addition to the manuscript of *Shaw on Vivisection* in 1948. The brackets indicate portions of the statement which were deleted before publication.

> In 1945 the physicists, not the vivisectors, discovered how to disintegrate the atom [with the result imagined by Mr H.G. Wells years before]. It stopped a ruinous world war instantaneously. The Anglo-American armies, who alone knew the process, wiped out two Japanese cities with it in a few seconds. The Japanese Alliance at once surrendered at discretion and laid down its arms, leaving the world completely terrorized, victors and vanquished alike [for nothing can now save civilization but that human kindness which the Vivisectors had trained us to repudiate]. With the ground thus cut from under our feet, and vivisectional amorality applied to ourselves more ruthlessly than to the dogs, we can do nothing so far but tremble.

166 Menu prepared by Charlotte Shaw for chefs of hotels and ships when the Shaws were travelling. In Blanche Patch's autobiography, *Thirty Years with G.B.S.* (1951).

> Mr. Bernard Shaw does not eat MEAT, GAME, FOWL OR FISH, or take TEA or COFFEE. Instead he will want one of the undermentioned dishes at lunch and dinner. He will eat green vegetables, puddings, pastry, etc., cheese and dessert like other people. He likes oranges and salads and nuts—especially walnuts.

167 Written interview: replies to questions by Dorothy Royal on vegetarianism and postwar food shortages. 2 pp. (paste-up), 3 March 1946.

> Vegetarians are rather more pugnacious and ferocious than carnivora. Bulls, elephants, and Hitlers (he was a vegetarian and teetotaller) are cases in point.

168 Statement on vegetarianism to be communicated by Shaw's assistant, Dr F.E. Loewenstein. Autograph note at the head of an autograph letter, dated 29 October 1946, from L.D. Kelsey, Washington, D.C.

> Say I have not eaten fish flesh nor fowl for sixty years, and am therefore a living proof that they are unne[ce]ssary as diet; but as my parents and many of my relatives, [none] of whom were vegetarians, were longlived, and centenarians are mostly carnivorous, I do not believe that diet affects the duration of human life. My objection to meat is that it costs too much and involves a slavery of men and women to edible animals that is undesirable.

169 Printed postcard on vegetarianism (dated 1947 in text, but postmarked 15 December 1946), with revisions for a new printing in 1948. Shaw first experimented with vegetarianism in January 1881 after suffering severe monthly headaches. Although the diet did not relieve the migraines, he remained a vegetarian until his death nearly seventy years later—except for a few lapses, as at Bayreuth on 28 July 1889, when he noted in his diary: 'Dined at the restaurant, eating some salmon in the absence of anything more vegetarian.' WITH: Typewritten 'Headaches' chart compiled by Shaw from entries in his pocket diaries, 1917–19; additional data for 1920, 1922, and 1923 are added in Shaw's autograph. A note at the foot, written by his secretary, Ann M. Elder, concerns the health of his sister Lucy, who died on 27 March 1920. Eva Schneider was her nurse-companion.

170 Letter on capital punishment, to an unidentified correspondent. Autograph draft, 23 March 1907. A young man named Horace Rayner had just been sentenced to death for the murder of a London merchant-prince, and Shaw had been asked to lend his name to an appeal for a reprieve of the sentence. Shaw had long viewed life imprisonment as 'a curious sort of mercy' for a man considered impossible to reform, useless to torture, and dangerous to release.

> Rayner seems to me to be a dangerous man; and as I am vehemently [opposed] to punishment of any kind, as a thing entirely vicious and mischievous, I am an advocate of the removal of dangerous men. People who go about vindicating popular morality with revolvers on their private responsibility are not fit for London life any more than a tiger or a mad dog is fit for it. You dont punish a tiger or a mad dog; but you kill it. . . .

171 Statement of views on cremation 'in its effect on the detection of crime.' Autograph note on a typewritten letter, dated 10 August 1910, from Frederick J. Higginbottom, editor of the *Pall Mall Gazette*. Shaw, a longtime advocate of cremation, owned shares for many years in crematoria.

> It is really inexcusable carelessness to get hanged at present. A brief study of our system of death certification will enable any intelligent person to commit such murders as he (or she) may desire with impunity, and with perfect consideration for the feelings of the relatives. . . . Our attachment to the practice of interment is not sentiment or respect for the dead, but superstition, stupidity, and slavery to the wrong sort of imagination—the imagination that conceives unseen things as they are not and cannot be as distinguished from the imagination that sees unseen things as they are and must be.

172 *Imprisonment*. This lengthy polemic on the faults of the British prison system was written as a preface to Sidney and Beatrice Webb's *English Prisons under Local Government* (1922). It presented Shaw's view that imprisonment as it existed in Britain 'is a worse crime than any of those committed by its victims; for no single criminal can be as powerful for evil, or as unrestrained in its exercise, as an organized nation.' In 1925 a special edition of *Imprisonment* was published in New York, 'issued by the Department of Christian Social Service of the National Council of the Protestant Episcopal Church.' Additionally it was serialized in the Hearst chain of newspapers; reprinted in Shaw's collected works and Standard Edition; reissued in Britain in 1944 by the Medical Reform Council; and republished in the United States in 1946 as *The Crime of Punishment*.

173 *Bernard Shaw on Capital Punishment*. Printed postcard. Addressed by Shaw's assistant, Dr F.E. Loewenstein, to the theatrical manager Roy Limbert, 12 October 1949.

Revenge, officially bowdlerized as Retribution, is natural to us: but it is ruled out as an evil passion by Christian civilization, involving as it does the horror of a State service of merciless tormentors, including warders and wardresses, hardly more free than their prisoners, having their lives wasted in vindictive cruelty.

*174 Temperance poster, series No. 260; undated. 'Alcohol makes men happy by dulling their consciences. George Bernard Shaw.' Issued by the Temperance Council of the Christian Churches of England and Wales.

175 *The Drink Question*. Typewritten manuscript, unfinished; revised by Shaw on the first page, with corrections on the remaining pages made later by his secretary Blanche Patch. 13 pp; undated (1919). The essay opens with a parody of Shakespear's 'To be or not to be' soliloquy, and goes on to consider the effect narcotics have on society in general and on artists in particular.

Coleridge and De Quincey did some very fascinating work on opium. How much Dante Rossetti did on drugs, I do not know: they certainly ended in his becoming impossible both as an artist and a human being. Wilkie Collins wrote some capital novels on Dutch inspiration; and De Maupassant assisted nature in the same way. But these and all the cases I have ever heard of shew that the artist who drinks or drugs pays for it with half his career. He may flash like a meteor across the horizon, and leave a radiance that secures him a tragic notice in the biographical dictionary; but premature collapse has always followed.

176 Written interview on prohibition, 29 January 1924, supplied to the American journalist Perriton Maxwell on his typewritten letter of 17 January. If Shaw were an American citizen, Maxwell asked, how would he deal with the constitutional amendment prohibiting manufacture, sale and consumption of alcoholic beverages?

> I should decree that all bootleggers and their customers should be held in jail and fed on alcohol until they implored to be allowed to swear off for life, and signed a thousand dollar bond to be forfeited on their first relapse.

177 *Bernard Shaw on Temperance.* Galley proof, with a few corrections, passed for press by Shaw on 18 June 1947. The text was reproduced from a printed postcard Shaw had just distributed to the press.

> I wrote many years ago that drink is the chloroform which enables the poor to endure the painful operation of living. The failure of prohibition has since proved that compulsory abstinence is impracticable. We must first get rid of poverty, and make reasonable happiness possible without anæsthetics.

178 Alphabet reform: experiments designed to determine the amounts of writing time saved. Autograph manuscript, undated. 3 pp. Shaw's findings were embodied in a letter to the editor, 'Orthography of the Bomb: Save as You Spell', published in the *Times*, London, 27 December 1945. Shaw endeavored for several years to obtain advice and assistance from some existing government department, learned society, or other body as to the setting up and putting into practice of his scheme for alphabet reform, which was, he emphasized, 'purely economic', its object being 'to save time and labor.' When his efforts failed, he directed in his will that the first claim on his estate be the financing of a reformed English alphabet along the lines he had suggested in his lifetime. After his Trustee informed the High Court in 1957 that he was unable to deal with the matter practically, Mr Justice Harman in the High Court of Justice, Chancery Division, issued a declaration that this provision in the will

was legally invalid. The moneys thus were diverted to the residuary legatees: the British Museum, the National Gallery of Ireland, and the Royal Academy of Dramatic Art. When the Shaw Society, backed by funds from I.J. (later Sir James) Pitman and other alphabet reform enthusiasts, indicated that it would appeal the decision, the Trustee and the legatees compromised by establishing a competition for the designing of a new alphabet and the publication, in 1962, as Shaw had wished, of his play *Androcles and the Lion* in that 48-character script.

Displayed is a copy of Shaw's play *Androcles and the Lion*: 'Printed in the Shaw Alphabet with a parallel transcription in traditional orthography'. This is one of the copies of the 'Public Trustee's Edition', published on 22 November 1962, bound in cloth boards, distributed gratis to principal libraries and institutions throughout the world. An inexpensive trade edition in paper wrappers was issued simultaneously by Penguin Books in Britain and the United States.

179 Press release drafted by Shaw for the Associated Press, in response to an American attack on his proposals for a phonetic English alphabet. Autograph manuscript, written on the reverse of a December 1945 calendar slip. Published on 3 January 1946. Dr Charles Funk, an American philologist, had alleged that a Shaw-styled alphabet would destroy literary ties between Britain and America. Shaw called this an absurdity.

> It is precisely the lack of a phonetic alphabet that makes possible the differences in pronunciation not only between the east and west of the Atlantic but between the east and west of London and of New York. These differences do break up social ties, and in fact make intimate ones impossible (I could not dine with a man who called me Boyned Shore or Bunned Shorr); but a phonetic alphabet is the remedy, not the disease.

180 *Colossal Labor Saving* (1947). A folio leaflet, printed on antique wove foolscap, deckle-edged. Three copies. No. 1 is a proof, 11 February 1947, with a request for a revise. No. 2 is the published text, issued on 9 May 1947. No. 3 is a copy of the published text revised and approved for press, 30 June 1947, for a second impression which did not materialize. This 'Open Letter' on alphabet reform was posted to 600 members of Parliament, 200 'active' members of the

House of Lords, 78 members of the Parliament of Northern Ireland, 139 members of the Irish Dail, and 60 members of the Irish Senate. WITH: *A Forty Letter British Alfabet.* Autograph draft for a printed postcard; undated (ca. 1947).

THEATER

181 To Florence Farr. Typewritten letter, 28 January 1892.

> You are wrong to scorn farcical comedy. It is by jingling the bells of a jester's cap that I, like Heine, have made people listen to me. All genuinely intellectual work is humorous. You can create your part in a farcical comedy: in Rosmersholm you can only offer yourself as an imitation of something created by Ibsen.

182 To Henry Arthur Jones. Autograph letter, 24 December 1894. A letter on dramatic art from one practising dramatist to another, Shaw having just completed his fifth play.

> Like you, I write plays because I like it, and because I cannot remember any period in my life when I could help inventing people and scenes. I am not a storyteller: things occur to me as scenes, with action and dialogue—as moments, developing themselves out of their own vitality.

183 Stage Society annual reports for its first five years, 1899–1904. Although Shaw was active in the Society from its inception (his play *You Never Can Tell* was its first production), he declined for several years to accept an official appointment to any of its committees to avoid charges of conflict of interest. Charlotte Shaw, however, served on the Reading and Advising Committee (with Shaw frequently subbing for her as a reader), and eventually both were appointed to the Committee of Management. WITH: Agenda for the executive meeting of 28 April 1908 covered with Shaw's doodles (to which is added an autograph note in 1929 acknowledging the 'art work' as his own); and readers' reports 1909–12, including Shaw's comments, on ten plays submitted to the committee, of which the following are displayed: George Moore, *The Apostle*; August Strindberg, *Creditors*; H. de Selincourt, *Love in a Mist*; Gilbert Cannan, *Miles Dixon*; Hermann Bahr, *The Fool and the Wise Man.* Of these, only the Strindberg and Bahr plays were produced, on a double bill, in the season 1911–12.

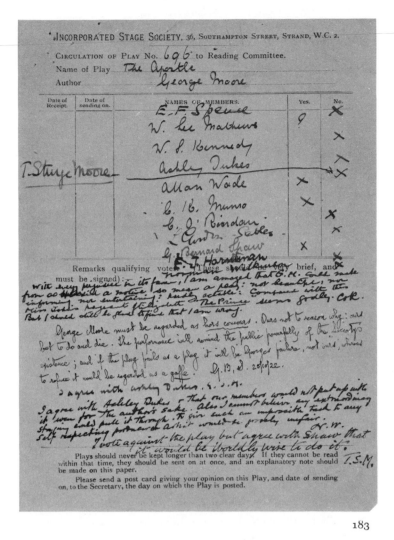

183

184 *Complimentary Dinner to Mr. J.E. Vedrenne and Mr. H. Granville Barker.* Souvenir of a dinner on 7 July 1907 to celebrate the successful completion of a three-year repertory experiment by John E. Vedrenne and Harley Granville Barker at the Court Theatre—an experiment which gave impetus to a movement for the creation of a National Theatre. Shaw, who had provided most of the financing for the experiment, and most of the plays (11 plays by Shaw were presented, for a total of 701 of the 988 recorded performances), delivered the major speech of the evening.

> I am glad to have the honour of speaking here for the Court Theatre authors, because if they had to answer for themselves they would be prevented from doing themselves justice by their modesty. Modesty, fortunately, is not in my

line; and if it were, I should . . . be modest on my own account, not on theirs. . . . We have, I think, proved that there is in this country plenty of dramatic faculty—faculty of the highest order too—only waiting for its opportunity; and it is the supreme merit of our guests this evening that they have provided that opportunity.

185 Memorandum of Agreement with Vedrenne-Barker. Autograph document, on leaves torn from a composition book; undated (July 1907). 11 pp. WITH: Typewritten Memorandum of Agreement, redrafted by Shaw's solicitor, J.G. Godard; undated (September 1907). 9 pp. The agreement provided for the formation of a guarantee fund of £4000 provided by Shaw for the season 1907–08 to secure the solvency of Vedrenne and Barker at the conclusion of their operations as managers of the Savoy Theatre, which they had just leased for the transfer of their operations to the West End, and as sponsors of a company touring the provinces with productions of Shaw's plays.

186 To Reginald Pound, journalist and author. Typewritten letter, 1 September 1923. This is actually a critique on the stage scenery of Joseph Harker and his contemporaries, intended for publication in Harker's autobiography *Studio and Stage* (1924), in which Pound was assisting.

187 To Hesketh Pearson, an actor who had appeared in the original production of *Androcles and the Lion* (1913), and who since the war had turned author. Twenty years later he became Shaw's biographer. Typewritten letter, 11 March 1920.

> What do you mean by Tchekov having no sense of the theatre? He had it in the rarest perfection. In matters of technique you must not judge a man by your enjoyment of his work, but solely on whether he produces the effect he aims at or bungles it. I dont know any playwright who has a surer or more cunning hand than Tchekov. You may not like it, but you cannot say that he muffs it.

The HRC possesses 80 pieces of Shaw correspondence (1918–50) to Pearson.

188 *Playwrights and Amateurs* (1920) and *What a Playwright Should Do with His First Play* (1921). These bits of advice were first published in the *Author*, house organ of the Society of Authors, of whose Dramatic Sub-Committee Shaw was a member. One hundred offprints of each article were run off for Shaw's personal use. He found them (like his printed postcards) so useful for dealing with correspondents that he ordered additional quantities on frequent occasions over the next twenty years.

189 *The Art of Rehearsal* (1928). Matthew Edward McNulty, a boyhood friend in Ireland, now in banking, who had written a play *Mrs Mulligan's Millions*, which he intended to direct, had solicited Shaw for advice on 'stage technique.' Shaw's practical theatrical advice, contained in a long letter on 9 June 1914, subsequently was published as a pamphlet, distributed by the New York playbroker firm Samuel French Inc. to interested novices.

190 To Kenneth Barnes, Secretary of the Royal Academy of Dramatic Art. Autograph note 'With Bernard Shaw's compliments', 16 May 1926, accompanying a 'Donation to be earmarked for the [Building] Fund'. The gift was £5000. Shaw was elected to the Academy's governing council in 1911, replacing the recently-deceased W.S. Gilbert. His first act was to chastize the council for lacking any distaff members, especially as the students were preponderantly female. By the end of 1912 the obdurate councillor won his battle with the appointment of the actress Irene Vanbrugh (sister to Barnes). For thirty years Shaw served the council faithfully and generously. Only once did he fail to perform a duty requested of him—when invited by Barnes to stand in as godparent at his son's baptism (Shaw's telegram on 4 January 1927 reads: 'After conscientious study of prayerbook find cannot comply without gross perjury . . . why tar helpless infant with my brush neutral tinted sponsor safer.'). On his 85th birthday, 26 July 1941, Shaw retired from the council, informing Barnes in a typewritten letter:

> Though I am ten years beyond the usual age for retirement I have been able to persuade myself that my lagging was not wholly superfluous; but 85 is the limit set by public decency as well as by my infirmity. . . .

The HRC possesses 62 pieces of Shaw correspondence (1914–50) to Barnes.

191 'For the Press.' Typewritten manuscript, with minor revision; undated (19 November 1938). A statement for the press, sent to the London producer of Shaw's new play *Geneva*, advocating modest ticket prices. Shaw had recently licensed the Federal Theatre in the United States to perform any of his published plays on the condition that the top admission price be fifty cents.

> I cannot imagine anything more ridiculous than an attempt to work out an equation between the price of theatre seats and the genius of the author of the play or of the performers. It would simply lead to pricing the stalls at a Shakespear or Shaw performance at a hundred guineas. . . .

THE PLAYS

(Dates are those of start and finish of original composition)

WIDOWERS' HOUSES (1884–92)

Shaw's first play was begun on 18 August 1884 under the provisional title *The Way to a Woman's Heart* (subsequently altered to *Rhinegold*), its plot suggested by the drama critic William Archer. Shaw struggled through two acts and an eventually abandoned fragment of a third, discarding Archer's plot along the way, and eventually dropping the project. He returned to the manuscript in 1887, but soon discarded it again—after Archer had fallen asleep while the two acts were being read to him. Another aborted effort followed in 1890. At last, encouraged by the critic J.T. Grein in 1892 to provide a play for his newly-founded Independent Theatre, Shaw was inspired to compose his third act and to prepare the manuscript for performance. Grein published it as No. 1 of the Independent Theatre Plays series in 1893.

192 Program of the first production, by the Independent Theatre Society, at the Royalty Theatre, London, 9 and 13 December 1892.

193 Revisions for the 1898 text of the play, in *Plays Pleasant and Unpleasant*. Autograph manuscript. 5 pp.

194 Program of the special production directed by Charles Charrington for the International Labour Festival on May Day 1900, at the Crystal Palace, London.

195 From Ben Iden Payne. Telegram, 23 July 1907, seeking permission for the Playgoers' Theatre Company, Manchester (precursor of the Gaiety Theatre) to produce the play for its first public run. WITH: Shaw's autograph draft of a message of approval.

196 From Ben Iden Payne. Typewritten letter, 24 July 1907, with autograph note by Shaw indicating that he had recommended the actress Mabel Hackney for the rôle of Blanche. The part eventually went to Mona Limerick, wife of Iden Payne.

197 Replies to inquiries by Floryan Sobieniowski, Shaw's Polish translator. Autograph manuscript, 31 March 1930. 2 pp. A signed note at the foot of the second page concerns the play *Heartbreak House*, scheduled for imminent production in Warsaw.

THE PHILANDERER (1893)

198 The play, which Shaw began on 14 March 1893, had its inception in a lurid encounter five weeks

The Independent Theatre
FOUNDED 1891.

Second Season—Sixth Performance.

"WIDOWERS' HOUSES,"

AN ORIGINAL
Didactic Realistic Play in 3 Acts,

BY

G. BERNARD SHAW.

Dramatis Personæ.

Harry Trench	...	...	...	MR. W. J. ROBERTSON
Cokane	...	...	...	MR. ARTHUR WHITTAKER
Sartorius	...	...	...	MR. T. W. PERCYVAL
Lickcheese	...	...	...	MR. JAMES WELCH
Waiter	...	...	...	MR. E. P. DONNE
Porter	...	...	...	MR. W. ALISON
Blanche	...	...	...	MISS FLORENCE FARR

By kind permission of Mr. C. HAWTREY.

Annie	...	*Parlour Maid*	... MISS N. DE SILVA

earlier between Shaw's rival paramours, Jane Patterson and Florence Farr (Mrs Edward Emery). Shaw recounted the episode in his diary on 4 February.

> In the evening I went to FE; & JP burst in on us very late in the evening. There was a most shocking scene, JP being violent and using atrocious language. At last I sent FE out of the room, having to restrain JP by force from attacking her. I was two hours getting her out of the house. . . . [*Transcription by Dr Stanley Rypins from Shaw's shorthand*]

199 To Florence Farr. Autograph letter on 19 small slips extracted from a pocket notepad, 1 May 1891, written on a joggling train after visiting Jane Patterson.

> At this moment I am in a contemptuous fury. . . . Not for forty thousand such relations will I forego one forty thousandth part of my relation with you. Every grain of cement she shakes from it falls like a block of granite on her own flimsy castle in the air, the work of [her] own imagination.

The HRC possesses 29 pieces of Shaw correspondence (1891-1909) to Florence Farr.

200 To Millicent Murby, a young Fabian, who had organized an amateur performance (and first theatre production) of *The Philanderer*. Autograph letter, 13 February 1905. Shaw indicates that he will attend one or two rehearsals.

201 To Florence Farr. Autograph letter, 8 February 1905. Shaw discusses Miss Murby's suspicions of his Superman theories relating to women as instruments of the Life Force.

202 Program and advertising flyer of the production by the New Stage Club, at the Cripplegate Institute, London, 20 February 1905.

203 Program of the first American production, by Winthrop Ames, at the Little Theatre, New York, 27 December 1913. WITH: Three photographs of Mr Ames's production at the Little Theatre, Chicago, during the 1914–15 season.

204 List of proposed alterations by Floryan Sobieniowski in the Polish translation of *The Philanderer*, with Shaw's notes of approval. Autograph manuscript, undated (ca. 1930–32). 5 pp. When Sobieniowski suggested the alteration of the Ibsen Club to the Bernard Shaw Club, Shaw responded: 'Yes (In England I should call it the St Bernard Club).'

> You have solved the problem . . . how to bring The Philanderer up to date and make it intelligible to people who have never heard of Ibsen.
> Naturally it never occurred to me; nor could I have becomingly suggested it if it had. But now that you propose it I see that it is the correct solution. . . .

MRS WARREN'S PROFESSION (1893)

205 Page proofs, datestamped 21 July 1897, for *Plays Pleasant and Unpleasant*, with revisions. These proofs of *Mrs Warren's Profession* were sent to Ellen Terry to read. She returned them with pencilled comments on small slips inserted in the appropriate places. In Act IV, when Vivie writes down her mother's qualifications—'the two words'—and then tears the paper to bits, Ellen Terry inquires: 'What are the two words?' The answer is supplied on the slip by Shaw: 'Prostitute and Procuress.'

206 To George Alexander Redford, Examiner of Plays in the office of the Lord Chamberlain. Autograph draft, 12 March 1898. Shaw, informed that the theatre manager has been denied a licence for a copyright reading performance of the play, asks the censor to bluepencil the allegedly offensive portions and to pass the remainder of the play to enable him to obtain protection against forfeiture of stage rights after the publication of the play in April. When Redford responded stubbornly that he had already issued 'an uncompromising Veto' and that 'dramatic expurgation' should be the work of the author, not of the examiner of plays, Shaw patiently prepared a new version of the play, converting Kitty Warren into a female Fagin and omitting the second act. Upon receipt of this emasculated version Redford authorized the issuance of a licence. The reading was held on 30 March.

207 To Harley Granville Barker, who had recently appeared as Eugene Marchbanks in the Stage Society production of *Candida*, and whom the Shaws looked upon as an adoptive son. Typewritten letter, 31 December 1901. Barker was rehearsing in *Mrs Warren's Profession* under Shaw's direction. Shaw, not content with writing plays, insisted through most of his dramatic career on controlling their stage destiny as well. He did his own casting and his own staging of virtually all of the first London productions (and many of the revivals and touring productions) from *Arms and the Man* in 1894 to *Saint Joan* in 1924, and thereafter frequently sat in on rehearsals, providing detailed notes and comments for the director and the cast.

> Instead of being incorrigibly good-for-nothing, you are incorrigibly the other thing. I have serious thoughts of having you to dinner on Sunday and making you very drunk; only I fear that you would become pious in your cups instead of gay. Instead of getting boundless amusement out of everything disastrous, you become the man of sorrows at every exhibition of human frailty, and seem to be bitterly reproaching me all through for the flippancy of my dialogue. Two rehearsals more, and you will draw tears even in the third act.

208 Program of the first performance, under the auspices of the Stage Society, at the New Lyric Club, London, 5 January 1902, autographed by Shaw on the first page. This was a private performance. The play was not approved for a public performance in England until more than 20 years later.

209 To Frederick H. Evans. Autograph letter, in pencil, 12 January 1902. Shaw is seeking to arrange for a photographic session with the cast. He is hesitant to invite Evans to take the pictures in his Adelphi Terrace flat, having doubts about the light, since the rooms are 'so low & so broad.' He thinks his mother's house in Fitzroy Square would probably be better. 'But I dont see how to manage the development of a plate in either house unless you get into a sack.' WITH: Three bromide prints by Evans: (a) Fanny Brough as Mrs Warren; (b) Granville Barker as Frank Gardner; (c) Madge McIntosh as Vivie Warren, writing 'the two words', with Julius Knight as Praed and Granville Barker looking on.
The HRC possesses 33 pieces of Shaw correspondence (1895–1922) to Evans.

210 Stage Society edition of *Mrs Warren's Profession* (1902), containing 12 photographs by Frederick H. Evans, with a new preface, 'The Author's Apology.' Inscribed on the halftitle (undated): 'to H.G. Wells | from G. Bernard Shaw. | MRS WARREN'S PROFESSION [*printed*] | or | Things One Tells | To a Man like Wells.'

ARMS AND THE MAN (1893–94)

211 Typewritten manuscript (dated 31 March 1894 by the typist), heavily revised and labelled 'AUTHOR' by Shaw on the cover of Act I. 76 pp. (each act separately covered). The typewritten title *Alps and Balkans* is altered on each cover, in Shaw's autograph, to *Arms and the Man*. He had earlier considered and discarded several alternative titles: *Emperor of Switzerland*, *Drums in the Rose Valleys*, *A Choice of Heroes*, *Indomitable!*, *There is But one Step—*, and *Two Sons of Mars*.

212 Three costume sketches, watercolored. These are part of a set of six pages of sketches by Shaw on cyclostyled stencils. The coloring may have been done by another hand. Unidentified pencilled handwriting.

213a

213 Four cabinet photographs (by Bullingham) of the first production, at the Avenue Theatre, London, 21 April 1894: (a) Act I: Alma Murray as Raina and Yorke Stephens as Bluntschli; (b) Act II: Bernard Gould as Sergius and Yorke Stephens; (c) Act II: Florence Farr as Louka and Bernard Gould; (d) Act III: James Welch as Petkoff and Alma Murray. WITH: Advertisement card: 'A Chorus of Approval from the Entire Press' (additional quotations on the reverse).

214 *Instructions to Producer*. Typewritten manuscript; undated. 2 pp.

> The most difficult part to cast is that of Sergius. Sergius is not a ridiculous personage, sent on the stage to be laughed at, but a superb man, brave, haughty, high-spirited, mag-

netic and handsome. The difficulty lies, not in finding an actor with these qualifications, but in inducing him to play a part in which all his attractions are reduced to tragic absurdity, in which he marries, not the heroine but the parlormaid, in which a rival actor repeatedly makes the audience laugh at his expense.

215 Research notes: autograph and shorthand, on four British Museum readers' tickets. These notes were gathered by Shaw for writing a defence of the play, published as 'A Dramatic Realist to His Critics' in the *New Review*, July 1894. WITH: Shorthand writers' notebook containing autograph research notes for the same article. 8 pp. (or fragments of pages).

216 Photograph (by Marceau of Philadelphia) of Arnold Daly as Bluntschli (1906).

217 Rehearsal notes for the 1911 production, which starred Arnold Daly, at the Criterion Theatre, London. 58 pp. Bound in is a list of performers seeking parts in the production. 2 pp.

CANDIDA (1894)

218 To Janet Achurch. Typewritten letter, 20 March 1895 (Shaw had begun to type his newspaper articles and correspondence, in March 1890, on a secondhand Barlock machine for which he had paid £13—on credit). WITH: Galley proof, revised by Shaw, of Dr F.E. Loewenstein's article 'What Richard Mansfield Thought of *Candida*' (1946). 'Interesting young woman', Shaw recorded in his diary in 1889 after attending the first performance of Ibsen's *A Doll's House*, in which Janet Achurch had appeared as Nora. ' "That one is a *divil*",' his mother remarked 'with intense conviction' as she sat beside Shaw in the theatre. Janet, her husband Charles Charrington, and Shaw quickly developed a warm personal friendship, and Shaw soon wrote *Candida* for her. Janet, unfortunately, was a hopeless drug addict, who burned out rapidly in spite of all of Shaw's desperate efforts to rehabilitate her. At the time of this letter Janet was in New York preparing to appear as leading lady to the American actor-manager Richard Mansfield, Shaw having insisted on her engagement as one of the conditions of his agreement with Mansfield. The latter, however, found her detestable, and eventually relinquished his rights in the unproduced play. 'I couldn't

have made love to your Candida', he told Shaw, 'if I had taken ether.'

219   To Frederick Whelen, founder of the Stage Society (1899). Two autograph postcards, 7 and 11 June 1900. Shaw insists on Henry V. Esmond for the rôle of Marchbanks in the Stage Society production: 'No Esmond, no Candida.' After seeing Granville Barker perform in the Society's production of Hauptmann's *The Coming of Peace* he allows his mind to be changed. '[Charles Charrington] was quite right about Granville Barker. . . . I am quite ready to try him.' And Barker it was who created the rôle in London.

The HRC possesses 36 pieces of Shaw correspondence (1893–1926) to Whelen.

220   Advertisement card for a series of special matinées sponsored by Granville Barker and J.E. Vedrenne at the Royal Court Theatre, London, in April and May 1904. The success of this first venture generated the Vedrenne-Barker repertory partnership.

221   Programs:

(a)   Copyright performance, Theatre Royal, South Shields, 30 March 1895 (a reading given by members of the touring company of *Arms and the Man*).

(b)   Première performance, Her Majesty's Theatre, Aberdeen, 30 July 1897, with Janet Achurch as Candida, Charles Charrington as Morell, Courtney Thorpe as Marchbanks, and Ellen Terry's daughter Edith Craig as Prossy.

(c)   Pirated first American performance by the Browning Society of Philadelphia, South Broad Street Theatre, 18 May 1903.

(d)   First authorized American performance, produced by Arnold Daly, Princess Theatre, New York, 8 December 1903. On this is a note by Shaw clarifying the sequence of the two American productions in 1903.

222   Report of royalties by Arnold Daly for the New York production, which began as a series of trial matinées and eventually completed a run of 133 performances between 8 December 1903 and 19 March 1904. The first matinée drew a house of only $19.17.

223   Photographs (by Hall) of the New York production, 1903: (a) Act II: Dorothy Donnelly as Candida,

Arnold Daly as Marchbanks, Dodson Mitchell as Morell; (b) Act III: Louise Closser as Prossy, Ernest Lawford as Lexy, and the three principals. [The latter is in the Leeds Gallery wall display.]

224   Portrait of Alice Archainbaud, who appeared as Candida in the first production in French translation (Brussels, 1907), photographed by P. Dupont-Emèra, Brussels. Inscribed: 'At [*sic*] Mr. Bernard Shaw the first and happy interpreter of so passionately interesting character of "Candida".'

*225   Poster for the French production of *Candida*, in the translation by Augustin and Henriette Hamon, Théâtre des Arts, Paris, 7 May 1908.

226   To Granville Barker. Autograph lettercard, undated (6 August 1908), from Munich, where Shaw has just viewed a performance of *Candida*, which he describes and illustrates.

227   From Katharine Cornell, the American actress-manager, who had first performed the rôle of Candida in New York in 1924. Typewritten letter, 16 June 1933, seeking permission to revive the play for a road tour. Shaw has noted on 29 June: 'Licensed for "as often as she likes". . . .' His shorthand reply to the letter is drafted on the reverse side. WITH: Photograph of Katharine Cornell as Candida and Marlon Brando as Marchbanks in her fourth and last New York production of the play in April 1946.

228   Tennessee Williams: college essay on *Candida*. Typewritten manuscript, with pencilled notes scribbled on reverse of the third page; undated. 3 pp. Speaking of the essay, Tennessee Williams commented recently: 'Since I attended 3 universities (Missouri, Washington & Iowa) I can't say where I wrote this piece. *Candida* does play better than it reads I discovered when I saw it years later. . . .' (*Shaw Review*, May 1977).

THE MAN OF DESTINY (1895)

229   To Janet Achurch. Autograph letter, 24 August 1895. Shaw, having just finished the first draft of *The Man of Destiny*, is writing about it to Janet. There is a sudden interruption. 'Great Heavens, I have just

rescued it from a frightful fate. I am lying in a field, writing in an old note book with a fountain pen. A foal came up behind me that time & was just stretching down for a mouthful of the little book with the play in it when I became aware of him.' WITH: Portrait in oils, 10″ by 12″, of Shaw at work on the play in the field, by Bertha Newcombe, an artist who was enamored of Shaw.

Everybody seems bent on recommending me to marry Bertha—a fact fatal to her hopes. . . . The feeling, as I understand it, is that there is a fearful danger of my marrying somebody, and that it is perhaps more prudent to pair me with Bertha than to run the risk of my being borne off by someone worse.

230 To Sir Henry Irving, noted British actor-manager. Shorthand draft of letter, 12 July 1896, with typewritten transcription, and autograph draft of a letter, 17 July. WITH: Memorandum of agreement, in an unidentified hand, signed by Shaw, witnessed by Edith Wardell (whose stage name was Craig). Ellen Terry, who liked the play, embarked on a campaign to induce Irving to produce it. Shaw, as an active drama critic, was fearful Irving would accept the play and pay a fee for the rights only as an attempt to buy him off, with no intention of performing it (which was Irving's custom in dealing with critics). Shaw therefore insisted upon protective terms and conditions which Irving eventually rejected. In the published Terry-Shaw correspondence in 1931, Shaw stated that the sequel proved that Irving, 'though contemptuously willing to pay me for control of the play, never had any serious intention of producing it'—even after Shaw had made him an extraordinary offer.

> PS. As to 1897, I will make one concession. If you produce a play by Ibsen—say Peer Gynt or The Pretenders . . . then I will not only consent to a postponement of 'The Man of Destiny' but will hand over the rights for all the world to you absolutely to do as you like with until your retirement, without fee or condition of any kind. But if you will excuse my saying so, I'm hanged if I'll be put off for Shakespear. Take him away: he lags superfluous.

231 Photograph (by Hall) of the New York production at the Carnegie Lyceum, 10 February 1904, with Arnold Daly as Napoleon and Edward Morrison as the Innkeeper. The presence of two little peasant girls, as well as of a soldier on guard duty in the background, suggests that it was an elaborate and expensive production.

232 From William Archer. Two autograph postcards from Tokyo, 8 June 1912, describing Archer's visit to Waseda University and to a performance of *The Man of Destiny* in a small private theatre. Scenes from the production are reproduced on the reverse side of the postcards. WITH: Photograph of the production, in which Shunsho Doi appeared as Napoleon and Sumako Matsui as the Strange Lady.

233 Memorandum of agreement with Frederick Harrison and Cyril Maude for production at the Haymarket Theatre, London. 5 pp. Shaw's signature was witnessed by Edward R. Pease, 26 February 1897. The play went into rehearsal on 9 April 1897, under Shaw's direction, but he was so dissatisfied with the casting, and the management so alarmed by his demands, that at the end of a fortnight of shared frustrations Shaw withdrew the production.

234 From Frederick Harrison. Autograph letter, 18 May 1897.

> I don't know how to express my appreciation of the way in which you met us over the withdrawal of your play. I sincerely hope that you will bring us another comedy presently, which we can carry to a successful issue.

235 Cyril Maude: *The Haymarket Theatre* (1903). Chapter XVI was ghostwritten by Shaw for insertion into Maude's history of the Haymarket Theatre. Typewritten manuscript, 7 pp., being a transcription made in 1913, with newly added revisions by Shaw, for translation by Augustin Hamon into French. Accompanied by a typewritten manuscript, 2 pp., dated January 1913, providing an explanatory introduction for French readers; it is headed, in Shaw's autograph, 'Bernard Shaw on the early history of his most popular comedy'.

236 From Daniel Frohman, New York theatrical producer. Autograph letter, 19 August 1896, expressing interest in a possible New York production. His brother Charles Frohman also sought to obtain the American rights in the play.

237 To Henry Arthur Jones. Autograph letter, in pencil, 23 August 1899. Shaw despairs of finding the players he needs.

> You Never Can Tell is a whited sepulchre. It looks as if a play with that waiter & those twins *couldnt* fail; but that ten minutes at the end of the second act requires a double-first comedian; and where is he to be found? Mrs Clandon too! who is to play her?

GARRICK THEATRE

HOYT & McKEE, Lessees.

CHARLES FROHMAN, Manager.
Also Manager of the Empire, Criterion and Herald Square Theatres,
New York City, and the
DUKE OF YORK'S and VAUDEVILLE THEATRES, LONDON, ENG.

Evenings, at 8.30.　　　　Matinees Wednesday and Saturday, at 2.15.

1905.

ARNOLD DALY

(LIEBLER & CO., Managers)

ANNOUNCES

BERNARD SHAW'S COMEDY,

YOU NEVER CAN TELL

The Cast

Mr. Crampton	George Farren
Mr. McComas	William H. Thompson
Mr. Valentine	Arnold Daly
Mr. Bohun	Harry Harwood
Philip Clandon	Summer Gard
William	John Findlay
Servants at the Marine Hotel {	Frank Hughes
	Leonard Gallager
Mrs. Clandon	Miss Jeffreys Lewis
Miss Clandon	Miss Drina de Wolfe
Dolly Clandon	Miss Mabel Taliaferro
Maid	Miss Eda Bruna

Programme continued on second page following.

238

238 Program of the first American professional production, by Arnold Daly, at the Garrick Theatre, New York, 9 January 1905. (There had been a prior performance in Chicago in 1903 by students of a local school of acting.) The scrawled notes were sent by Daly to Shaw, after the successful opening ('Really a triumph'), to boast of his high-salaried cast. The play ran for 129 performances. WITH: Act I photograph of Daly as Valentine and Mabel Taliaferro and Sumner Gard as the twins Dolly and Philip.

239 Textual cuts made by Arnold Daly for the New York production. Typewritten manuscript, 6 pp., iden-

tified in Shaw's hand. Notes by Daly indicate that some of the cuts subsequently were restored.

240 *Shavians at the Savoy.* Photographic reproduction, from the *Bystander* (London), 2 October 1907, of sketches by Chas. Sykes of the audience at a performance of *You Never Can Tell*, produced by Vedrenne and Barker at the Savoy Theatre.

241 To J.E. Vedrenne. A list of six translation titles of the play, in Spanish, French, German, Swedish, Danish-Norwegian, and Italian. Autograph manuscript, 1 February 1909. 1 p.

> Dutch & Russian are piracies (no international copyright) so I dont know the names. Bohemian & Hungarian translations are not yet named.

The HRC possesses 75 pieces of Shaw correspondence (1904–27) to Vedrenne.

242 To Anmer Hall, a London theatre manager and fellow member of the council of the Royal Academy of Dramatic Art. Typewritten letter, 22 January 1941.

> Dickens does not dramatize well, because his most excruciatingly funny characters do not develop. I have stolen some of them, and I know. The barrister in You Never Can Tell is obviously a rechauffée of Jaggers in Great Expectations, and he is effective enough; but he has only one entry and one scene. I could not have carried him through a whole play.

THE DEVIL'S DISCIPLE (1896)

243 List of queries concerning courts martial and military executions; undated (1896). 6 pp. Dictated to Charlotte Payne-Townshend (the future Mrs Bernard Shaw), who was serving as his secretary.

244 Research notes on General John Burgoyne, written on both sides of a British Museum readers' ticket; undated (1896? 1900?). May have been obtained for the 'Notes to The Devil's Disciple' appended to the play when published in *Three Plays for Puritans* (1901).

245 Program of the copyright performance, Bijou Theatre, London, 17 April 1897. For this reading Shaw conscripted Richard Mansfield's brother Felix and his family, who were visiting London. He himself, billed as 'Cashel Byron' (the pugilistic protagonist of his 1882 novel), played the Reverend Anthony Anderson.

*246 Poster for the copyright performance, Bijou Theatre, London, 17 April 1897.

247 To Richard Mansfield, whose production of *The Devil's Disciple* was then in rehearsal. Autograph draft of a postscript to a letter of 8 September 1897, concerning fees. (On the same leaf is the draft of a letter to Shaw's American agent, Elisabeth Marbury, informing her of the terms quoted to Mansfield.) WITH: Program of the first production, at the Fifth Avenue Theatre, New York, 4 October 1897, and a photograph of Mansfield as Dick Dudgeon.

> The moral of the figures is that you should break the back of this provincial sharing business by building a theatre for yourself, and pay me 15% instead of 10. It is no use trying to beat down the authors. . . . As to my own terms I am astonished at my moderation. I ought to have 25% to cover the risk of dealing with a genius void of conscience and the incarnation of caprice.

248 Boxoffice returns from the first production in England, presented by the actor-manager Murray Carson, at the Princess of Wales Theatre, Kennington (a suburb of London), 26 September (misdated October by the boxoffice manager) to 7 October 1899. The thirteen performances grossed just under £500.

*249 Program of the German production, in its second year in the repertory, at the Berliner Theater, Berlin, where it was first presented on 25 February 1903. Translated by Siegfried Trebitsch under the title *Ein Teufelskerl* (*A Devil of a Fellow*), this was the first Shaw play to be performed in translation.

250 Design for the Acts I and II fireplace, sketched by Shaw, with an undated autograph note, evidencing his concern for production details.

251 Note on costumes, on a small notebook leaf; undated (ca. 1907). 'All that need be said is that the Dudgeon family wear very sober colors, but Dick may be as flamboyant as he pleases. Forbes Robertson played the part in a flowered silk waistcoat, very ele-

gant.' WITH: Cabinet photograph (by Window & Grove) of Johnston Forbes-Robertson in the touring production of the play, which opened at the Coronet Theatre, Notting Hill Gate (London), 7 September 1900.

252 To Frederick Whelen. Autograph postcard, 28 March 1917. The play, Shaw informs Whelen, is very much in demand 'because it exploits anti-British sentiment; and for that reason I have withdrawn it.'

253 Two set designs and three stage designs by Shaw for the French production, in Augustin and Henriette Hamon's translation, at the Odéon, Paris, 23 March 1926.

CAESAR AND CLEOPATRA (1898)

254 Shaw's research notes, with a drawing of the Alexandria lighthouse on the first page; dated 1898 on the second page. 3 pp.

255 Typewritten (carbon) manuscript, with revisions in pencil; undated. 142 pp. On p. 13 of Act III, Shaw provides words and music to Apollodorus's Barcarolle; these have been inserted by hand. Inlaid at the front is an autograph postcard to an unidentified correspondent, 2 July 1916, tentatively authenticating the manuscript.

*256 Poster for the copyright performance, at the Theatre Royal, Newcastle-on-Tyne, 15 March 1899, with Mrs Patrick Campbell as Cleopatra. Granville Barker read the part of Lucius Septimius.

257 Autograph draft of the program for the copyright performance (1899). 4 pp. Two copies of the program, one with Shaw's autograph revisions for the program of the Johnston Forbes-Robertson production at the New Amsterdam Theatre, New York, 30 November 1906.

258 *Three Plays for Puritans* (1901). First edition, containing *The Devil's Disciple*, *Cæsar and Cleopatra*, and *Captain Brassbound's Conversion*. Unsigned presentation inscription on the halftitle: 'to Edward McNulty, my foster brother | in letters. | Jan 1901.'

*259 *Cæsar and Cleopatra. Exclamations & Interruptions for Extra Ladies & Gentlemen with Cues.* Autograph manuscript, dated 1906, on rectangular slips, consisting of specific phrases of dialogue to be assigned to each extra performer throughout the play. 17 pp. An example of Shaw's extraordinary concern for preciseness in his staging.

260 From Johnston Forbes-Robertson. Autograph letter, 22 August 1906, containing a transcription of textual refinements Shaw had provided for Act I (later retitled Prologue). Shaw sends him by return post a small slip on which he has further improved the passage.

261 From Johnston Forbes-Robertson. Cablegram from New York, 31 October 1906, after the appearance of the morning's critical notices. A one word message: 'Hurrah.' WITH: Program of the first production, at the New Amsterdam Theatre, New York, and a photograph (by Hart) of Act IV, with Forbes-Robertson as Cæsar and his wife Gertrude Elliott as Cleopatra. A second photograph (by the Daily Mirror Studios) is of Forbes-Robertson's 1907 London production: Act I, Cæsar and Cleopatra seated on the paws of the sphinx.

262 Typewritten manuscript of a 'Prologue' to be substituted for the original Act I; it was subsequently captioned 'An alternative to the Prologue.' 5 pp. The length of the play had long been a production problem, with the third act as a rule having to be omitted. In 1912 Shaw wrote a 'Prologue' for Forbes-Robertson's 'farewell tour' revival of the play, allowing him to drop Act I and restore Act III. Proofs were printed, datestamped 16 August (Second Proof) and 26 August (Third Proof). Shaw's note on the typescript indicates that he abridged the prologue for Barry Jackson's production at the Kingsway Theatre, London, 21 April 1925, in which for the first time Acts I and III both were performed in full: 'Barry Jackson produced the play with only one interval, thereby saving time enough to avoid all the old omissions, but also making part of the prologue superfluous.'

On the reverse of the last leaf is an inscription by Floryan Sobieniowski inaccurately identifying the manuscript as the original, uncut prologue, and misdating it 1911.

263 Photograph of Helen Hayes as Cleopatra, in the Theatre Guild production, New York, 13 April 1925. The Cæsar was Lionel Atwill.

CAPTAIN BRASSBOUND'S CONVERSION (1899)

264 Typewritten questionnaire prepared by Shaw for R.B. Cunninghame Graham, Scottish traveller and

writer, on physical details for the play. Cunninghame Graham returned it with autograph responses; undated (1900). 5 pp. (on 4 leaves). Shaw asks how a missionary in Mogador would be dressed on a hot afternoon; how one pronounces Sheikh, Mogador, and Franguestan; and whether he may 'safely cull flowers of Eastern speech from Captain Burton's Arabian Nights.'

*265 Poster for the copyright performance, at the Royal Court Theatre, Liverpool, 10 October 1899, with Ellen Terry as Lady Cicely and Laurence Irving as Captain Brassbound.

266 To Ada Rehan, Irish-born American actress. Typewritten letter, 5 July 1904. Shaw had written the play, under the title *The Witch of Atlas*, especially for Ellen Terry, but she disappointedly found it unsatisfying ('I couldn't do this one', she wrote to Shaw, 'and I believe it would never do for the stage.') In 1904 he sought to persuade Ada Rehan to perform the play, first in London and then in America, informing her untruthfully that *she* had been in his mind when he created the play. He flattered, cajoled, and humored her for several months, but eventually was defeated by her prior managerial commitments and ill health. By that time Ellen Terry had changed her mind and agreed to appear in the play for the Vedrenne-Barker management.

The HRC possesses 24 pieces of Shaw correspondence (1901–07) to Ada Rehan.

267 To Ada Rehan. Two picture postcards bearing photographs of Shaw, both postmarked 10 August 1905, from Rosscarbery, Ireland. Each has a caption in Shaw's autograph below the portrait. The first reads: 'GOLD HAIR before Lady Cicely jilted him.' The second reads: 'WHITE HAIR after Lady Cicely jilted him.'

268 From Lillie Langtry, actress-manager, called the Jersey Lily. (The west Texas town of Langtry was named for her by Judge Roy Bean.) Autograph letter, 26 March 1902 (dated by Shaw). Miss Langtry was one of many British and American actresses who made bids for the play. Shaw decided, after consulting William Archer, that she could not do justice to the rôle and declined her offer.

269 From Ellen Terry. Autograph letter, 30 December 1905, addressed to 'Dear Silly' and apologizing to Charlotte Shaw 'for calling her husband a "wicked" name!' With rehearsals for the Vedrenne-Barker production in the offing, under Shaw's direction, Ellen has begun to worry about her ability to handle the rôle of Lady Cicely, and advises Shaw: 'I sh^d like a month's rehearsals, please.' 'Chris' was Ellen's young companion Christopher St John, who later edited the Terry-Shaw correspondence. With: Photograph of the production at the Royal Court Theatre, 20 March 1906, with Ellen Terry as Lady Cicely Waynflete and Frederick Kerr as Captain Brassbound.

270 To Harley Granville Barker. Autograph letter, 14 March 1906. Rehearsals had commenced in February, and the performance was now only six days away. Ellen Terry's insecurity had become something of a problem. To ease her tension Shaw allowed Barker to take over the rehearsals.

> Do not let Ellen repeat any scene. When she gets through she always wants to do it over and over again until it is right. There are two fatal objections. 1. She always goes to pieces the second time & discourages & demoralizes herself more & more every time. 2. She has just strength enough to get through the play once without tiring herself . . . and the repetition of a scene means a corresponding omission at the end. Go straight through & dont let them stop for anything.

*271 Chanty composed by Shaw for Act III. Autograph music manuscript, with Shaw's lyrics inserted; undated (1906).

*272 Dialogue for the five extras representing Brassbound's crew. Autograph manuscript, dated 'Oct 1912 Little Theatre'. 2 pp. Shaw was directing a revival of the play with Gertrude Kingston as Lady Cicely.

THE ADMIRABLE BASHVILLE (1901)

273 Program of the Amateur Boxing Championships, Lillie Bridge Grounds, London, 17 March 1883. Shaw entered both the Middle Weight and Heavy Weight classes, but his name was not drawn for competition in either class. Entered with him was his friend and chief sparring partner, the poet Pakenham Beatty. WITH: Envelope, postmarked 28 March 1882, comically addressed by Beatty to 'Gully Belcher Shaw', on which Shaw has drawn two ink sketches of pugilists. Shaw was in Leyton, at the home of his uncle, Dr Walter Gurly, convalescing from a light attack of scarlet fever.

274 From Pakenham Beatty. Autograph letter, [8 March 1901], with Shaw's autograph comments added. Beatty has just read a typescript of *The Admirable Bashville*, Shaw's adaptation in Elizabethan-styled (and parodied) blank verse of his 1882 novel *Cashel Byron's Profession*.

> In your old age you will be able to say, as poor Simon Finighty once said to me—after four 'goes of gin'—'It's no use a-denying of it—*I was clever.*' Your blank verse is admirable—indeed some lines are so really fine that I had intended to prig them.

275 To Pakenham Beatty. Autograph letter, 6 April 1901, in reply to Beatty's letter of 8 March.

> Glad you found only one Irish trysyllable: there were several in my first draft, the best of them being forearm (four are um). I mentioned this & your discovery of fighersides to [Sydney] Cockerell; but he poured forth such a flood of precedents from Morris & other eminent poets that I came to the conclusion that Poe's fire-higher rhyme [in 'The Bells'] is classical.

276 *Novels of His Nonage No. 4: Cashel Byron's Profession. Newly Revised* (1901), containing the first publication of *The Admirable Bashville; or, Con-*

stancy Unrewarded. The author's own copy, containing his stage directions, notes, and set plans for two productions of the play. For the first, presented by the Stage Society at the Imperial Theatre, London, 7 and 8 June 1903, the notations are in black ink. For the second, presented by the After Noon Theatre at His Majesty's Theatre, London, 26 January 1909, the notations are in red ink.

277 To Harley Granville Barker. Autograph letter, 23 April 1903, from Orvieto. Shaw authorizes a Stage Society production of the play, but warns Barker that 'it is not a burlesque', and 'should be announced simply as Bernard Shaw's celebrated drama in blank verse . . . being the only authorized dramatic version of the author's famous novel entitled "Cashel Byron's Profession." "If you have tears, prepare to shed them now." Shakespear.' He then provides a series of comic announcements for the program.

278 Photograph of the play *Cashel Byron's Profession*, an unauthorized dramatization of the novel by Stanislaus Stange (who was later to provide the English libretto for *The Chocolate Soldier*), at Daly's Theatre, New York, 8 January 1906. James J. Corbett, former world's champion prizefighter, played Cashel.

MAN AND SUPERMAN (1901–02)

279 Added dialogue for Act IV, with revisions; undated (ca. 1901–02). 1 p. At the foot are four drawings by Shaw of set plans, one of which is scribbled over for deletion. *Man and Superman*, which was Shaw's first attempt to deal dramaturgically with 'Creative Evolution', his religion for the XX century, is one of very few Shaw plays for which no draft manuscript survives.

280 Research inquiries, headed 'Look up at Museum &c. for Superman'; undated (1902). 2 pp. These are questions relating to the preface, the stage directions, and the appended text of John Tanner's *The Revolutionist's Handbook*; they range from the accuracy of references to Bunyan's *The Pilgrim's Progress* to the history of Spain and the legends of Don Juan.

Folkestone Sunday fares.
Title of Delaroche's Beaux Arts painting . . .
Solitary confinement 6 or 9 months?

Was Little Faith attacked by Wildhead Incon[siderate] & Prag[matick]? . . .
Alphonse de Royer 1863 gave a translation. 'Séducteur de Seville.'

*281 Poster for copyright performance, at the Victoria Hall (Bijou Theatre), Bayswater, 29 June 1903. The poster is hand-lettered in black ink, on brown butcher paper.

282 Instructions to the printer for a proposed 'Acting Version'. Typewritten manuscript, heavily revised; undated (ca. 1905). 2 pp. This version of the play, designed to omit the entire third act, including the dream of Don Juan in Hell, and to provide a number of small but significant textual alterations, was never published. The textual revisions were subsequently discarded.

283 Rehearsal text, labelled 'Malone', consisting of unbound quires of the 1903 published text. Stamped 'The property of | Vedrenne & Barker | Royal Court Theatre'; additional dialogue (in Charlotte Shaw's hand) is affixed to p. 145 (renumbered p. 73 in ink). The rôle of Hector Malone in the 1905 Court Theatre production was played by Hubert Harben.

284 Program of the first American production, presented by Charles Dillingham, at the Hudson Theatre, New York, 5 September 1905. WITH: Photograph (by Hall) of Act I. Fay Davis as Ann Whitefield, Lewis Massen as Roebuck Ramsden, Robert Loraine (seated on desk) as John Tanner, Lois Frances Clark as Mrs Whitefield, and Alfred Hickman as Octavius Robinson.

320   The Admirable Bashville   [Act II

Aiming beside the angle of the jaw
And landing with a certain delicate screw
I without violence knock my foeman out.
Mark how he falls forward upon his face!
The rules allow ten seconds to get up ;
And as the man is still quite silly, I
Might safely finish him ; but my respect
For your most gracious majesty's desire
To see some further triumphs of the science
Of self-defence postpones awhile his doom.

PARADISE. How can a bloke do hisself proper justice
With pillows on his fists?

THE CROWD.   Unfair!   The rules!

CETEWAYO. The joy of battle surges boiling up
And bids me join the mellay.

THE CHIEFS.   Victory and Isandhlana!

LUCIAN. Forbear these most irregular proceedings.
Police! Police!

A POLICEMAN. Give us a lead, sir.   Save the English
flag.
Africa tramples on it.

CASHEL.   Africa!
Not all the continents whose mighty shoulders
The dancing diamonds of the seas bedeck

Act II]   Constancy Unrewarded   321

Shall trample on the blue with spots of white.
Now, Lydia, mark thy lover,

LYDIA.   Hercules
Cannot withstand him.   See: the king is down ;
The tallest chief is up, heels over head,
Tossed corklike oer my Cashel's sinewy back;
And his lieutenant all deflated gasps
For breath upon the sand.   The others fly
In vain: his fist oer magic distances
Like a chameleon's tongue shoots to its mark ;
And the last African upon his knees
Sues piteously for quarter.   [Rushing into CASHEL's arms]
Oh, my hero :
Thoust saved us all this day.

CASHEL.   Twas all for thee.

CETEWAYO [trying to rise] Have I been struck by
lightning?

LUCIAN.   Sir, your conduct
Can only be described as most ungentlemanly.

POLICEMAN. One of the prone is white.   Tis Paradise.

CASHEL.

POLICEMAN. He's choking : he has something in his
mouth.

LYDIA [to CASHEL] Oh Heaven! there is blood upon
your hip.
Youre hurt.

CASHEL.   The morsel in yon wretch's mouth
Was bitten out of me.
[Sensation.   LYDIA screams and swoons in CASHEL's
arms.

*285 Five photographs (by Hall) of the first American production of *Man and Superman*, at the Hudson Theatre, New York, 5 September 1905.

286 Charles Ricketts: Costume sketch of the Devil, in watercolor and brown ink, on reverse of an undated (May 1907) autograph letter from Ricketts to Shaw concerning his costume designs for the production of *Don Juan in Hell* (the third act, hitherto unperformed in Britain, of *Man and Superman*) by Vedrenne and Barker at the Royal Court Theatre, London, on 4 June 1907, to be presented for a series of eight matinées. This is one of three undated letters concerning the production, each with a Ricketts drawing, bound together.

> I have altered the character of Mephistopheles' dress. He no longer looks like that of Gounod. . . . [T]his dress allows for quite a stout man[.]

287 *Don Juan in Hell.* 'Analytical programme' by Shaw for the edification of the firstnight critics, inserted into the programs at the first performance on 4 June 1907.

> As this scene may prove puzzling·at a first hearing to those who are not to some extent skilled in modern theology, the Management have asked the Author to offer the Court audience the same assistance that concert goers are accustomed to receive. . . .

JOHN BULL'S OTHER ISLAND (1904)

*288 Autograph manuscript, in four pocket notebooks. 314 pages on 275 leaves (including 25 dictated pages, in Charlotte Shaw's hand, with revisions and additions by Shaw). Dated 18 March 1904 on the first text page of the first notebook. On the inner side of the upper cover of the first notebook is a presentation inscription: 'This is the original manuscript of John Bull's Other Island. Presented to Sydney Carlyle Cockerell on St Patrick's Day 1922 by G. Bernard Shaw'. The notebooks also contain 21 pages of notes (partly in Charlotte Shaw's hand) on Free Trade; shorthand notes in both the Henry Sweet and Pitman systems; a draft of a postscript to a letter; and a list of persons to whom letters were owed. Each notebook contains the bookplate of Louis H. Silver.

*289 Preface. Autograph manuscript in ink and pencil, revised; incomplete; dated 3 April 1906. 59 pp.,

several of which are composite pasteups. Bound by Rivière in dark blue morocco with gilt dentelles. Presentation inscription on the front free endpaper, to Sydney Cockerell from Shaw, dated Christmas 1929. Contains the bookplate of Louis H. Silver. Bound in with the manuscript are 13 letters and postcards from Shaw to Cockerell and 3 photographs of Shaw, mounted. Loosely inserted in the volume is a four-page fragment of a shorthand manuscript of Shaw's preface to the sixpenny 'Home Rule Edition' of the play, 1912.

290 From Hilaire Belloc, poet and essayist. Typewritten letter, 4 September 1903. A long, detailed response to Shaw's inquiries relating to the character Peter Keegan.

> Quite simple. If a priest goes mad, or whatnot, that has nothing to do with his apostolical succession. It sticks to him for ever, but that has nothing whatever to do with the doctrines he may choose to preach in his madness. . . . [If] you make your priest in your play take to practical Christianity, or any other horror, you must have his papers taken away from him—a phrase that will be easily understood by your audience, and especially by the un-frocked priests who will come in shoals to hear.

John Bull's Other Island. A play in four acts

Act I — Bernard Shaw — (title page)

first floor

A sitting room, half sitting room, half office, in Great George St, Westminster. Door in flat L to staircase landing. Door down R to bedroom. Fireplace R. Big table, consisting of a broad board on trestles, covered with engineer's plans, against flat R.C. Double writing table facing R & L in C, with chairs. Telephone &c, on desk. File cabinet L, with cupboard on top. Standing desk with stool down L, Umbrella stand R of door in flat. Electric bell push above fireplace R.

Four o'clock in the afternoon

Enter Hodson from landing, carrying large Gladstone bag and straps of rugs. He carries them into the bedroom, coming in at one door & out at the other without speaking. Hodson is a ...

288

291 To Harley Granville Barker. Two autograph postcards, 24 and 25 August 1904. Shaw is in a worried mood, expressing concern about the casting, the date of opening, problems of revision, and the tone of the title.

> There is no ending at all: only a transcendental conversation which will stagger the very soul of Vedrenne & send the audience away howling. . . . Rule Britannia will not do [as a title]: it is too frankly a jest; and we shall have to play off the piece as a very advanced and earnest card in the noble game of elevating the British theatre.

292 To Harley Granville Barker. Autograph postcard, 7 September 1904. Shaw has completed the play, and has sent the manuscript to be typed: 'To my horror I find on a rough computation that the thing contains about 32,000 words of dialogue. . . . I am too floored to attempt cutting as yet.' The play, even after subsequent drastic cutting, ran over three hours in performance. This, Shaw admitted in his typewritten *Instructions to the Producer* (see No. 300), 'is extremely exhausting to the audience; but the piece will hold them for that time better than a more cut version will hold them for a shorter time.' Although this proved to be the case in London, the New York critics thought the long play insufferably dull, and it closed after 13 performances. In America it remains the least known and most underrated of any of Shaw's major works.

293 Watercolor by Shaw for the Act III setting (1904). Autograph note in pencil on reverse, indicating the need for a practicable house door, gate, and path round to the back of the house. 'This means that the house must not be painted on the back cloth. The ambig[u]ous object near the tree is the inverted basket on which Haffigan sits. The tree is dispensable.'

294 Added dialogue for Patsy in Act II. Autograph manuscript; undated. 1 p. This fragment does not appear in any published edition of the play. It seems to be a reply to Nora's admonition of Patsy, as he enters loaded up with parcels and provisions, for the unsanitary act of taking the goose's neck in his mouth.

> An' how would a poor boy like me know what the likes of *you* would think right? It's little thanks I do be gettin' for me throuble, an' me offerin to let the weight of the goose maybe pull the teeth out o' me head, God help me.

295 Rehearsal notes for the first production at the Court Theatre, London, 1 November 1904. 21 pp.

296 To J.L. Shine, who played Larry Doyle in the first production. Two typewritten letters, 29 October and 1 November 1904, containing final instructions, voicing concern about audibility, and offering congratulations.

> You [and Louis Calvert, playing Broadbent] will both be remembered in the parts; and nothing is rarer than a really memorable performance.
>
> I think you owe St Peter a candle or two; but your church policy was excellent at such short notice, though the martyrs got a little extra martyrdom.

297 To William T. Stead, editor of the *Review of Reviews*. Autograph postcard, 23 November 1904. Shaw has been getting assistance from Stead in dealing with technical details of the play.

> I have just learned that the correct technical term to substitute for 'disfrocked priest' is 'silenced priest.'
>   By the way, Patsy isnt half witted. That's complete mental competence in Ireland.

298 William Archer, *A Record and Commentary of the Vedrenne-Barker Season 1904–1905*. Illustrated pamphlet, containing photographs of the principal performers in *John Bull's Other Island*. WITH: Small advertisement card, announcing six 'Special Matinees' of the play between 1 and 11 November 1904.

299 Typewritten manuscript, labelled by Shaw on the cover of each separately bound act 'Cut Copy for Stage use only', with pencilled revisions by Shaw and Charlotte Shaw and insubstantial cuts; undated (1904). 113 pp. Bound in is an autograph letter from Arthur Conan Doyle, 6 October 1905, expressing his enjoyment of a performance: 'It is the very best play, the wisest and the wittiest that I can ever remember.' Also bound in is the Court Theatre boxoffice final return for the 'Performance—at the King's Request' on 11 March 1905. Shaw, who had refused to sanction a command performance, noted on the boxoffice statement: 'Sent me with cheque for £16–8–3 royalty at 10%, which I returned, not making any charge for the performance.'

300 *The Author's Instructions to the Producer*, dated Christmas 1904. Typewritten (carbon) manuscript, with revisions. 7 pp. A guide for the American producer (presumably Arnold Daly, who presented the play in New York in October 1905).

> Unless the most unsparing vigilance be exercised, the scene-painter, the company, and the costumier will proceed on the assumption that an Irish Round Tower resembles a ruined mediaeval castle; that an Irish land-agent's house is a thatched hovel with magnificent tree wings; that all Irishmen wear very long frock coats with large holes in them stuffed with wisps of straw, knee breeches, and battered hats with clay pipes stuck through them; and that mean is pronounced mane, sleep slape etc. by Irish people of all classes.

301 Autograph memorandum on costume, undated, labelled 'File John Bull'. Beside a portrait of an Irishwoman ('The late Miss Younge'), extracted from a journal, Shaw has noted: 'Typical Irish Victorian dress XIX century, say 1875. — for Nora in John Bull's Other Island.'

302 *John Bull's Other Island* (1920). This volume, known as the 'heros and martyrs' copy, was the only work by an Irish author allowed to circulate in the wards of the Women's Gaol at Kilmainham, Ireland, towards the end of the civil war, in 1923. The political prisoners signed and circulated it to identify themselves to each other and to pass along messages. It was presented to Shaw some years later by the proprietor of the Four Courts Book Store, Dublin.

*303 Henry Tonks: Portrait of William Poel as Peter Keegan in *John Bull's Other Island* (1932). Oil painting, 18⅛″ by 14¼″. Poel had succeeded Granville Barker in the rôle in September 1906. In 1909 he toured in the play, and recreated the rôle in a 1912 London revival.

HOW HE LIED TO HER HUSBAND (1904)

304 To Harley Granville Barker. Autograph letter, 18 August 1904. The unexpected, overwhelming success of *Candida* in New York the preceding year, as a result of an almost cult-like critical affection for the play's central character, inspired Shaw to write a play mocking what he termed 'the Candidamaniacs.' His opportunity came when Arnold Daly asked for a brief curtain-raiser to pad out a double bill with *The Man of Destiny*. The *Candida* references were deleted when Shaw revised the play for his collected edition in 1930.

> I have polished off Daly in four days with a screaming curtain raiser . . . specialized for a theatre at which Candida has been raging, and for an actor who has played Eugene.

305 Typewritten (carbon) manuscript, with revisions; undated (August 1904). 26 pp. Shaw had originally set the play in a house in New York, but soon altered the setting to a flat in the Cromwell Road. This necessitated a few geographical alterations in the text. WITH: Bodley Head Bernard Shaw *Collected Plays with Their Prefaces*, Vol. II (1971). Definitive edition, displayed at pp. 1048–1049 for textual comparison.

306 The Lord Chamberlain's provisional licence (22 August 1904) and formal licence (29 August), for the copyright performance in the Victoria Hall. WITH: Boxoffice report of sale of one ticket at a guinea, evidencing that the reading was a 'public' performance. As Shaw was vacationing in Scotland, Florence Farr arranged for the copyrighting, to avoid any delay in sending the play to New York. She herself read the part of Aurora Bompas.

307 To Harley Granville Barker. Autograph letter, 1 March 1905. Barker and Gertrude Kingston appeared in the play at the Court Theatre for a special season of nine matinées. Shaw offers his evaluation of the opening performance the previous afternoon, concluding 'For the rest, it's all right & will come righter. You both do not need any compliments over an idiotic farce, do you?' WITH: Program of the London production.

308 Advertisement of the film version, produced by British International Pictures, as shown at the Malvern Festival, August 1931. WITH: Photograph of Vera Lennox as Aurora and Robert Harris as Henry Apjohn. This first screen version of a Shaw play was poorly received by critics and public alike, as was the screen version of *Arms and the Man* by the same producers the following year. It was not until the release of Gabriel Pascal's production of *Pygmalion* in 1938 that Shaw achieved a film success.

309 Photograph of Shaw surrounded by the cast and producer of the first television production of a Shaw play, by the B.B.C., on 8 July 1937. Greer Garson appeared as Aurora. Shaw made a brief appearance on the screen after the performance, at which time he was charmingly deprecatory about this offspring of his less mature genius.

MAJOR BARBARA (1905)

310 *Major Barbara: A Discussion in Three Long Acts.* Typewritten manuscript, with revisions and cuts; undated (1905). 98 pp. The subtitle was dropped before publication.

311 To J.E. Vedrenne. Autograph letter, 2 October 1905. Shaw had just attended a special memorial meeting of the Salvation Army 'to commemorate dead comrades', presided over by General William Booth, leader of the Army, in the Albert Hall. It was a scene he would recreate fictionally in the film version of *Major Barbara* (1941), with music by William Walton.

312 From Gilbert Murray. Two typewritten letters (with typed signatures), 2 October and 3 December 1905. Accompanying the first letter are two pages of notes and suggestions concerning the Act II ending and Act III. Murray, after whom Shaw modelled the role of Cusins, the professor of Greek, has been reading the manuscript of the play and suggests revisions ('Excuse the cheek of this interference.'). He provides an alternative text for a scene in Act III. 'It makes Cusens [*sic*] come out much stronger, but I think that rather an advantage. Otherwise you get a simple defeat of the Barbara principles by the Undershaft principles. . . .'
Murray's views prompted Shaw to rewrite the entire third act. After the opening performance of the play on 28 November, however, Murray indicates he still is dissatisfied with the third act, although he

has found the second act 'moving to emotions and intellect at once'. The rapidity of the change in Barbara between these two acts, he insists, is unacceptable. 'It would, of course, be against your principles to re-write the end (again!) making it into four acts, and you are so dogmatically attached to your principles.'

313 Advertisement (on back page of a program of Ibsen's *The Wild Duck*) of the Vedrenne-Barker matinées of *Major Barbara*, billed as 'A New and Unpublished Play in Three Acts', at the Royal Court Theatre, London, 28 November to 15 December 1905. WITH: Two photographs (by E.H. Mills) of Act II. Louis Calvert as Undershaft and Granville Barker as Adolphus Cusins; Annie Russell as Barbara Undershaft and her husband Oswald Yorke as Bill Walker.

314 From Beatrice Webb. Autograph letter, 4 December 1905. Like Gilbert Murray, Mrs Webb has been left dissatisfied by the ending of the play.

> You made me doubt my own criticism of the ending . . . by your persuasive exposition of it. But you don't get your meaning into the mind of the audience: the impression left is that Cusins and Barbara are neither of them convinced by Undershaft's argument, but that they are uttering words, like the silly son, to bridge over a betrayal of their own convictions.

315 From Alex M. Nicol, Commissioner of the Salvation Army. Typewritten letter, 18 December 1905, accompanying a 14-page typewritten criticism of the play by an unidentified Salvationist who had attended the matinée on 15 December. The report is ingenuous, superficial, and uncomprehending, yet it reveals that Shaw's play has had its effect, as the writer concludes: 'You come away feeling not very sure of yourself. Human nature is shewn as such a rotten sort of thing, that you even wonder if you aren't a bit of a humbug yourself.'

316 From Harley Granville Barker. Autograph letter, 17 December 1915, describing the New York production of *Major Barbara*, after viewing the first two acts. WITH: Program of the first American production, presented by William A. Brady, at The Playhouse, New York, 9 December 1915; and a photograph (by White Studio) of Brady's wife, Grace George, as Barbara.

> It lacks quality of course . . . Barbara played soft and sweet—attractive enough in Act I. Useless in Act II—the scenes with her and Bill are just not played. . . . This audience doesnt know good acting from bad and has precious little chance to learn. . . . And I fear that 'My God why hast thou forsaken me' is cut if not drowned in the brass band.

PASSION, POISON AND PETRIFACTION (1905)

Passion, Poison and Petrifaction, or The Fatal Gazogene: A Brief Tragedy for Barns and Booths was written for the annual Theatrical Garden Party, for which a prominent dramatist was invited each year to contribute a burlesque of oldstyle melodrama, to benefit the Actors' Orphanage Fund. Several performances were given during the afternoon of 14 July 1905 in the Regent's Park Royal Botanical Gardens, in a tent booth called 'The Theatre Royal', with an allstar cast that included Cyril Maude and Irene Vanbrugh. During the day Shaw's manuscript was auctioned off to further aid the charity. Throughout his lifetime Shaw presented all royalties earned by the play to the Actors' Orphanage, and in his will bequeathed the copyright to the organization.

317 Autograph manuscript, written in a ruled composition book, dated 4 June 1905 at the end. 41 pp. Inscribed on the first page by Shaw, dated June 1905: 'This is the true and original copy written by me, mostly in Great Northern Express trains: hence the joggly handwriting in many places.' The leatherbound manuscript contains the bookplate of the American collector Robert Hoe.

318 Typewritten (carbon) manuscript, with an added leaf of typewritten 'Notes' at the back; undated (June 1905). 20 pp.

> As it is extremely difficult to find an actor capable of eating a real ceiling, it will be found convenient in performance to substitute the tops of old wedding cakes for bits of plaster. There is but little difference in material between the two substances; but the taste of the wedding cake is considered more agreeable by many people.

319 Playbill for the production at 'The Theatre Royal', Regent's Park, 14 July 1905.

320 From Harry Furniss, illustrator and author. Autograph letter, 1 August 1905. An appeal for a contribution of 'a few lines' on the drama for inclusion in Furniss's new Christmas annual. To his surprise Shaw contributed the text of his Theatrical Garden Party farce (based on a story Shaw had earlier written for William Archer's small son Tom, concerning a cat which lapped up some liquid plaster of Paris and became petrified).

321 *Harry Furniss Christmas Annual* (1905). First publication of Shaw's play, illustrated by Furniss. Inscribed by Shaw on the first page, 13 July 1929: 'Harry Furniss was at school with me in Dublin. How he got there I have never been able to make out. But the fact explains how he hit off the vein of this piece of tomfoolery so exactly in his illustrations.' Furniss, born in Wexford, came to England at 19. He was a caricaturist for *Punch* and illustrator of Lewis Carroll's *Sylvie and Bruno*, as well as of editions of the complete works of Dickens and Thackeray.

THE DOCTOR'S DILEMMA (1906)

322 To Lillah McCarthy (now the wife of Harley Granville Barker), who created the rôle of Jennifer Dubedat. Autograph letter, 1 September 1906. Shaw is certain it will be a lucky play for all concerned, as he was confronted that morning by 'an extraordinarily poetic effect': a beautiful snake with 'a perfect design in lozenges on its back.'

323 To Harley Granville Barker, who created the rôle of Louis Dubedat. Autograph postcard, 28 September 1906. Shaw is struggling with the revisions.

> It is a rotten play: the first act is proving very unmanageable: cutting makes it horribly dull.

324 Program of the first performance, at the Royal Court Theatre, London, 20 November 1906 (one of a series of 8 matinées). The play was moved into the evening bill on 31 December.

325 To the editor of the *Saturday Review*. Autograph draft of a letter, incomplete, December 1906. 1 p.

Shaw disagrees with a correspondent's interpretation of his play.

> It is my invariable practice to state my meaning with laborious exactness; and it is the invariable practice of my critics to ignore my statements, not in malice, but in a condition of glamor & bedazzlement which makes them incapable of attributing any straightforward prosaic procedure to me. I am to them a god—the god Mercury, wonderful, subtle, artful, fascinating, elusive, supremely deceitful. Naturally I am flattered; but I am also misunderstood. . . .

326 To Elizabeth Robins, Ibsen actress and writer. Typewritten letter, 8 March 1907, completed in Shaw's autograph on 12 March. Shaw offers a criticism of her play *Votes for Women!* by discussing his own technique in Act I of *The Doctor's Dilemma*.

The HRC possesses 25 pieces of Shaw correspondence (1891–1936) to Elizabeth Robins.

327 Preface. Typewritten manuscript, with revisions; undated (ca. 1909–10). 83 pp.

328 *Der Arzt am Scheideweg.* Program of the German production by Max Reinhardt, at the Kammerspiele des Deutschen Theaters, Berlin, 28 October 1910 (the third year in the repertory). Autograph notes on the program are by Lillah McCarthy, who sent it to Shaw. In the margins she has noted 'This is a *perfect* theatre' and 'Epilogue quite good—though Ridgeon showed some signs of a phthisical cough!!!'

329 To Cecil Lewis, radio producer and screen writer. Autograph postcard, 15 December 1926. Shaw informs Lewis that the death scene is derived—'not to say stolen'—from a short story by Richard Wagner. 'Read Goldsmith on "originality".'

The HRC possesses 28 pieces of Shaw correspondence (1923–37) to Lewis.

330 Photographs: (a) Alfred Lunt as Dubedat, Lynn Fontanne as Jennifer, and Baliol Holloway as Ridgeon. Theatre Guild production, New York, 21 November 1927. (b) Geraldine Fitzgerald as Jennifer and Roddy McDowall as Dubedat. Phoenix Theatre production, New York, 11 January 1955.

°331 Marcel Vertès: Portrait of Katharine Cornell as Jennifer, New York, 1941. Watercolor, 13½" by 10½".

332 Typewritten manuscript, with extensive revisions; undated (1908). 142 pp. Bound with this is a typewritten manuscript of the preface, with revisions; undated (1910). 62 pp. The play, originally titled *Any Just Cause or Impediment?* (from the Church of England marriage service), and its lengthy preface are concerned with the English marriage laws and their ramifications, absurdities, illogicalities, and injustices —and even their immoralities where divorce is concerned. Marriage, Shaw argues, is an insoluble problem, but there is no alternative to it. It is bad, but to reject it is worse.

333 *Getting Married, An Instructive Conversation. In One Piece.* Typewritten manuscript, with revisions: 'Corrected copy for Hugo Vallentin' (Shaw's Swedish translator). 113 pp. On the third page of Act I Shaw has provided an amusing drawing to illustrate the term 'Dundreary whiskers'.

334 Mock-up by Shaw of a program emphasizing the producers' credits. Drawn on the reverse of a correspondence card to J.E. Vedrenne, 8 May 1908, four days before the opening of the Vedrenne-Barker production (in association with Frederick Harrison) at the Haymarket Theatre for a series of six matinées. Although the critics were, as usual, generally negative in their reviews, the audiences received the play with sufficient warmth to encourage the producers to transfer it to the evening bill, where it survived for 48 performances.

335 To J.E. Vedrenne. Autograph letter, 22 May 1908. Shaw had slipped into the theatre that afternoon for another look at the production.

> The cast finds out more every time of what it is all about; and so, consequently, does the audience. It just wants to be made an hour longer & played every day for the next ten years, like Madame Tussaud's.

336 From Sir Alfred Douglas. Typewritten letter, 25 May 1908, in response to Shaw's letter of the same date. WITH: Typewritten transcriptions of Shaw's letters to Douglas of 25 and 27 May (the originals of which do not appear to have survived). The *Academy*, a literary weekly which Douglas edited, had published an erratic, negative notice of *Getting Married*. Shaw, puzzled by the review's errors and inconsistencies, and noting a distinctly libellous remark, was convinced that the critic had been intoxicated. He wrote to Douglas to ask, 'Who on earth have you been handing over your dramatic criticism to?' and to suggest that he 'volunteer' in the next issue to withdraw the article. Douglas replied indignantly, 'As a matter of fact I wrote the article myself', and, ever litigious, supplied the name of his solicitor. In later years, when the two men became good friends, Douglas assured Shaw that he had not been drunk, but that 'I hated your play. It bored and exasperated me. . . .' and he had departed long before the final curtain.

337 List of boxoffice returns for the Vedrenne-Barker 'Special Matinées' of the six new Shaw plays produced between 1904 and 1907, with additional returns for productions of Ibsen's *Hedda Gabler* and Elizabeth Robins's *Votes for Women*. The 8 matinées of the Ibsen play in 1907, it is interesting to note, drew one of the highest grosses of all the series.

338 To William Faversham, American actor-manager. Autograph postcard, 6 October 1916. This was one of a series of communications advising Faversham on the casting and staging of the play in New York.

> I forgot to urge . . . the great importance of casting Father Anthony and Lesbia, as they balance Hotchkiss and Mrs George in such a way that the least attempt to play them low down as a comic monk and old maid would utterly destroy the atmosphere necessary for their two contrasted opposites. You need a tragic player of Irvingesque intensity for Anthony. . . .

The HRC possesses 21 pieces of Shaw correspondence (1915–17) to Faversham.

339 Program of the first American production, at the Booth Theatre, New York, 6 November 1916. WITH: Photograph (by White), in the *Theatre* (New York), January 1917. Act I: Edith (Virginia Fox Rhodes): 'Cecil, I must speak to you particularly. Papa, go away. Go away, everybody.' William Faversham, as the Bishop of Chelsea, is at the far right.

THE SHEWING-UP OF BLANCO POSNET (1909)

*340 Shorthand manuscript (incomplete) in a pocket shorthand notebook, dated 16 February 1909. 39 pp. The notebook also contains the incomplete shorthand manuscript of 'The Italian Play' (subsequently titled *The Glimpse of Reality*), written aboard the cruise ship Derfflinger on a Mediterranean cruise en route to Algiers and Tunisia, dated 8, 16, 25 [28?] March 1909. 20 pp. WITH: Shorthand manuscript fragment of the last scene of *Blanco Posnet*; undated (1909). 6 pp. Autograph manuscript of a scenario for the play, dated September 1909. 1 p.

341 Typewritten (carbon) manuscript, with revisions, for the production by the After Noon Theatre, which was cancelled during rehearsals in May 1909 when the Lord Chamberlain denied the management a licence to perform it on the grounds that the play was blasphemous. 64 pp.

342 Typewritten (carbon) manuscript, with revisions. 39 pp. This copy was used by the printer for typesetting. Bound in are five pages of rehearsal notes (undated) and a typewritten letter from Lady Gregory, dated 'Wednesday 18th' [July 1909]. As the Lord Chamberlain's censorship powers did not extend to Ireland, Shaw offered his play to Lady Gregory for the Abbey Theatre. See Nos. 148–150 for additional materials relating to the controversy.

343 Lady Gregory's diaries: extracts. A poorly typewritten (carbon) transcription, with a few corrections. 14 pp. This fragment, which covers diary entries for 12–15 and 20 August 1909, was sent by Lady Gregory to Shaw in Parknasilla, where he was on holiday. On 20 August she records an interview by Yeats and herself with the Viceroy (Lord Aberdeen) concerning the disputed play.

344 Rough Proof rehearsal copy, sent by Shaw to Lady Gregory, inscribed by him on the upper cover 'This is the censored play.' On the inside of the cover is a notice: 'Printed for private use in the Theatre at rehearsals and not for publication or circulation.' Shaw found it expedient to have his plays typeset as rapidly as they were written and, as soon as they were proofed, to have small quantities of 'Rough Proofs' printed in paper wrappers for use by actors and translators and for distribution to friends. When a play underwent textual alteration during production, revised rehearsal copies would generally be run off. *Blanco Posnet* was the first of Shaw's plays to be designedly printed for rehearsal purposes, although Shaw previously had utilized specially pulled thin-paper proofs from existing plates for productions of *You Never Can Tell*, *The Devil's Disciple*, *Candida*, and *Man and Superman*. Some of these proofs were unbound; others were cased in blank flexible paper wrappers.

345 Souvenir linen print (brown on tan) of a scene from *Blanco Posnet*, portraits of principal members of the Abbey Theatre company, and quotations (with facsimile signatures) from Lady Gregory's play *The Jackdaw* and W.B. Yeats's poem 'The Gift.' Copies were sold by the Irish Players at one dollar on their 1913 American tour, to raise funds 'towards a building to save Sir Hugh Lane's Great Gift of Pictures for Ireland'. Lane, who was Lady Gregory's nephew, had willed his art collection to Ireland on the condition that the government provide a proper gallery for housing it. He died in the Lusitania in 1915. For nearly half a century England and Ireland quarrelled over its ownership. Eventually they divided it.

346 From Count Leo Tolstoy, Russian novelist and humanitarian. Autograph letter in English (in a secretary's hand), 9 May 1910. Tolstoy acknowledges receipt of a copy of *Blanco Posnet* which had been forwarded to him by his British translator Aylmer Maude. In an accompanying letter, on 14 February, Shaw had summed up his religious views and indicated how these were reflected in the play. He concluded: 'You said that my manner in [*Man and Superman*] was not serious enough—that I made people laugh in my most earnest moments. But why should I not? Why should humor and laughter be excommunicated? Suppose the world were only one of God's jokes, would you work any the less to make it a good joke instead of a bad one?' Tolstoy replied:

> Concerning . . . what you say about God and about evil I will repeat the words I said, as you write, about your 'Man

and Superman', namely that the problem about God and evil is too important to be spoken of in jest. And therefore I will tell you frankly that I received a very painful impression from the concluding words of your letter. . . .

347 Photograph of the Japanese production, translated by Dr Ōgai Mori from the German translation of Siegfried Trebitsch, under the title *Uma dorobō* (*The Horsethief*), at the Yurakuza Theatre, Tokyo, 23 November 1910, with Masao Inoue playing Blanco Posnet. This was the first Shaw play to be performed in Japanese. It was successful, commented the poet Yone Noguchi, because 'the simple dramatic motive is not difficult to handle, even by Japanese actors, who are not yet well acquainted with such a Western dialogue play, since they were educated on a stage where action is everything. . . . I simply wondered whether a new age had reached even Japan, which has hitherto been able to understand morality, but not philosophy, and passion, but not intellect; and the actors also appeared to adapt themselves to the new situation, which is sad and happy alternately.'

PRESS CUTTINGS (1909)

348 Typewritten (carbon) manuscript, with revisions copied in by Shaw's secretary Georgina Gillmore, and some deletions; undated (May 1909). The printer set the text from the original of this typescript.

349 To Bertha Newcombe. Autograph postcard, 11 May 1909, and typewritten letter, 14 May. 'The sketch' which Shaw had promised to write for the Civic and Dramatic Guild, and which he had drafted 'in odd spare moments in Algeria', is completed. 'Perhaps the best plan would be to read it to you and Forbes Robertson—though really the thing is such a ghastly absurdity, that a reading is hardly bearable.' The leading rôle of General Mitchener apparently was intended for Johnston Forbes-Robertson. His reaction to the play may be surmised from the fact that the rôle eventually was performed by Robert Loraine, with Forbes-Robertson confining his participation in the program to a reading from *The Ancient Mariner*!

The HRC possesses 30 pieces of Shaw correspondence (1896–1926) to Bertha Newcombe.

350 From G.A. Redford, Examiner of Plays for the Lord Chamberlain, to the Acting Manager of the Royal Court Theatre, 24 June 1909, calling attention to the endorsement on each 'Licence for Representation' issued by his office: 'No offensive personalities, as representation of living persons to be permitted on the stage'. He returns the Topical Sketch 'in order to give you the· opportunity of eliminating all personalities, expressed or understood.' When Shaw altered the names of the Prime Minister and the General from Balsquith and Mitchener to Bones and Johnson (traditional names for the minstrel-show endman and interlocutor) and made a few insignificant textual revisions, a licence for the 'revised version' (also displayed) was issued on 17 August.

351 *Press Cuttings* (1909). Two copies of the published text, in pink wrappers (variant states of printing on cover). One is marked '"cut" copy' in pencil on the cover; the other is labelled 'AUTHOR'S COPY' on the cover. There are variant cuts in the two copies; the first contains some revisions inserted by Shaw's secretary Georgina Gillmore.

352 To Frederick Whelen. Autograph letter, 23 October 1912. Shaw authorizes the New York Stage Society to play *Press Cuttings* provided 'they dont cut it and dont tomfool with it. Tell them . . . to play all the parts seriously on the assumption that they are human beings and not Punch & Judy puppets.'

353 To St John Ervine, Irish playwright and journalist. Typewritten letter, 24 January 1921, containing a rundown on Shaw's censored plays. He identifies the prototype of General Mitchener as 'the old Duke of Cambridge, the now forgotten George Ranger of the parks, Commander in Chief of the British Army, and brother to Queen Victoria.'

The HRC possesses 88 pieces of Shaw correspondence (1912–50) to Ervine.

MISALLIANCE (1909)

354 Shorthand manuscript, incomplete, written in a pocket shorthand notebook, dated 8 September 1909 on the first page. 114 pp. Revised shorthand passages pasted in. Accompanied by discarded typewritten manuscript fragments. 3 pp. With the exception of the first two acts of *Widowers' Houses* (1884), all of Shaw's plays through *The Doctor's Dilemma* were drafted in longhand. The companion plays *Getting Married* and *Misalliance* were the first that Shaw composed in shorthand in their entirety.

355 From Spencer Brothers, Ltd. Autograph letters of 28 June and 2 July 1906, concerning arrangements for a balloon flight by Shaw, his sister-in-law Mary Cholmondeley, Granville Barker, and Robert Loraine. WITH: Certificate attesting to a two and a half hour ascension in the 'Norfolk', piloted by Percival Spencer, on 3 July. Maximum altitude: 9000 feet. The party landed near Cobham on the property of an irate squire. The incident and the pilot found their way into Shaw's play, metamorphosed into an aeroplane crash by Joey Percival and his passenger into the Tarletons' greenhouse.

356 Scene plan, drawn by Shaw in pencil, with ink notations; undated (1909). This was the plan from which Shaw worked in devising the stage directions he inserted into the final typescript for the printer.

357 Program of the first production, in the Charles Frohman repertory, at the Duke of York's Theatre, London, 23 February 1910. Disparaged by almost all the London critics, *Misalliance* survived in the repertory only for eleven performances, giving way to more popular pieces like Galsworthy's *Justice* and the revival of Pinero's *Trelawny of the 'Wells'*. In recent years, however, it has become one of Shaw's most popular successes both in England and the United States.

358 To Lena Ashwell, the actress who played the Polish acrobat Lina Szczepanowska. Typewritten letter, 11 March 1910.

> I indulged in the luxury of a peep at you at the matinée yesterday. I had in my box W.B. Yeats who, being a poet, occasionally says the right thing. At the end of the 2nd Act he said 'That is what is so extremely rare: *beautiful gaiety*.' So you see it is not quite completely a secret between you and me.

The HRC possesses 34 pieces of Shaw correspondence (1898–1926) to Lena Ashwell.

355

359 To William Faversham. Autograph letter and cablegram, both dated 9 December 1917. Faversham's production of *Misalliance*, at the Broadhurst Theatre, New York, on 27 September 1917, disappointed the critics and survived only for 54 performances. WITH: Program of the post-Broadway touring production at the Plymouth Theatre, Boston, November 1917. Shaw, apprised that the text had been drastically cut, writes to inform the producer that he can not be trusted with any further Shaw plays.

> You dont understand audiences psychologically; you dont understand plays technically; and you dont keep your contracts. I could look after the first two, if you were sound on

the third; but the three together beat me. Henceforth you are useful to me only as a terrible example of a manager who succeeded when he did what I told him, and failed when he thought he knew better than I what was my business and not his.

360 Three photographs of the Teatr Polski production, Warsaw, in Floryan Sobieniowski's translation, with Boguslaw Samborski as Tarleton. March 1930.

361 'Extra and final corrections' for the text of the play in Shaw's collected edition. Autograph manuscript, 1 April 1930. 1 p. For the limited collected edition, 1930–32, Shaw made a number of significant alterations in his plays, including the modernization of one passage in *Misalliance*.

FANNY'S FIRST PLAY (1910–11)

362 Shorthand manuscript. 146 pp. The play originally was titled *Just Exactly Nothing*. Composition was begun with Act I, in Rosscullen, Ireland, 13 August 1910. Shaw completed Act I in the Caribbean and Act II while passing Turks Island, en route to England after a visit to his Fabian colleague Sydney Olivier, then Governor-General of Jamaica, B.W.I. The Induction and Epilogue were afterthoughts, composed in February and March 1911. Bound in with the manuscript are: the shorthand text of the preface, 2 pp.; a corrected typewritten transcription of the preface, 3 pp.; a draft of a telegram to Granville Barker concerning American production arrangements, 11 July 1911; and a photograph of Act III of the original production, with Lillah McCarthy as Margaret Knox wrestling a struggling Shiel Barry (as Bobby Gilbey) down onto the table, crying 'Pig! Beast!', with Dorothy Minto (as Dora Delaney) and H.K. Ayliff (as the footman Juggins) looking on. WITH: Program of the first production, at the Little Theatre, London, 10 April 1911.

The HRC also possesses four pages of manuscript, constituting a new ending for Act II, bound in with rehearsal notes for Overruled.

363 Typewritten manuscript, with revisions; undated. 131 pp.

364 From Sir Herbert Beerbohm Tree, the actor-manager who later appeared as Higgins in *Pygmalion*.

Typewritten letter, 5 May 1911. Tree had enjoyed the play enormously.

> I thought that . . . you touched your highest, often striking the human note. . . . I have not read any of the notices, but the play is bound to be a great success. I do wish you would write Don Quixote.

365 *The Author's Testimonial.* Limerick for the actress Dorothy Minto on the occasion of the 500th performance of the play. Inscribed by Shaw, 28 June 1914 (the date is erroneously written as 1912) in a copy of the 1911 Rough Proof.

> The parts I entrust to Miss Minto
> She throws herself thoroughly into.
>   If the part were a Jap
>   She would study the map,
> And change her religion to Shinto.

366 Rhyming prologue: 'To be substituted for the Induction when the Play alone can be performed.' Shorthand and autograph manuscripts; undated (15 September 1916). Each is 5 pp. During the war an early curfew necessitated the abbreviating of Shaw's play to permit two performances to be presented back-to-back in the late afternoon and early evening. Shaw accordingly gave permission to the producer, Charles Macdona, to drop the Induction and the Epilogue on his provincial tour and to open the performance instead with an explanatory rhyming prologue to be delivered by the actress playing Fanny. It was first performed in Birmingham on 18 September 1916, with Shaw in attendance. WITH: Printed first proof of the prologue, datestamped 23 September 1916. 3 pp. A small number were printed for rehearsal use. The text was not published in any edition of the play until after Shaw's death.

ANDROCLES AND THE LION (1912)

367 Shorthand manuscript, with autograph directions on the first page, dated Edstaston (home of Charlotte Shaw's sister), 2 January 1912. Completed 6 February 1912. 78 pp. Bound in at the front are three of Shaw's pencilled set sketches.

368 Set sketch and rehearsal notes, 28 August 1913, for the first production, at the St James's Theatre, London. 5 pp. WITH: Set drawings in pencil, on both sides of a single leaf.

369 Photograph of Lillah McCarthy as Lavinia, signed 'To | Charlotte and C.B.S. | From Lillah. as "Lavinia" in "Androcles | & the Lion" | Xmas 1919.' 9⅝″ by 6¾₁₆″, mounted and framed.

370 From John Galsworthy. Autograph letter, 9 September 1913. Despite high praise from most of the drama critics, as well as from Galsworthy, Wells, Chesterton, and other discerning colleagues, the audiences grew sparse after the first few weeks and the play was withdrawn after only 52 performances.

> I write hot-handed after seeing 'Androcles' to give you joy of it. It's splendid—goes deep, & hits all round. The fun of it is great, but the fun is not—as the poor critics seem to have thought—its prime blessing & beauty. I like it best of any of your plays. . . . It's a splendid subject, and you've done justice to it. I haven't cried so much for a long time—with laughter, & something more.

371 First publication in English. *Everybody's Magazine*, New York, September 1914 (with cover design by Oliver Herford). Siegfried Trebitsch's German translation preceded it in 1913.

372 *A note to 'Androcles and the Lion' written for the New York production by Bernard Shaw* (1915). A printed leaflet distributed to audiences at Wallack's Theatre. WITH: Wallack's Theatre program for the last week (26 April–1 May 1915) of the McCarthy-Barker season.

373 Postcard photograph of Ludvik Veverke as Androcles and Charles Koler as the Lion, in the Prague National Theatre production, 17 September 1915.

PYGMALION (1912)

*374 *The Phonetic Play.* Shorthand manuscript, dated 7 March 1912 on the first page. 135 pages, mounted and bound in red morocco by Sangorski and Sutcliffe.

*375 Typewritten manuscript, with revisions; undated (1913). 121 pp. The last three pages provide a new ending to the play, lacking in the shorthand manuscript. This manuscript was used by the printer for typesetting.

373

*376 Poster for the first production of *Pygmalion*, in Siegfried Trebitsch's translation, at the K.K. Hof-Burgtheater, Vienna, 16 October 1913.

377 From Henry Dana (Sir Herbert Beerbohm Tree's business manager) to Bourchier F. Hawksley (Mrs Patrick Campbell's solicitor). Typewritten (carbon) letter, 17 February 1914, concerning negotiations for Mrs Campbell's services. Tree's 'absolutely final' offer is a salary of £130 a week for six performances, guaranteed for a minimum of five weeks, with an additional £21.13.4 for each matinée. Mrs Campbell would also receive 2% of the gross weekly receipts above £700.

Inigo Jones's Church of
St Paul's, Covent Garden

Wall of Church

Cobble stones.

Plan roughly stated

$4\frac{1}{2}$ $13\frac{1}{2}$ $4\frac{1}{2}$ 18 feet $4\frac{1}{2}$ $13\frac{1}{2}$ $4\frac{1}{2}$ 28' 24'

Edge of pavement
63 feet

378 From Sir Herbert Beerbohm Tree. Autograph and typewritten letters, both dated 18 February 1914, concerning Tree's production of the play. He reports that Mrs Campbell 'has at last succumbed' to his offer, and defends himself against Shaw's criticisms of his efforts at casting.

> After reading your letter, were I not buoyed up by self-esteem, (which may or may not be justified), I should seek some dusty corner of the stage and weep my eyes out. You are addressing me very much as 'Bottom the Weaver' addressed his company of players. . . . I consider that though I do not presume to be a playwright, I may be allowed to know something about acting, and perhaps as Manager, I may claim a courtesy right in the casting.

379 Sketches by Shaw of Inigo Jones's church of St Paul's, Covent Garden (1914). 'The scene should be built to the full size of the original, shewing only as much as the stage will hold of the church'.

380 From Henry James to Hugh Walpole. Autograph letter, 21–23 April 1914. The novelist, after attending a performance of 'Shaw's Tree-and-Mrs-Campbell play', informs Walpole that his 'whole impression' of the 'rotten' play is 'one of the blackest'. It is, he announces, shallow, vapid, vulgar, and senseless.

The HRC possesses 85 pieces of James correspondence (1908–15) to Walpole.

381 Programs of the first London production, at His Majesty's Theatre, 11 April 1914, and of the first American production in English, at the Park Theatre, New York, 12 October 1914 (the German translation of Siegfried Trebitsch had been produced at the Deutsches Theatre, New York, on 24 March 1914). Mrs Patrick Campbell appeared as Eliza Doolittle in both productions, with Higgins performed in London by Beerbohm Tree and in New York by Philip Merivale. On the American tour, when Merivale withdrew from the cast, he was replaced by Mrs Campbell's new husband George Cornwallis-West. WITH: Photograph (by White) of Mrs Campbell in the New York production.

382 From George C. Tyler, manager of the American production. Typewritten letter, 13 October 1914. Tyler has cabled the news to Shaw: 'Apparently very successful. Press unintelligently enthusiastic.' He then, nonchalantly, drops a bombshell: he has restored the original line at the end of the play—a line Shaw had deliberately discarded—which brings Eliza back on stage to determine the size of the gloves Higgins had asked her to buy. 'Frankly', Tyler admits, 'I was *afraid* to omit the line. I felt it would have an enormous commercial value with sentimental America. . . .' Four weeks later, Tyler filed for bankruptcy, and the production was transferred to another management and another theatre. Shaw lost the first month's royalties, but one suspects he must have been overjoyed at Tyler's getting so quick a comeuppance after tampering with a Shaw text!

383 From Mrs Patrick Campbell. Cablegram, 18 July 1915, informing Shaw that 'business has been vile' in Portland. His draft reply of 20 July is inscribed at the foot of the cable: 'Cheer up much worse here why not disband and rest'. The touring company, following a nine week run in New York, opened in Detroit on 14 December 1914 and closed in Elmira, New York, on 22 March 1916, playing engagements coast to coast, north and south, full week and split week, in 106 American cities, and making several brief excursions across the border into Canada.

384 Sequel to *Pygmalion*. Typewritten manuscript, with revisions, of the narrative postscript written for the published book text in 1916, establishing that Eliza married Freddy and became the proprietress of a flower shop. 15 pp. Bound with this is a typewritten manuscript of the preface to the 1916 edition. 5 pp. WITH: Autograph letter, to R. & R. Clark, Ltd., 17 September 1915.

> Put a row of asterisks after the last line of the play and then follow on with the sequel, in roman, not in italic. The play, in fact, changes into a novel without a break.

385 To Feliks Topolski. Autograph postcard, 20 May 1940. Shaw criticizes Topolski's costuming of his figures, and suggests the proper styles. Affixed to the card is Shaw's drawing, in red and black ink, of Eliza carrying her flower basket, with the three ostrich plumes on her hat soaring above her.

The HRC possesses 28 pieces of Shaw correspondence (1939–46) to Topolski.

From Bernard Shaw.

4, WHITEHALL COURT (130) LONDON, S.W.I.
TELEGRAMS: SOCIALIST, PARL-LONDON.
TELEPHONE: WHITEHALL 3160.

AYOT ST LAWRENCE, WELWYN, HERTS.
STATION: WHEATHAMPSTEAD, L.&N.E.R. 2¼ MILES.
TELEGRAMS AND PHONE: CODICOTE 218

The costumes do not matter chronologically, because by the time the book is finished and in circulation the fashions of today will be as obsolete as those of 1913. But 1913 will give you Eliza's shawl and hat with three ostrich figures, now quite vanished; and the Rossettian Mrs Higgins in her Burne Jones costume and Morrison drawingroom. I think I have photographs of Mr Morris, and of the original production, that would help.
The men's dress has not changed much, except that Higgins should have a frock coat and tall hat instead of a lounge suit and derby. GBS

LIZA

385

386 Feliks Topolski: Three drawings (ca. 1940–41) for the Penguin edition, with Shaw's autograph notes and his sketches of Eliza and of Doolittle. Black ink and sepia and black wash, 10″ by 8″. WITH: The final drawings as they appear in the published book.

No, no, no Mrs Campbell, except in her gutter dress, was wildly unlike Liza.
All wrong. Eliza is not an impudent hoyden: she is a tired pathetic figure, dragging her basket *wearily*, pretty through her dirt, and altogether pitiable.
At Doolittle's first appearance he is playing the part of a stern father come to save his daughter's honor or to avenge her ruin. . . . When he finds that Higgins is more than a match for him at this game he becomes the genial irresistible philosopher and humorist. . . . In the last act he must not look ridiculous. . . . *He is no longer a comic character.* There should be 3 different Doolittles.

MY FAIR LADY (1955–56)

Shaw had on several occasions rejected offers to musicalize *Pygmalion.* A few years after his death, however, the Public Trustee succumbed to Gabriel Pascal's blandishments and, as executor of Shaw's estate, authorized Pascal to produce a musical version of the play. After several years of false starts, financial entanglements, and the death of Pascal, the musical treatment emerged as *My Fair Lady,* produced by Herman Levin, with music by Frederick Loewe and lyrics and libretto by Alan Jay Lerner. It was given its first performance in New Haven on 4 February 1956, and arrived at the Mark Hellinger Theatre, New York, on 15 March 1956, where it proceeded to make a mockery of all previous theatrical records for longevity, achieving the unprecedented number of 2717 performances and an unmatched gross in excess of $20,000,000 before it ended its run on 29 September 1962. Comparable records were subsequently established in London, Berlin, and other theatrical centres throughout the world.

387 Programs of the original New York production, 15 March 1956, and of the 20th Anniversary revival by the original producer, Herman Levin, at the St James Theatre, New York, 25 March 1976. WITH: Souvenir brochures of the original New York production and of the first German production, at the Theater des Westens, Berlin, 25 October 1961.

388 Ten photographs (by Fred Fehl) of the first production, New York, 1956. Rex Harrison as Henry Higgins; Julie Andrews as Eliza Doolittle; Stanley Holloway as Alfred Doolittle; Cathleen Nesbitt as Mrs Higgins; Robert Coote as Colonel Pickering. Production designed by Oliver Smith. Costumes designed by Cecil Beaton. Lighting by Abe Feder.

The HRC's Hoblitzelle Theatre Arts Collection houses the Fred Fehl Collection of 7300 photographs, 1000 slides, and more than 40,000 negatives of American theatre productions from 1940 to 1967.

389 Record sleeves for recordings of the original American and British stage productions, and for the Danish, German, Hebrew, Hungarian, Italian, and Spanish stage versions, and the French-dubbed screen version. From the Dan H. Laurence Musical Comedy

Collection of recordings (in the Hoblitzelle Theatre Arts Collection).

390 Shooting script for the Warner Brothers film version, produced by Jack L. Warner, directed by George Cukor. Screenplay by Alan Jay Lerner.

OVERRULED (1912)

391 *Trespassers Will be Prosecuted*. Shorthand manuscript, completed on 'Gt Northern train passing Holloway', 23 July 1912. 44 pp. Bound with this is a shorthand manuscript of the preface. 10 pp. The title was discarded when Shaw discovered there was currently another play with the same name.

392 Typewritten manuscript, with revisions, including one inserted autograph page. 41 pp. Bound with this is a typewritten manuscript of the preface, with revisions. 21 pp.

393 Rough Proof (1913). Augustin Hamon's copy, with a pencilled note by Shaw on the halftitle explaining to its present owner the change of title, 19 October 1929.

> I changed it to a single word—rather a farfetched one—so as not to make the title of the volume of three plays in which it appeared too cumbrous.

394 Rehearsal notes for the Duke of York's production, which Shaw staged in October 1912. 2 pp.

395 Program of the first production by Charles Frohman at the Duke of York's Theatre, 14 October 1912, in a triple bill with Pinero's *The Widow of Wasdale Head* and Barrie's *Rosalind*.

396 To Sir Arthur W. Pinero. Autograph letter, 15 October 1912. Charles Frohman had commissioned short plays from Shaw, Barrie, and Pinero, in an experiment to combine the work of the three principal London dramatists in one bill. The morning after the opening performance, Shaw wrote to Pinero, who had not been present, to tell him that Barrie had stolen the evening. As for the audience reaction to Shaw's play and Pinero's:

> They simply loathed us. They weren't indifferent: we didnt fall flat: they were angrily disgusted: we were trampled on, kicked, and hurled downstairs and out into the street.

Shaw suggests that the management advertize: 'WARNING: Mr Barrie's piece does not begin until 10.'

GREAT CATHERINE (1913)

397 Shorthand manuscript, begun at Torcross on 29 July 1913 and completed at Sandwich on 13 August. 57 pp. Bound in at the front is the Lord Chamberlain's licence for representation, 17 November 1913, for the production at the Vaudeville Theatre.

398 Three variant typewritten manuscripts, each revised (1913).

(a) 58 pp. Transcribed from the shorthand manuscript.

(b) 63 pp., carbon, with shorthand fragment of the preface and a production note, 2 pp., bound in at the back. This was Shaw's production copy.

(c) 70 pp. With typewritten manuscript of the preface, the first four pages of which (on green paper) are revised by Shaw; the remainder (on white paper) contain revisions copied in by Shaw's secretary Ann M. Elder. This is the text which was sent to the printer.

399 To Frederick Whelen, co-producer of the production scheduled for performance on 18 November. Autograph postcard, 31 October 1913. The casting has not yet been completed; the script has still to be submitted to the Lord Chamberlain for licensing; and Shaw has not yet completed the revisions.

> I have with some difficulty finished the first scene. Heaven only knows when I shall be able to get through with the rest. I shall have to send it to the typist scene by scene.

400 Notes of interviews by Frederick Whelen with the Lord Chamberlain at St James's Palace on 13 and 14 November 1913. Typewritten (carbon) manuscript, with minor corrections. 4 pp. and 2 pp. Although the examiner of plays had found Shaw's play to be 'inoffensive', the Lord Chamberlain, under the influence of his comptroller, Brigadier General Sir Douglas, Dawson, had denied the play a licence because the drunkenness of Patiomkin and the act of the Empress coarsely tickling the English soldier and throwing him on the bed might give offence to Grand Duke Vladimir of Russia, a visitor of the English royal family. Dawson also expressed concern about the uniform to be worn by Edstaston. Whelen brought all his powers of persuasion to bear, and finally extracted a promise that they would attend the next day's rehearsal. When they had done so, they withdrew their objections without requiring any modification. They warned, however, that if any 'diplomatic representations' be made subsequent to the first performance, 'we must be prepared to hear from [them].' The first interview also included a discussion of the continued denial of a licence to *The Shewing-up of Blanco Posnet.*

401 Photograph of the production at the Vaudeville Theatre, London, 18 November 1913, directed by Shaw, with Gertrude Kingston as the Empress and Edmond Breon as Captain Edstaston. It was performed on a double bill with Hermon Ould's *Between Sunset and Dawn.*

402 To Ignaz Lilien. Typewritten letter, 22 February 1930. Lilien had approached Shaw with the score of an opera *Die Grosse Katharina*, based on Siegfried Trebitsch's German translation. Shaw authorized the performance after Lilien, at his insistence, travelled from Czechoslovakia to London to audition the work. In the letter Shaw indicates his satisfaction that, when completed, the score 'will be brilliant and witty enough to do much more than justice to my unpretentious little play.' Lilien's score was published by Universal-Edition, Vienna, in 1930, and performed successfully at the State Theatre in Wiesbaden in 1932. It has since vanished from the stage completely.

PLAYLETS OF THE WAR

Shaw collected, under this heading in the volume also containing *Heartbreak House* and *Great Catherine*, four short plays written as *pièces d'occasion* between 1915 and 1917. Three are represented here; the fourth, *O'Flaherty V.C.*, will be found in the display case on Ireland (Nos. 602 and 603).

THE INCA OF PERUSALEM (1915)

403 Typewritten manuscript, with extended revision, including the insertion of autograph text pages. 38 pp. This copy was used for typesetting. The play originally was titled *The Royal Chancellor.*

404 From the office of the Lord Chamberlain to the actress Gertrude Kingston, who was preparing to produce the play. Typewritten letter, 15 November 1915, passing it for performance subject to the omission of personal references to 'The Inca's Grandmother' (Queen Victoria), 'The Inca's Uncle' (Edward VII), and 'King George's abstinence from wine'. Miss Kingston is also requested to 'kindly see that the make up of the Inca does not too closely resemble the German Emperor.' WITH: Rough Proof (1915), labelled by Shaw on upper cover 'Cut to comply with License.' Due to the reaction against his unpopular war position, Shaw resorted here (and elsewhere) to the masking identification 'By a Fellow of the Royal Society of Literature'.

405 To Helen Arthur, director of the Neighborhood Playhouse, New York. Autograph draft of cable, 15 September 1916. It was Shaw's firm belief that election campaigns were detrimental to the boxoffice. As America was in the midst of a political race between Woodrow Wilson and Charles E. Hughes, he cabled: 'You must not produce in Newyork until after presidential election middle November'. Miss Arthur delayed the opening until 14 November.

406 Rough Proof (1918), with autograph revisions by Shaw on p. 24, incorporated in the published text in 1919. Pp. 21–24 are loose tearsheets.

407 Photograph of an unidentified French contemporary production, presumably in Augustin Hamon's French translation, taken by Studio G.L. Manuel Frères, 47 Rue Dumont d'Urville, Paris.

AUGUSTUS DOES HIS BIT (1916)

408 To the drama editor, *Evening Standard.* Autograph postcard, 13 December 1916. A statement identifying the play as 'only a sketch, and a very trifling one at that', written for Lalla Vandervelde (wife of the Belgian Socialist leader Emile Vandervelde), who performed in the play, under the auspices of the Stage Society, for the benefit of Belgian refugees. 'It was suggested by the recent appeal of the Government . . . for didactic sketches inculcating war saving. Augustus is my patriotic response to that appeal.' WITH: Program of the first production, at the Royal Court Theatre, London, 21–22 January 1917.

409 Rough Proof, with autograph revisions; undated (1918). This was the last bound proof prior to publication of the play in 1919. Only two copies are known to exist. The corrections appear in the published text.

ANNAJANSKA, THE BOLSHEVIK EMPRESS (1917)

410 Shorthand manuscript, titled *The Wild Grand Duchess*, was begun at Ayot St Lawrence on 4 December 1917 and completed three days later at 10 Adelphi Terrace, London. Bound with this are a prefatory note and an 'Addition to Annajanska' (in shorthand). 3 pp.

411 *Annajanska, the Wild Grand Duchess. From the Russian of Gregory Biessipoff*. Rough Proof (1917), with corrections. G.B. Essipoff was a variant pseudonym used by Shaw in 1930 as signature to a letter in the *Daily Herald* dealing with religious persecution in England. The title of the play was altered in the published text (1919) to *Annajanska, the Bolshevik Empress*.

412 Rough Proof (1917), used as 'PROMPT COPY' for the first production, at the Coliseum Theatre, London, 21 January 1918. Interleaved, with Lillah McCarthy's notes and stage directions. This is a variant proof, with the pseudonym on the title but not on the upper cover. WITH: Photographs of Lillah McCarthy in the Coliseum production.

413 To Lillah McCarthy. Autograph letter, 25 January 1918. A series of criticisms of the performance, which Shaw had monitored that afternoon, revealing his concern for every theatrical nuance.

Why, after I took the trouble to get Strammfest out of your way by the window trick, leaving you the centre all to yourself, and prolonging the anticipation sufficiently to enable the audience to take it fully in, have you undone it all? . . . Do kick the dynasty *out* with your left foot, and not *in* with your right. It makes all the difference in the intelligibility of the gesture.

HEARTBREAK HOUSE (1916–17)

414 *Heartbreak House*. Rough Proof, datestamped 28 December 1917. The rarest of all of Shaw's play proofs, of which only two other copies (one of them a variant) are known to exist. The text was severely pruned and revised for publication in 1919.

415 *Heartbreak House, Great Catherine, and Playlets of the War* (1919). First edition, with a presentation inscription 'to Ellen O'Malley, | by whom Ellie Dunn was born to | be played, | from G. Bernard Shaw.' The volume contains Ellen O'Malley's rehearsal notes in pencil.

Heartbreak House.
A Dramatic Fantasia.
By Bernard Shaw.

Constable and Company
Ltd. London: 1917.

416 To Ellen O'Malley, who had created the rôle of Nora in *John Bull's Other Island* in 1904. Autograph letter, 25 January 1921, seeking information as to her availability for *Heartbreak House*.

> Are you engaged after Easter? How old are you? What is your weight? Can you look eighteen still? Can I insist on your playing Ellie without making myself and you ridiculous? . . . *Do* let me have a line . . . answering the last two questions in the affirmative.

The HRC possesses 20 pieces of Shaw correspondence (1904–23) to Ellen O'Malley.

417 Two series of autograph rehearsal criticisms and directions for Ellen O'Malley, consisting of 6 and 3 postcards respectively; undated (October 1921).

> The speech 'I suppose you think youre being sympathetic' and so on is becoming pathetic. This is fatal: it must be brutal and fierce. I want you to shew that you have this stop on your organ as well as the gentle ones. Besides, that is where Ellie comes out as a stronger woman than Hesione.

> 'That would be best of all' [to marry a sailor] Make a cadence of it.

> Force the revulsion at 'to get a glass of rum' for all you are worth.

418 To Ellen O'Malley. Typewritten letter, 6 November 1921. Shaw had acceded to the demands of the manager, James Fagan, to quicken the pace of the performance, in response to reviewers' criticisms that the play moved too slowly. The viewing of another performance leaves him agitated and despondent.

> In my youth I used to play piano duets with my sister: mostly Beethoven's overtures. We secured a very stimulating prestissimo by abandoning every care except as to which of us should get to the final chord first. If you and Mary [Grey] had been playing a Beethoven overture, it would have been all right. As you were playing a scene in which contrast of character, and consequently contrast of speed, of tone, of feeling, of age, of everything[,] is all important, the result was disastrous.

419 To Arnold Bennett, novelist and playwright. Typewritten letter, 20 October 1921. Bennett, like everyone else from the managers to the critics, had found Ellen O'Malley physically wrong for Ellie Dunn because of her age (she was past 40). Shaw resolutely defends the casting, arguing that the reaction is based on a misconception that Ellie is an ingenue and 'a sweet little sexual attraction.'

> I spotted Ellen as 'a heavy' nearly 20 years ago. . . . I knew all through her career that she would never make good until she got her teeth into a heavy part. And I gave her Ellie, not in the least because I wanted an ingenue, but because Ellie is technically the heavy lead in the play, just as I should give her Lady Macbeth.

The HRC possesses 15 pieces of Shaw correspondence (1910–30) to Bennett.

420 To St John Ervine. Two typewritten letters, 23 and 28 October 1921, in reaction to Ervine's criticism in the *Observer* on 22 October.

> I note from The Observer that you believe that the British public can think faster than a rhinoceros. Have you any ground for that tribute?

> Why the devil should Ellie Dunn seem in her element in Heartbreak House? I took the greatest care that she should not be—that she should be in the sharpest contrast to all the heartbreakers, and that when she is lured into it she should walk over Hector and Hesione straight to the Captain, the positive efficient man on whose shoulders the whole structure is carried.

421 Memorandum of Agreement with the Theatre Guild, 24 August 1920. Draft copy and final copy, the latter with J.M. Barrie's signature as witness.

422 Photographs of (a) the first production (by Ira Schwarz), as produced by the Theatre Guild, at the Garrick Theatre, New York, 10 November 1920 (Act II. Ariadne: 'Papa: dont say you think Ive no heart.'); (b) Cedric Hardwicke as Shotover (by Pollard Crowther), Birmingham Repertory Theatre, 3 March 1923; (c) Orson Welles, at the age of 23, as Shotover (by Alfredo Valente), Mercury Theatre, New York, 29 April 1938.

423 From John Houseman, director and co-manager of the Mercury Theatre, New York. Typewritten letter, undated (30 April 1938), reporting on the reception the preceding night of the Mercury's revival of the play, and enclosing the morning critical notices.

> What they cannot describe to you is the spell under which that audience sat for over three hours last night. I think you would have liked Orson Welles' production—it had intelligence, vitality and an extraordinary sort of beauty.

424 Replies to inquiries by Floryan Sobieniowski on 15 March 1930 for the Polish production. Autograph manuscript, 4 pp.; Shaw's notes are undated. WITH: Replies to inquiries of 17 March on *Misalliance* and *Heartbreak House*. Autograph manuscript, 3 pp., dated 29 March by Shaw.

> The two sisters should be as strongly contrasted in appearance as in character. . . . They are the daughters of a respectable English lady. They are the demon daughters of the Witch of Zanzibar by the devil to whom Shotover is said to have sold himself solely in a mystical sense, just as Ellie is the Captain's wife in a mystical sense only. From the prosaic point of view it is a family joke.

BACK TO METHUSELAH (1918–20)

425 To Harley Granville Barker. Autograph letter, 18 December 1918. Shaw, who has just read 'The Gospel of the Brothers Barnabas' (Part II of the play) to Barker and his future wife Helen Huntington, announces that he is thoroughly bored with it: 'it has never seemed quite so tedious before.'

> I shall have to get the picture better composed. . . . The idea is not to get comic relief . . . but to exhibit the Church, marriage, the family, and parliament under shortlived conditions before reproducing them under longlived conditions. . . . I may have to disregard the boredom of the spectator who has not mastered all the motifs, as Wagner had to, but I daresay I shall manage to make the people more amusing, some of them more poetic, and all of them more intelligible than they now are in this first draft.

426 Press release drafted by Shaw for the Constable & Co. first book publication; undated (ca. April 1921).

> Messrs Constable & Co have to announce the publication . . . of an important and even extraordinary work by Mr Bernard Shaw: one which will interest biologists, religious leaders, and lovers of the marvellous in fiction as well as lovers of the theatre. It is the author's scientific, religious, and political testament as well as his supreme exploit in dramatic literature.

427 To St John Ervine. Typewritten letter, 21 September 1921. Shaw responds to Ervine's criticisms of the recently-published play.

> [I]t is not experience of life but expectation of life that determines our conduct, our attitude, and the effort we call upon ourselves for. If Louis XV had expected to live three centuries he would not have said 'Après moi le deluge': he would have tried to build an ark with the help of Turgot.

428 Photograph of Part IV, 'The Tragedy of an Elderly Gentleman' (setting and costumes by Lee Simonson), Theatre Guild production, at the Garrick Theatre, New York, 6 March 1922 (Parts I and II were first performed on 27 February). Albert Bruning as the Elderly Gentleman and Margaret Wycherly as the Oracle. WITH: Photographs of the production in the 'Shaw Festival' souvenir program sold in the theatre.

429 To H.K. Ayliff, director of the Birmingham Repertory production in 1923. Autograph letter, 29 August 1923. Shaw insists that Edith Evans as the serpent should be heard but not seen, and provides drawings to illustrate the suggested staging.

> You must get an artist . . . to design a very slender snake's head and neck to rise out of the Johnswort and quiver there while Edith, sunk in the cut with her head just above the level of the stage, and hidden by the Johnswort, speaks the lines. She must stand on something resonant . . . and tick out her words with deadly distinctness in a tone that suggests a whisper, but isnt.

Needless to say, Shaw's suggestion was vetoed by actress, director, and manager. Edith Evans, in an elaborate cobra costume, was very much in evidence on opening night. WITH: Photograph (by George Dawson) of Part I, 'In the Beginning' (set and costumes by Paul Shelving), Birmingham Repertory production, 9 October 1923. Edith Evans as the Serpent, Colin Keith-Johnston as Adam, and Gwen Ffrangcon-Davies as Eve.

430 Textual revisions, corrections, and cuts for the Birmingham Repertory production, undated (9–12 October 1923), written in pencil on two small slips.

431 Autograph rehearsal notes for productions at the Birmingham Repertory Theatre, 1923 (7 pp.); the Court Theatre, 1924 (10 pp.); and the Old Vic, 1929 (5 pp.). (The last page of the Old Vic notes also contains a note for *The Apple Cart*, dated 18 July 1929).

> Adam [listen to] the Voice — not to Eve — brooding[.] generally she should attend to him & he be preoccupied.
>
> Snake legend of Lilith — why not fall down again & hiss it at Eve?
>
> luskry ate wotzwill [Edith Evans's slurring of the phrase 'at last create what we will']

432 Jacket blurb written by Shaw for the Penguin edition, 1939. Typewritten (carbon) manuscript, with revisions. 2 pp.

Parknasilla. Kenmare. Co. Kerry. 29th Aug. 1923.

Dear Ayliff

No property head that the clumsiest pantomime property man could perpetrate could be half so fatal as Edith Evans's torso offering itself as the voice that breathed oer Eden.

You must get an artist (or get Sir Whitworth Wallis to choose one) to design a very slender snake's head and neck to rise out of the johnswort and quiver there while Edith, sunk in the cut with her head just above the level of the stage, and hidden by the johnswort, speaks the lines. She must stand on something resonant, not on anything solid, and tick out her words with deadly distinctness in a tone that suggests

Cobra hood spread

a whisper, but isnt.

The hood may be practicable or may not. The serpents neck should be vibrant, not rigid. It is impossible to say more without experiments on the spot, and a real artist doing the design and coloring and lighting.

If I had known Edith was to be in it I would have written in a proper part for her. Why dont you make her play the Envoy's wife? she would lift it to a leading part at once. Anybody can play the oracle. She is going to play Lady Utterword in Heartbreak House, I hope.

ever

G.B.S.

Back to Methuselah . . . first appeared in 1921, when the world was still bleeding dangerously from what the deepest living Conservative thinker described as 'a foolish and unnecessary war,' and when even those who thought its revolutionary destruction of three empires, and its inauguration of a great social experiment in Russia, well worth a world war, were nevertheless appalled by the fact that nothing could have been further from the intentions of the statesmen who made the war than these consequences of it.

SAINT JOAN (1923)

433 Photograph of Winifred Lenihan, the first Shavian Joan, in the Theatre Guild production, at the Garrick Theatre, New York, 28 December 1923. WITH: Program of the production.

434 To Sydney Cockerell. Typewritten letter, 27 February 1924, tipped in at the front of a 1924 Rough Proof, containing three autograph corrections. (An autograph letter of 21 February 1924 is written on the halftitle). Shaw confesses that he is not 'inordinately proud' of *Saint Joan*.

[I]t was very easy to write: the materials were there, and even the historical manufacture had been worked over by so many hands that I am only the author in the sense that Michael Angelo was the architect of St Peter's. . . . I have had only to pull it together and fit it in. . . . However, though this affects my feeling towards the work, it has no effect on anyone else: it is the most satisfactory result, and not the most troublesome or individual one, that best pleases the reader. And Joan is very satisfactory.

435 Rehearsal notes for the first London production, at the New Theatre, 26 March 1924. 14 pp. on 10 leaves. WITH: Rough Proof rehearsal copy (wrappers missing), 1924. Revised extensively for the printer; a note by Shaw on the flyleaf, 23 May 1931, authenticates the volume, although 'I cannot account for its passing out of my hands.' He apparently had forgot that he sold a large quantity of unexamined proofs, pamphlets, foreign translations, and other superfluous publications to Gilbert Fabes of Foyle's Rare Books Department before vacating Adelphi Terrace in 1927.

436 Two photographs (by Graphic Photo Union) of Sybil Thorndike as Joan in Scene VI (The Trial) of the London production, 1924, in one of which Lawrence Anderson appears as Brother Martin. Photograph (by W.S. Campbell) of O.B. Clarence as the Inquisitor. WITH: Program of the London production, at the New Theatre, 26 March 1924, containing a 'Note by the Author.'

437 First edition (1924), with a presentation inscription 'to Shayle Gardner | first of the de Baudricourts | on his birthday | from | G. Bernard Shaw', dated 22 August 1924, and signed on several pages by 21 members of the cast, including Sybil Thorndike, Lewis Casson (De Stogumber), Ernest Thesiger (the Dauphin), and Raymond Massey (D'Estivet).

438 Limited edition, with tipped-in color reproductions of Charles Ricketts's set and costume designs. London: Constable, 1924. One of 750 copies. The displayed plate is No. 1, 'Joan and the Executioner'. WITH: Photograph of Ricketts's design for Scene IV (Tent Scene), which was displayed in the Royal Academy winter exhibition in January 1933.

433

439 To T.E. Lawrence. Inscribed presentation copy (1924, but not first printing): 'to Shaw from Shaw | to replace many stolen copies until | this, too, is stolen.' Dated 7 February 1934. On the reverse of the same leaf is a note of explanation by Lawrence, signed 'T.E. Shaw', dated February 1934.

> G.B.S. gave me first a copy of the acting version of S. Joan. It was borrowed from me by an R.T.C. [Royal Tank Corps] reader, who lent it to another, and he to a third. So it disappeared.
>
> Then G.B.S. sent me another Joan, like this, inscribed 'To Pte Shaw from Public Shaw'. This was one of my chief joys at Clouds Hill: but in 1932 it also vanished.
>
> Hence this third copy, with its pessimistic inscription.

440 From Karel Čapek, Czech dramatist, author of the play *R.U.R.* Autograph letter, 30 October 1924, reporting (in faulty English) on the Czech première of *Saint Joan*, and inviting Shaw to visit Prague.

> [I]t is a great joy for me to can announce you that [the production] was a really good performance. Joan (Mme [Leopolda] Dostalová) was more passionate than Miss Thorndike . . . the Dauphin less ingenious and more pitiable than in London. . . . [Y]ou were celebrated [in the press] more than ever; only a Catholic journal discovered, you are an irreverent haeretic, which perhaps cannot be denied.

*441 Oskar Strnad: Three set plans for Max Reinhardt's lavish, revolving-stage production of *Saint Joan*, in Siegfried Trebitsch's translation, at the Deutsches Theater, Berlin, 14 October 1924. Strnad was a highly reputed Viennese scene and costume designer.

*442 Lithographed poster of the French production, at the Théâtre des Arts, Paris, 28 April 1925, with a portrait of Ludmilla Pitoëff 'd'après Van Dongen'.

THE APPLE CART (1928)

443 Shorthand manuscript. Dated 5 November 1928 on the first page. Completed 29 December at Cliveden, where the Shaws were guests of Lady Astor. 89 pp.

444 Typewritten manuscript fragments, consisting of the first page each of Acts I, II, and III, and the lower half of the final page. These were retained by Shaw to preserve the dates of composition. The bal-

ance of the original typewritten transcription from the shorthand was destroyed.

445 First page proofs, heavily revised, datestamped 6 February 1929. 23 additional lines of typewritten text are inserted on p. 38 into Magnus's long speech defending the Royalist position, from which nearly 5 lines of the typeset speech have been eliminated.

446 To Floryan Sobieniowski. Two autograph postcards from Venice, 31 May and 8 June 1929, concerning the world première production in Warsaw.

> Contrast—continual contrast—is essential to my dialogue: if the performers take their tone and speed from one another, all glibly picking up their cues and rattling on in the same way, the scene will be unintelligible. Unless every actor speaks and behaves as if he had never heard his cue before, and is surprised by it, or wounded, or pleased—all involving some change of tone or pace, however subtle—the whole affair will be about as amusing as a gabbled-through church service.

The HRC possesses 20 pieces of Shaw correspondence (1929–36) to Sobieniowski.

*447 Poster for the production of *The Apple Cart*, in the Polish translation of Floryan Sobieniowski, under the title *Wielki Kram*, at the Teatr Polski, Warsaw, 14 June 1929.

448 Photographs: (a) Warsaw, 1929: Marja Przybylko-Potocka as Orinthia (by St. Brzozowski); (b) London, at the Queen's Theatre, 17 September 1929: Cedric Hardwicke as Magnus, and Barbara Everest and James Carew as Jemima and Vanhattan (by Pollard Crowther); (c) New York, at the Plymouth Theatre, 18 October 1956: Maurice Evans and Signe Hasso as Magnus and Orinthia (by Fred Fehl).

449 *Der Kaiser von Amerika* (Berlin, 1929). The first publication of the play, in Siegfried Trebitsch's German translation. The English text was not published until 1930.

450 To Clarence H. Norman. Autograph postcard, 9 January 1930, headed *Private*. Shaw rebukes Norman for misunderstanding the play.

> I am disgusted at the ease with which nice clothes and a pleasant address, with rank, imposes on everybody. My

infernal old scoundrel of an inquisitor in St Joan got away with it like a cathedral canon; and now here are you swallowing my gentlemanly Magnus as a god! I'm surprised at you.

TOO TRUE TO BE GOOD (1931)

451 Unbound page proofs, extensively revised. Containing a note to the printer, William Maxwell, dated 2 December 1931: 'I shall want 50 copies bound in paper for rehearsal . . . as usual, as I shall have to hold up publication for a year, probably'; and an inscription, dated 13 December 1931, 'This can now be added to William Maxwell's private collection of badly shopsoiled literary curiosities'.

452 To R. & R. Clark, Ltd. Two autograph notes, 13 December 1931, and an autograph postcard, 18 December 1931, providing corrections. '*Now* you may go to press.'

453 Shaw's drawings of set plans for Acts I and II.

454 Rough Proof rehearsal copy (1931), inscribed to Lady Rhondda, publisher and editor of *Time and Tide*, with additional typewritten text affixed to the last text page, and an autograph note explaining its importance to the actor, Cedric Hardwicke, on stage alone at the end of the play.

455 Programs of the first production by the Theatre Guild, which opened at the Imperial Theatre in Boston on 29 February 1932, and in London by Barry Jackson, at the New Theatre, 13 September 1932 (after 8 performances at the Malvern Festival, commencing 6 August).

456 Photographs (by Vandamm) of the New York production (1932): (a) Julius Evans as the Monster; (b) Beatrice Lillie as Sweetie, Hope Williams as the Patient, and Hugh Sinclair as the Burglar; (c) Ernest Cossart as Col. Tallboys. WITH: Photograph (by Sasha) of Ernest Thesiger as the Monster and Leonora Corbett as the Patient in the London production (1932).

457 Charlotte F. Shaw to St John Ervine. Autograph letter, 9 October 1932. In his drama column in the *Observer* that morning Ervine had asked: 'What right has an old man to throw up his hands and surrender every belief he holds? That game soldier, Shaw, who has hitherto valiantly put up his fists and been the foremost in every fight, is now whimpering in corners and assuring his followers . . . that they had better all lie down and die. . . . Better indeed that [he] should have died a dozen years ago than live to write this whining play . . . [in which he] recants all his beliefs.' Charlotte instantly penned an impassioned rebuttal.

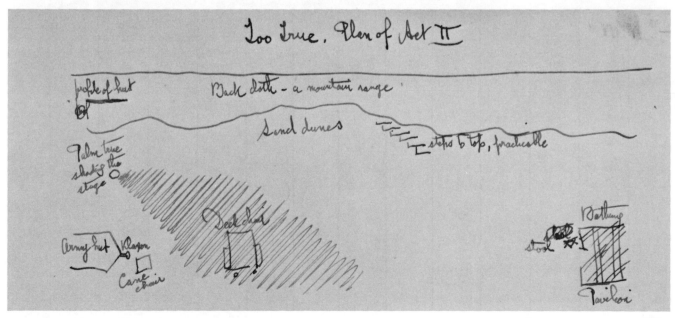

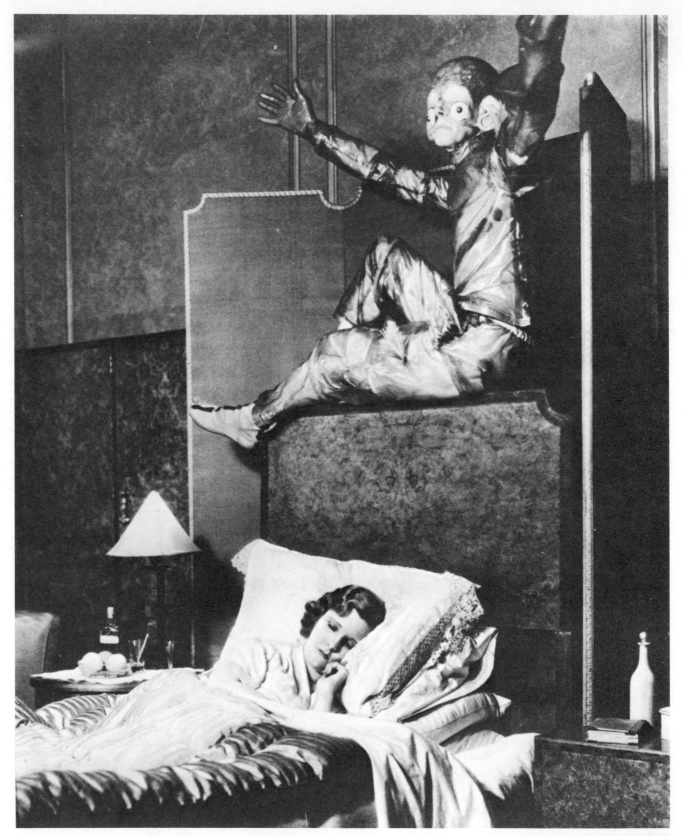

456 (London)

I, who am G.B.S.'s severest critic, specially like this play. To my mind it is not pessimistic, not despondent & not a recantation of any of his beliefs. It is a play of revolt. One character after another declares that this is 'not enough': that they are getting glimpses of the 'reality that was hidden'. . . . Everything in the play points to the fact that there is a 'way of life', & that all these people, some consciously some unconsciously, are struggling to find it. Honestly, St. John, I do think that in the future, when things straighten out, it will be understood that this is among G.B.S.'s big plays. The voice of one crying in the wilderness!

ON THE ROCKS (1933)

458 Shorthand manuscript, first and last pages, preserved for the dates of composition. The balance of the manuscript was destroyed. Composition was begun 'In the Gulf of Siam' on 6 February 1933, and completed on 4 July at Ayot St Lawrence.

459 List of characters, with physical descriptions and characteristics. The names of actors suggested for the rôles are underlined in red ink. Typewritten (carbon) manuscript, with autograph notes. 1 p.

460 Programs of the first production: in London, at the Winter Garden Theatre, 25 November 1933, with a cover design by John Farleigh; and in New York by the Federal Theatre, at Daly's Theatre, 15 June 1938.

461 Three photographs of the London production (1933): (a) Inset of front door to No. 10 Downing Street; (b) World map drop-curtain; (c) Act II: Meeting in the Cabinet Room. Nicholas Hannen as Sir Arthur Chavender. Two photographs of the Federal Theatre production (1938): (a) Ardis Gaines as Alderwoman Aloysia Brollikins and Philip Bourneuf as Chavender; (b) Bourneuf, Lyster Chambers as Sir Broadfoot Basham, and Harry Irvine as Old Hipney.

462 Review by Alan Bott, 'A Salute to Guy Fawkes', in the *Tatler* (London), 13 December 1933, with caricatures of the performers by 'Tomtitt'.

The HRC's vertical files contain more than 5000 newspaper and magazine articles by and on Shaw, letters to editors, reviews of his plays, and obituary notices from all parts of the world. Most of these were supplied to Shaw by British and international news-cutting bureaus to which he subscribed for more than half a century.

463 To Esmé Percy, a veteran of the Bernard Shaw Repertory Company, with which he toured as leading man for many years. Autograph postcard, 6 July 1934. Percy had expressed a desire to appear in the play in New York. However, the Theatre Guild, still hurting from the failure of *Too True to be Good* two years earlier, had turned it down 'very decisively', Shaw reports, 'and the play is too doubtful to justify a move [of the London production] to America on the chance of its running more than 6 weeks.'

The HRC possesses 31 pieces of Shaw correspondence (1913–50) to Percy.

VILLAGE WOOING (1933)

464 Shorthand manuscript, originally titled *The Red Sea*, dated 2 January 1933 on the first page and 27 January 1933 'In the Sunda Strait' at the end. 18 pp. Written aboard the Empress of Britain during a world cruise. The title was later revised to *A Village Wooing* before it attained its final form.

465 First Rough Proof (1933). Inscribed to Floryan Sobieniowski, 30 September 1933.

466 Photographs of the first production, by the Dallas Little Theatre, 17 April 1934, with Charles Meredith as 'A' and Keith Woolley as 'Z'. The initials stem from Shaw's long practice, when working out a scenario, of labelling his characters by a sequence of letters of the alphabet, forward from A for the males and backward from Z for the females.

467 To Lillah McCarthy. Autograph letter, 25 May 1934, rejecting the idea of a B.B.C. broadcast of the play, in which she would appear, as this would kill 'stone dead' the upcoming London production and a provincial tour he had just licensed.

I do not see myself as the Man: he is intended as a posthumous portrait of Lytton Strachey.

468 Rehearsal notes for the first London production, at the Little Theatre, 19 June 1934. 12 pp. (bound) and 1 p. (unbound). Shaw's caricature of Sybil Thorndike appears on one of the bound pages. WITH: Program of the play at the Little Theatre, on a double bill with John Galsworthy's *The Little Man: A Farcical Morality*.

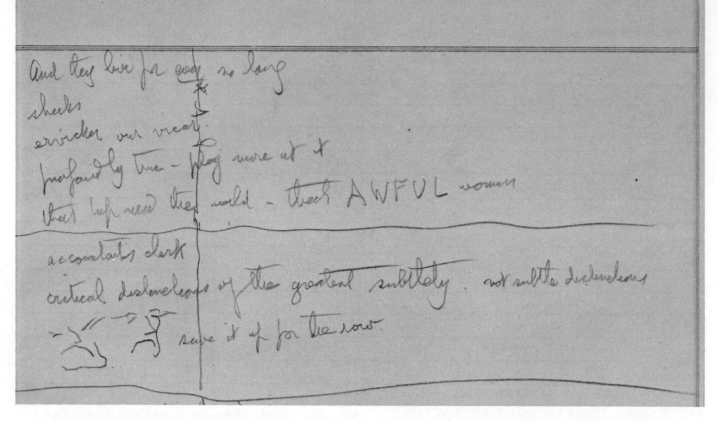

THE SIMPLETON OF THE UNEXPECTED ISLES (1934)

469 To Leonora Ervine, wife of St John Ervine, who was Shaw's neighbor in Whitehall Court, London. Autograph letter, 12 May 1934, aboard the Rangitane, returning from New Zealand.

> I have written two plays on the double voyage. . . . Playwriting is becoming a Platonic exercise with me. . . . My bolt is shot as far as any definite target is concerned and now, as my playwright faculty still goes on with the impetus of 30 years vital activity, I shoot into the air more and more extravagantly without any premeditation whatever—*advienne que pourra.*

The HRC possesses 20 pieces of Shaw correspondence (1916–45) to Leonora Ervine.

470 Page proofs, bound in plain brown wrappers, labelled by Shaw on the upper cover: 'The Simpleton | of the | Unexpected Isles | by | Bernard Shaw'; presentation inscription, 16 December 1934, on the halftitle: 'To Floryan Sobieniowski | for translation'.

471 To Floryan Sobieniowski. Two typewritten letters, 12 and 21 January 1935, and two autograph postcards, 25 January and 13 March 1935, all of them dealing with the Polish translation and offering suggestions for the production at the Teatr Polski.

> The third scene of the prologue is taken from the caves of Elephanta, an island near Bombay. The giant figures are of Indian deities. It is impossible to describe them.
>
> The four young creatures, in their exquisite dresses, never utter a word naturally. They declaim, their speech is musical, rhythmical, artificial in the last degree. When Maya is making love she coos like a dove.
>
> Prola is a woman of overpowering sexual attraction; and the blundering and inexperienced simpleton is trying to describe this effect on him without fully understanding it when she, understanding it perfectly and knowing that it is a thing *sui generis* for which there is no language, pushes him with her foot . . . and says 'Let the unspeakable remain unspoken.'

472 Program of the first production, by the Theatre Guild, at the Guild Theatre, New York, 18 February

1935. WITH: Photographs (by Vandamm) of Romney Brent as Iddy Hammingtap and Alla Nazimova as the priestess Prola, and of one of Lee Simonson's settings.

473 To Mrs Patrick Campbell. Autograph letter, 17 March 1935. Shaw had encouraged the Theatre Guild to give the part of the priestess to Mrs Campbell, who was living in America. Due to a misunderstanding, the part eventually was offered to Nazimova. Shaw chastizes Mrs Campbell in the letter, but also offers the solace that the production was a disaster.

> As it turns out you are lucky to have missed the part . . . for the critics have fallen on it with such fury that it has flopped completely. . . . The politest notice describes me as a dignified monkey shying cocoanuts at the public.

The HRC possesses 13 pieces of Shaw correspondence (1915–39) to Mrs Campbell.

474 Program of the first British production, at the Malvern Festival, 29 July 1935. WITH: Photograph (by J.W. Debenham) of Stephen Murray as the Simpleton, Curigwen Lewis as Maya, and Elspeth March as Vashti.

THE MILLIONAIRESS (1934)

475 Rough Proof, labelled 'Private' by Shaw in red ink on the upper cover, inscribed to Floryan Sobieniowski on the halftitle, 13 December 1935. One of 25 copies printed in July 1935. The subtitle 'A Jonsonian Comedy' on the rehearsal copies persisted through 1940, despite the fact that the published text in 1936 was subtitled simply 'A Comedy'.

476 Programs of the première production (second performance), by the Burgtheater, in Siegfried Trebitsch's German translation, at the Akademie Theater, Vienna, 8 January 1936; and of the first production in England, by the Matthew Forsyth Repertory Company, at the De La Warr Pavilion, Bexhill, 17 November 1936.

477 Three photographs (by Press Photo Service) of a production in Prague, 17 January 1936. The settings were designed by A. Heythum.

478 Rehearsal Copy (1940). An autograph letter to the writer Charlotte Haldane, 4 July 1942, is inscribed on the halftitle, informing her that a passage in which she is interested begins at the foot of p. 151: 'American men of business are all like that. They will give a rake-off to the nearest hobo rather than be alone in any enterprise. An amiable weakness: the secret of their great successes and their ruinous follies.' At the end of the text in this 1940 impression Shaw added a new passage, stating:

> And that is how the story ends in capitalist countries. In Russia, however, and in countries with Communist sympathies, the people demand that the tale should have an edifying moral.

He therefore has provided an alternative ending for Communist countries.

479 Photograph (by Angus McBean) of the first London West End production, at the New Theatre, 27 June 1952. An earlier production starring Edith Evans toured the provinces in 1940, but its London engagement was cancelled because of the Blitz. Shaw had encouraged the Theatre Guild to produce the play with Katharine Hepburn as the millionairess Epifania, but Miss Hepburn, unimpressed by the script, vetoed the suggestion. Fifteen years later she changed her mind and performed the play both in London and New York with Cyril Ritchard as Adrian Blenderbland and Robert Helpmann as the Doctor.

THE SIX OF CALAIS (1934)

480 (a) First preface. Typewritten manuscript, revised. 4 pp. Discarded. (b) Second preface. Shorthand draft, dated 28 May 1935 'On The High Seas'. 2 pp. Written aboard the S.S. Winchester Castle en route from Cape Town to England. WITH: Published text of the preface, in *The Simpleton, The Six, and The Millionairess* (1936).

The HRC also possesses the original shorthand manuscript, under the title Les Bourgeois de Calais, *dated 15 to 18 May 1934 'In the Atlantic'. 8 pp.*

481 First Rough Proof, datestamped 5 June 1934, with revisions. Note on the upper cover, in the hand of the printer William Maxwell, 16 June 1934: 'Given to me by G.B.S. for the shop soiled collection of literary curiosities.' Second Rough Proof, datestamped 19 July 1934, with further revision for a printing of the First

Proof after Rehearsal. This is bound with uncorrected proofs of the book text, published in 1936.

482   From John Cammidge, a specialist in historical pageantry. Typewritten letter, 4 June 1934. Cammidge offers his services to see that the play is 'accurately dressed and equipped.' An undated autograph note by Shaw on the letter instructs his secretary: 'Say he must deal with Mr [Sydney] Carroll, as I care nothing for historical accuracy if I can get a handsome pictorial effect.'

483   To Sydney Carroll, who produced the play at the Open Air Theatre, Regent's Park, London, 17 July 1934, on a triple bill with Shaw's *Androcles and the Lion* and Michael Martin-Harvey's mime play *Joan*. Autograph letter, 7 June 1934, on the halftitle of a copy of the first proof. WITH: Shaw's watercolor set design.

> As to the scenery, a few castellated profiles sticking up out of the bushes and a couple of pavilions and a few tents, with a royal seat for the king, is the most you can do; and we could do with less at a pinch.

GENEVA (1936)

484   Photograph (by J.W. Debenham) of the London production, at the Saville Theatre, 22 November 1938. Act III: Walter Hudd as Battler, Alexander Knox as the Judge, and Cecil Trouncer as Bombardone.

485   Watercolor and crayon sketches by Shaw of 'The Jew' and 'The Widow'. 12″ by 9½″.

486   To Roy Limbert, Malvern and London theatrical manager. Autograph letter, 17 September 1939. The rapid sequence of European political events between 1937 and 1939 made it difficult for Shaw to keep his play topical. He revised endlessly, producing a flood of variant rehearsal copies, like the 1938 SECOND REHEARSAL COPY, REVISED AFTER BOMBARDONE'S CONVERSION TO ANTI-SEMITISM (with a presentation inscription on the halftitle to Blanche Patch, 8 October 1938). Now he discusses with Limbert the effect on the play of the outbreak of war.

> The declaration of war is the making of Geneva, which has always lacked a substantial climax. . . . I have written a new scene—the arrival of the news of Battler's attack—which will just do the trick.

The HRC possesses 152 pieces of Shaw correspondence (1930–50) to Limbert.

487   Feliks Topolski: Sketch of Shaw and himself, with an autograph note by Shaw on its mount. 8¾″ by 6½″. Reproduced in facsimile in the first edition of *Geneva* (1939).

488   Feliks Topolski: Ink sketch of Herr Battler and Signor Bombardone at Geneva. 8″ by 10″.

489 To Dr F.E. Loewenstein. Autograph note, on typewritten letter from Harold O. White of the Leagrave Press to Loewenstein, 4 July 1947, requesting permission to reproduce Feliks Topolski's *Geneva* sketch of Shaw and himself in Loewenstein's book *Bernard Shaw Through the Camera*. Shaw, now under the spell of the artist Clare Winsten, a neighbor in Ayot, vetoes the reproduction.

I object to this. Topolski's work is always attractive and interesting; but it creates a Shaw that does not exist and damages my reputation. It is 40 years out of date.

I have refused to have my latest books illustrated by T, though he has pressed me to let him do so.

Shaw does not mention that Topolski, a year earlier, had outraged him with a series of irreverent sketches for a proposed Penguin Books edition of *Saint Joan*. 'Saint Joan is sacred', he had spluttered in a postcard to Topolski on 9 April 1946. 'You of all men must not touch her. Your speciality is monstrous burlesque. . . . Penguin can see no difference between Pygmalion and La Pucelle.'

IN GOOD KING CHARLES'S GOLDEN DAYS (1938–39)

490 To Roy Limbert. Autograph postcard, 24 December 1938. Shaw has begun an ambitious new work.

I never know what a play is going to be until it is finished. What I am aiming at so far is an educational history film. The people will wear XVII century costumes regardless of expense, numbers, and salaries. It may be beyond the resources of Malvern even if Pascal does not get in first.

491 From Sir James H. Jeans, English physicist and astronomer. Autograph letter, 7 July 1939. From Sir Arthur S. Eddington, English astronomer, director of the Cambridge Observatory. Typewritten letter, 21 June 1939. Shaw had sent to each of these men a copy of the play in Rough Proof, asking for their assistance in dealing with the scientific aspects of the play. Jeans did the logarithms for him. Eddington jibbed at the anachronism in Shaw's use of the term 'perihelion of mercury', which belonged to the XIX century, and confessed there were 'some sayings attributed to Newton which make me shudder as a mathematician'. He conceded, however, that these were pedantic criticisms, and that one must allow for 'dramatic license.' This was sufficient encouragement for Shaw to retain the 'perihelion' phrase as a guaranteed stage laugh that he could not afford to sacrifice.

492 Feliks Topolski: Sketches for the cover of the paper boards issue of the book and the dustwrapper of the issue in cloth binding; with Shaw's notes (1939). Of the image of the artist at work Shaw comments: 'This is a very pretty design'; of Shaw at work: 'My wife likes this.'

493 First edition (1939), illustrated by Feliks Topolski, issued simultaneously in cloth and in paper boards. One copy contains a presentation inscription, dated 13 November 1939, to Topolski: 'my more attractive collaborator'.

494 Page of notes, December 1939, seeking to amend a former error in calculation. ('The figures on page 24 are wrong', Shaw confessed to H.G. Wells; 'I added the Leap Years instead of deducting them.')

495 To G.M. Trevelyan, the historian. Autograph postcard, 20 January 1940. Shaw discusses his errors in the play, notably his blunder in miscalculating Calvin's death by a century. At his present age (83½) 'I find myself doing all sorts of silly things.'

496 Program of a performance in the presence of King George VI and Queen Elizabeth, 29 October 1948, at the People's Palace, Mile End Road, London. This was a revival by Roy Limbert which toured the provinces before being performed at the 1949 Malvern Festival.

BUOYANT BILLIONS (1936–46)

497 Autograph note by Dr F.E. Loewenstein, 2 August 1945, '11.45 a.m. G.B.S. told me to make a note of this date. He is starting a new play and will do nothing else until it is finished.' The play, called provisionally *O Bee Beeze Beez*, was one that Shaw actually had begun en route to Honolulu in February 1936, under the working title *The World Betterer*, and then set aside after a week's work. He returned to it briefly in August 1937 before abandoning it completely. The new version was completed in November 1946, but Shaw continually revised it for more than two years, during which time it was called *A World Betterer's Courtship* and, later, *The Buoyant Billions*.

498 Autograph list of 'World Betterer Names', written on the reverse of a printed postcard proclaiming the Society of Authors to be Shaw's agent for play licensing.

499 Six pages of revised typescript, undated, discarded after being copied. Preserved by Shaw's secretary Blanche Patch.

500 To Roy Limbert. Autograph letter, 18 November 1946. The new play, Shaw announces, is finished, and will be ready for the 1947 Malvern Festival 'if it ever comes off'. The Festival was not revived until August 1949, when *Buoyant Billions* attained its first British production.

> It is so bad that I ought to burn it; but it will serve your turn for a few performances. . . . There are 12 characters and 3 scenes, costing more than they are worth.

501 To Roy Limbert. Autograph letter, 6 November 1948. Instructions are given for the production.

> No character is to make-up to resemble the author. . . . No ugliness, vulgarity, or low comedy.

*502 Poster for the first London production, at the Princes Theatre, 10 October 1949.

503 *Zu Viel Geld* (Zürich, 1948). First book publication, in Siegfried Trebitsch's German translation.

504 *Buoyant Billions: A Comedy of No Manners in Prose*. Illustrated by Clare Winsten. Limited to 1025 copies. Dated 1949, but not issued until May 1950. The cover drawings are by Mrs Winsten's daughter Theodora. Despite the pleading of his printer William Maxwell, Shaw allowed the Winstens to control the design of the book. The result was a monstrosity.

505 To R. & R. Clark, Ltd. Autograph letter, 4 January 1949, with a sketch by Shaw of the title page for the limited edition. 'This is to be set in the most Gothic looking type you have, and must be solid because it has to fit into the lower half of the pictorial title page which Mrs Winsten has designed. . . .'

506 Watercolor sketch by Shaw of Clementina Buoyant, 9⅞″ by 7¹⁵/₁₆″, on reverse of an autograph letter of 6 August 1949 to Clare Winsten. Shaw has decided there should be two additional drawings in the limited edition of *Buoyant Billions*.

> There must be one of her at the beginning of the Panama scene, threatening the intruder. My daub on the back of this is more like a Pirate King than a woman; but it gives the attitude and expression.

FARFETCHED FABLES (1948)

507 To St John Ervine. Typewritten letter, 17 August 1948.

> I have actually begun another play but it is only a dodge to keep me alive. I call it provisionally Shawsop's Fables.

508 Typewritten (carbon) manuscript, with revisions copied in by Blanche Patch, 25 September 1948, and shorthand additions to the text by Shaw. 38 pp. WITH: Scrap of shorthand discarded from 'The New

Play', with a dated note, 28 July 1948, in Dr F.E. Loewenstein's hand.

509 First rehearsal copy, 'By a Fellow of the Royal Society of Literature', undated (July 1949). One of 48 copies.

510 To Esmé Percy. Autograph postcards of 12 and 19 July 1950. Percy was preparing to direct the first production of the play. *Farfetched Fables*, Shaw informs him, is not a full-length play, but 'a string of short scenes . . . not intended for professional production, but for amateurs with unlimited time for rehearsal, making their own dresses and painting their own scenery. Also shifting it.' Upon learning that there is to be a full-scale production sponsored by the Shaw Society, he warns that he did not bargain for 'a regular West End first performance; and it must not be announced as such. . . . Another fiasco like that of Buoyant Billions would damage me seriously.'

511 To Dr F.E. Loewenstein. Autograph note on Shaw's printed licence form, partially filled out by Loewenstein; undated (ca. June 1950). The Shaw Society had undertaken to produce the play in celebration of Shaw's 94th birthday on 26 July, but production complications necessitated a delay until autumn. Shaw apparently had not been informed of the postponement, or had forgot. 'But why September?' he inquires. 'The birthday is in July. Where is the connexion?'

512 Program of the first production, by the Shaw Society, at the Watergate Theatre, London, 6 September 1950. (The juxtaposition of the play's title and the theatre's name is comic irony.) WITH: Photograph of the Sixth Fable, in which Ellen Pollock appears as the teacher.

WHY SHE WOULD NOT (1950)

513 *Why She Would Not: A Little Comedy*. Shorthand manuscript, dated 17 July 1950, with a note at the top to the typist (Shaw's half cousin and former secretary Georgina Musters): 'Green & Yellow. A complete new play', indicating that, as usual with typescript copies of Shaw's plays, the top copy was to be on green paper and the carbon copy on yellow. 11 pp. A note by Shaw on the last page indicates 'End of Scene 5 and of the Play'. WITH: Typewritten manuscript, 16 pp., containing Shaw's revisions and informing the printer in what was destined to be the last printing instruction he ever gave: 'Standard Edition format as usual'; and typewritten (carbon) manuscript, 3 pp., of material deleted from the play, but published in 1974 in the Bodley Head definitive edition of Shaw's *Collected Plays with Their Prefaces*, Vol. VII.

514 Page proofs, labelled by the printer FIRST PROOF and datestamped 29 September 1950. 14 pp. By the time these proofs were ready for correction, Shaw had suffered the accident which led to his death on 2 November, and never saw them.

515 Clare Winsten: Pencil drawing of Shaw, 1950. 12″ by 8½″. Captioned by Mrs Winsten in pencil: 'G.B.S. telling us about his last play: "I am writing a play in which there is an old man who has a housekeeper who is so houseproud that she gradually eliminates everything that is personal in the house until he feels a perfect stranger there".'

516 'Bernard Shaw is 94 Today: And he still has a punch'. Press cutting of a written interview in reply to questions by F.G. Prince-White, *Daily Mail*, 26 July 1950.

> I've written another play. . . . It is in five scenes. I wrote the whole thing in seven days. . . . People seem to think that I ought to go on writing big plays like 'Back to Methuselah' and 'The Doctor's Dilemma'—but why should I? I've said all I wanted to say; now I can write little things to amuse myself.

517 *Theatre Arts*, New York, August 1956, containing the first publication of *Why She Would Not*, preceded by an article by Dan H. Laurence, 'The Facts about "Why She Would Not".' WITH: Announcement of the first performance, by the Shaw Society of America, on 21 January 1957.

SHAKESPEAR

As a critic Shaw launched a one man crusade against the idolatrous worship of Shakespear. To dramatize his point, Shaw inevitably resorted to exaggeration as he damned the practice of making 'a fetish of our Swan.' Failing to recognize that Shaw's weapons of deflation were aimed at the worshippers of Shakespear rather than at the playwright, the idolators bitterly denounced him for disparaging Shakespear's genius. In actuality, Shaw was a great admirer of Shakespear. He had read all of the plays before he reached his teens, re-read them constantly, and possessed so thorough a familiarity with the texts that he could (and often did) accurately quote passages from memory from almost any of them. His knowledge of Shakespear was firsthand, uncolored by scholarly exegesis and actors' interpretations; few commentators have ever shared Shaw's degree of sensitivity to the subtleties of Shakespear's works.

Admittedly he criticized his illustrious predecessor for being, like Dickens, 'concerned with the diversities of the world instead of with its unities', and for lacking a social conscience. Shakespear's test of the worth of life was, said the supernally optimistic G.B.S., 'the vulgar hedonistic one', which led him to the barren, pessimistic view and futile doctrine that 'life is a tale told by an idiot'. Yet, though Shakespear lacked intellect, he 'has outlasted thousands of abler thinkers, and will outlast a thousand more', for in such gifts as 'sonority, imagery, wit, humor, energy of imagination, power over language, and a whimsically keen eye for idiosyncrasies, Shakespear was the king of dramatists.'

518   To Edith Nesbit Bland, poet and children's author. Autograph postcard, 5 June 1910. Mrs Bland, who subscribed to the Baconian theory of the authorship of Shakespear's plays, had borrowed Shaw's facsimile copy of the First Folio for research purposes. Shaw mockingly constructs a 'Baconian' case to prove that Sidney Webb was the real author of Bernard Shaw's plays.

> Shaw was an utterly ignorant man. . . . He was a disgrace to his school, where he acquired little Latin & less Greek. . . . And this is the man to whom people attribute the omniscience, the knowledge of public affairs, of law, of medicine, of navigation &c&c&c which informs the plays & prefaces of G.B.S. Absurd! Webb, the L.L.B, the man who carried all before him in examinations . . . was clearly the man.

519   To Harley Granville Barker. Autograph postcard, [25 November 1910]. Shaw on the previous day had attended the first of two matinées of his play *The Dark Lady of the Sonnets*, written for and performed on behalf of the Shakespeare Memorial National Theatre, in which Barker appeared as Shakespear. WITH: Program of the production at the Theatre Royal, Haymarket, on a bill that included J.M. Barrie's *A Slice of Life* and two short plays by George Paston.

> Forgot to warn you that you made an astonishingly XIX century start by saying 'On the contrary' instead of 'Far from it.' . . . The costume was killing: there has been a great rally of the old adoration.

520   *The Dark Lady of the Sonnets*. Rough Proof, labelled 'Printer's Sample' by Shaw on the upper cover, which also bears the initials of Charlotte F. Shaw, who copied in the corrections and revisions. Undated (November 1910).

521   *The Dark Lady of the Sonnets*. Seven galley proofs, dated 10 December 1910, with corrections copied in by Shaw's secretary Georgina Gillmore. Published in the *English Review*, January 1911.

522   *Macbeth Skit*. Shorthand manuscript, dated 10 January 1916. 2 pp. WITH: Typewritten manuscript, to which some of Shakespear's speeches for Lady Macbeth are affixed, interspersed with Shaw's revised dialogue in modern idiom for Macbeth. Stage directions typed in red. 7 pp. This travesty was written for Lillah McCarthy and the light comedian Gerald Du Maurier to perform at a war charity matinée. It was unused, Shaw recorded on the manuscript, because 'Gerald would not burlesque himself. Probably he considered himself an ideal Macbeth.' Published in the Bodley Head Bernard Shaw *Collected Plays with Their Prefaces*, Vol. VII (1974).

523   *Cutting Shakespear*. Typewritten manuscript of a letter to the editor of the *Star*, incomplete and unpublished; undated (November 1920). 5 pp. One of Shaw's principal targets as a drama critic (1895–98) had been the incompetent editing of Shakespear's plays by XIX century actor-managers, especially the acting versions made by Sir Henry Irving, which Shaw told Ellen Terry 'are past all bearing.' To Shaw this was playing Shakespear 'with his brains cut out'. The abandoned letter to the *Star* had been motivated by a performance Shaw had seen of *Macbeth*, revived at the Aldwych Theatre, London, 2 November 1920, by an actor with a symbolically apt name, J.K. Hackett. Mrs Patrick Campbell appeared in the production as Lady Macbeth.

> A play is not a string of pearls which you can shorten by taking out some of the pearls when you are casting it before swine. It is at best an organism and at worst a machine.

524 To Cecil A. Lewis, B.B.C. broadcast writer-director. Typewritten letter, 31 May 1923. Lewis had sent to Shaw a script of a prologue he and Cathleen [Nesbitt?] had prepared for a B.B.C. reading of *Twelfth Night*.

> Your prologue is beyond human patience. . . . Shakespear began his play with a musical overture to establish the poetic mood in which he meant the audience to take the story of Viola. That overture is spoken by the Duke, and is the most famous overture in the world. Your idea is to bring on Viola first, and have an overture afterwards, or cut it out altogether. . . . Scrap all that foolish twaddle, and read the play straight through just as Shakespear (who really knew better than you) wrote it. . . .

525 Nancy Catford Stone: Sculpted plaster bookends representing Shakespear and Shaw (1930). Shakespear, seated on a copy of *You Never Can Tell* and reclining against a copy of *Saint Joan*, is reading a passage from *Man and Superman*: 'What is the matter with the poor is poverty. What is the matter with the rich is uselessness'. Shaw, seated on a copy of *Much Ado About Nothing* and reclining against a copy of *Hamlet*, is reading a passage from *Twelfth Night*: 'Some are born great. Some achieve greatness . . .' Mrs Stone, who obtained Shaw's authorization to offer her work to manufacturers, also produced a carved version of the bookends in walnut wood.

*526 William Shakespeare, *The Tragedie of Hamlet Prince of Denmarke*. Cranach Press, 1930. One of 300 copies on handmade paper; bound in red morocco boards. This was one of the eight volumes which Shaw inscribed for sale at Sotheby's in 1949. The autograph commentary covers the rectos of the first three front flyleaves.

> Brought up as a pagan prince to believe that vengeance, expiation by sacrifice, blood feud and the like are sacred institutions and divine attributes, he holds that it is his religious and social duty to kill his uncle. . . . But when it came to the killing he could not bring himself to do it. . . .

> The pagan prince had evolved into a Christian gentleman. And he does not understand what has happened to him. . . . Nor is Shakespear clear about it; for Creative Evolution was not then in our mental frame of reference; but there is a Christian in every man. It must have been very strong in Shakespear. And there you have the whole meaning of Hamlet as plain as a pikestaff.

527 Broadcast talk on the National Theatre, as prologue to a B.B.C. performance of *The Dark Lady of the Sonnets* on 22 April 1938. Autograph manuscript, dated 8 April. 3 pp., on 2 leaves. WITH: Typewritten transcription. 5 pp. Shaw informs his auditors that he had agitated for the building of a National Theatre on the site of Whitehall Palace overlooking the banks of the Thames, 'where the sweet swan of Avon . . . did oft delight Eliza and our James.' Instead the government tore down all the old houses and filled the site with blocks of offices. 'So we have had to buy a magnificent site in Kensington, which Shakespear knew only as a far-off village.' Eventually the theatre was built, not in Kensington, but on the south bank of the Thames, not far from the site of the original Globe Theatre. It opened in 1976.

528 *Cymbeline, by William Shakespeare and Bernard Shaw.* It had long been Shaw's view that the last act of *Cymbeline* was weak and ineffective as theater. When it was proposed to revive the play at Stratford in the 1930s Shaw undertook to provide a new, shortened last act. (He also gave his promise to stage a production of *Macbeth*, but was obliged to withdraw from the commitment when Charlotte Shaw dragged him off on another world cruise. It would have been the first time he had directed any dramatic work but his own.) In the unbound page proofs of the new fifth act (January 1937) the title was given as *Cymbeline Up to Date*. This was altered by Shaw to *Cymbeline Refinished: A Variation*, and 50 copies were printed 'for private circulation' in March 1937. (The HRC copy is inscribed by Shaw to Blanche Patch.) The act was not performed at Stratford; it received its first production at the Embassy Theatre, Swiss Cottage, London, on 30 November 1937, with the program linking the names of Britain's two greatest playwrights as collaborators.

529 *Shakes versus Shav.* Typewritten (carbon) manuscript, with revisions; undated (January 1949). 5 pp.

529

THE LANCHESTER MARIONETTE THEATRE

under the direction of WALDO and MURIEL LANCHESTER
assisted by M. & C. L. Stavordale

DURING

THE MALVERN FESTIVAL
AUGUST 9th — SEPTEMBER 3rd, 1949

We present a programme selected from our repertoire and a dialogue
specially written for our Marionettes by

GEORGE BERNARD SHAW

entitled

"SHAKES v. SHAV"

with the recorded voices of a celebrated cast directed by
SIR LEWIS CASSON

The Performances will be given in the

LYTTELTON HALL
CHURCH STREET, MALVERN

(under the Clock Tower)

EXCEPT
MONDAYS

DAILY at 2.45 p.m. & 8.15 p.m.

ALL SEATS 2/6 including Tax

(Seats are not reserved, but a Ticket guarantees a Seat)

Tickets obtainable after July 23rd from the Lanchester Marionette
Theatre Headquarters, 28 Worcester Road, Malvern, Worcestershire

Booking Hours: 10 a.m. to 4 p.m., or by post, if
money is sent with a stamped addressed envelope

Remaining Seats, if any, will be obtainable at the doors half an hour
before the commencement of the Performance. Please book for the
Evening Performances if possible, leaving space for children at Matinees

STEVENS, PRINTERS, MALVERN

Originally identified as 'Dialogue for Malvern Puppet Show', the work was written for performance by the Waldo Lanchester Marionette Theatre. Accompanying the typescript is a later typewritten manuscript of the play, 5 pp., further revised, undated; bound with a typewritten manuscript of the preface, 4 pp., dated 3 February 1949. WITH: Flyer advertizing the performances during the Malvern Festival, in the Lyttelton Hall, 9 August to 3 September 1949, and the issue of the *UNESCO Courier* for June 1955, in which photographs of the production are reproduced.

WOMEN

530 To John Francis (Earl) Russell, a barrister and later a Fabian, brother of Bertrand Russell. Autograph letter, 11 April 1892. Shaw indicates he is in favor of a bill introduced in Parliament to amend the divorce law, which was grossly unfair to women. The bill subsequently was defeated.

> If people only realized before marriage that they might come to dislike one another, and that to have to live with one whom you dislike is penal servitude of the worst kind, they would face anything in the way of social ostracism sooner than run such a risk. . . . I am inclined to think that the upholders of the marriage contract will eventually be forced to lighten & loosen the chains in order to prevent their falling out of use altogether.

531 To Bertha Newcombe, an artist and Fabian who was in love with Shaw, and whose friends conspired unsuccessfully to pair them off. Autograph letter, 31 March 1896.

> Your sex likes me as children like wedding cake, for the sake of the sugar on the top. If they taste by an accident a bit of crumb or citron, it is all over: I am a fiend, delighting in vivisectional cruelties, as indicated by the corners of my mouth.

532 To Janet Achurch. Typewritten letter, 16 May 1895. A discussion of the play *Candida*, Janet's husband Charles Charrington, her daughter Nora, and her enslavement by drugs and drink leads Shaw to the subject of marriage.

> It is no use: marriage is a damnable thing, root and branch. If I were married to you, I should be jealous of everybody; and I should be the one person of whom nobody else would be jealous. I used to think that this invariable fact that I am never jealous of the husband of the woman whom I love was only a part of the fact that I am, as I thought, so amiable that I am never jealous of anyone. But it must really be the moral of [Ibsen's] 'The Lady from the Sea' that is at work. Only, ladies who are not from the sea, like their slavery and exploit it. Before they are married they shirk their responsibilities by pretending to themselves and to others that their conduct is determined by their mothers: when they marry, the unhappy husband is made the scapegoat.

533 To unidentified correspondent: a Socialist debater who has asked Shaw for advice. The arguments set forth by Shaw anticipate his preface to *Getting Married* (1911). Autograph letter, 15 March 1899.

> [Y]our opponent defends marriage. What does he mean by marriage? Is it legal marriage? If so, according to what law and what canon? In England marriage is regarded as indissoluble by Roman Catholics, who do not recognize divorce. The law grants divorce for adultery & cruelty, but not for crime, drink, madness, or incompatibility of temper. Does your opponent consider that those who think that divorce should be extended to rescue people from drunkards, criminals & lunatics, as you hope every humane man, Socialist or not, [does], are advocates of Lust?

534 To 'Miss Charmer | Poste Restante | Godalming | Surrey.' Autograph letter, 28 September 1905. In this pseudonymous manner (which Shaw drew upon two years later for *Getting Married*) Erica Cotterill entered Shaw's life. A passionate, irrepressible young woman of 24, Erica bombarded Shaw with letters—strange, effervescent, rambling effusions, often unintelligible, and generally illegible. Her blandishments appealed to Shaw's vanity; he answered at length, supplied her with theatre tickets, had Charlotte invite her to lunch, and encouraged her to attend his Fabian lectures. Eventually she became a dreadful nuisance and, when her protestations of love for him became alarming, Shaw cunningly applied restraint by having Charlotte send her a letter which he himself had drafted.

The HRC possesses 25 pieces of Shaw correspondence (1905–12) to Erica Cotterill.

535 To Erica Cotterill. Autograph letter, 11 July 1907.

> You will always be exasperating until you achieve something which will cause people to accept you as a woman of distinction & encourage you to discharge the duties of that

position & take its proper attitude. There are other ways for untalented women—religion, which makes them realize their divinity, or bearing children, which makes them realize their humanity; but for you I suppose the safest way is to do something.

536 To Erica Cotterill. Autograph letter, 27 November 1907.

Marriage is a difficult business no matter how it turns out: but you had better get married all the same. . . . If you are to teach the world and move the world—and that is what being a writer means—you must share its cardinal experiences; and you cant do that without marrying, as things are arranged at present. You will find many women who denounce marriage, and with good cause; but you will never find a woman who regrets having gone through the experience of marriage, though you will find many who regret having missed it.

537 To Erica Cotterill. Autograph letter from Charlotte Shaw, 11 October 1910. WITH: Shaw's draft letter, copied by Charlotte with a few significant variations.

You have made a declaration of your feelings to my husband; and you have followed that up by coming to live near us with the avowed object of gratifying those feelings by seeing as much as possible of him. If you were an older and more experienced woman I should characterize that in terms which would make any further acquaintance between us impossible. As you are young and entirely taken up with your own feelings, I can only tell you that when a woman once makes such a declaration to a married man . . . there is an end of all honorable question of their meeting one another again. . . .

538 Introduction to a lecture by the drama critic H.M. Walbrook on 'The Women of Bernard Shaw's Plays', ghostwritten by Shaw to be read by the actress Margaret Halstan (at that time appearing in a revival of Shaw's play *How He Lied to Her Husband*). Typewritten (carbon) manuscript, with corrections copied in by Charlotte Shaw; undated (8 December 1911). 3 pp.

I will venture to tell [the lecturer] beforehand just one little secret. There are no women in Bernard Shaw's plays. Dont think that I mean that they are untrue to life. I mean exactly the contrary. For I will tell you another secret. There are no women in the real world. Believe me, ladies and gentlemen, woman, of whom we hear so much, is a stage invention, and . . . a very tiresome one. There is no such thing as a woman; and Bernard Shaw's greatness consists in his having discovered that fact, whilst all the others were turn-

ing out heroines that were getting womanlier and womanlier and womanlier until they had lost all semblance of humanity, and bored everybody to distraction except young men under nineteen and old men over 90. Bernard Shaw once told me . . . that the reason the women in his plays were so uncommonly good is that he always assumes that a woman is just like a man.

539 To Mrs Rosemary Frost, a London housewife who had left her husband. Autograph letter, 1 July 1919.

Any reasonable woman ought to be able to live with any reasonable man; for they are all much alike when the glamor wears off; and the sober, honest, and industrious ones are the best to live with; but sometimes there are inscrutable antipathies and incompatibilities that cannot be overcome.

540 To Matthew Edward McNulty. Autograph postcard, 25 December 1924.

The Victorian theory about Woman is a ludicrous delusion. She is the most dangerous of all the animals, if you come to that view of the situation. The attempt to hypnotize her into believing herself weak was bound to fail; and it *has*.

The HRC possesses 24 pieces of Shaw correspondence (1891–1939) to McNulty.

541 *The Intelligent Woman's Guide to Socialism and Capitalism* (1928) was begun in August 1924 under the provisional (and unwieldy) title *A Guide for the Study Circles and Other Bodies desirous of investigating Socialism.* Claimed by Shaw, in a self-drafted publisher's advertisement, to be the first book on economics and political science addressed specifically to women instead of to 'a sort of abstract reader who is conceived as aridly and academically male as far as he is conceived of having any sex at all', it was inspired by a letter from Shaw's sister-in-law Mary Cholmondeley requesting a few of his ideas on Socialism to bring before her local study circle in Shropshire. When it was published four years later Shaw dedicated the book to Mrs Cholmondeley (misspelling her name in the process), and provided the dedication copy with a special title page THE BOOK OF MARY THAT SHE CAUSED BERNARD SHAW TO WRITE, a proof of which is displayed. The book's page proof corrections were copied in by Charlotte Shaw (who failed to note the spelling error in her sister's name!). WITH: Hebrew translation by Pesah Ginzburg (Tel Aviv: 1931–33, in 3 volumes, bound in one), containing a special preface, written on 14 February 1930, addressed to 'The Intelligent Hebrew Woman'.

From Karl Marx and Ferdinand Lassalle to Walter Rathenau and the pioneers of Russian Communism, the Jew has been the inspirer, leader, and pleader of the European movement towards collectivism and Internationalism. I was converted to Socialism as a young man by Karl Marx, and Rathenau's mentality and outlook on life were far less foreign to mine than that of the anti-Semite statesmen who were then blundering into the war. Zion must sink or swim with the whole of modern civilization, and the Jews can save themselves only by saving the Gentiles and sharing their salvation. That is why I send my book unto the tents of Shem as earnestly as into the libraries of the Philistines.

542 *The Need for Expert Opinion in Sexual Reform.* Transcription of a lecture delivered extempore before the Third International Congress of the World League for Sexual Reform, 13 September 1929. Extensively revised for publication in the proceedings of the Congress, 1930. Typewritten (carbon) manuscript, torn up by Shaw and discarded, but mended with cellulose tape and preserved by his secretary Blanche Patch. WITH: Two corrected galley proofs, dated 24 January 1930.

The Pope is the Chief Priest of Europe; and he speaks very strongly on the subject of sex appeal. I, of course, should never dream of appealing in that matter to the Chief Priest of Europe; but if there were such a person as the Chief Prostitute of Europe I should call her in immediately. I should say, 'Here, clearly, is a person who deals professionally in sex appeal, and will lose her livelihood if her method is wrong. She can speak to us with authority.'

Unfortunately . . . there is no such person as the Chief Prostitute of Europe. . . . Therefore it is that I proffer myself as being the next best authority to the prostitute, that is to say, the playwright.

543 Written interview: replies to questions by Louise Morgan on the rights of women. 2 pp., dated 9 November 1943. Shaw is asked, *inter alia*: 'If you could summon a meeting of 5,000 women as Minister of Labour and National Service, what would you tell them?'

I would tell them what I have been telling them for the past forty years—to press for a Constitutional Amendment making it compulsory for every public body to be governed by men and women in equal numbers, no matter how they are elected or appointed. Votes for Women failed to send even one woman to parliament, although several conspicu-

ously able women contested seats. The Vote kept them out instead of letting them in. It does so still. I told them it would.

544 List of the number of men and women in Parliament, with a clumsy mathematical effort to seek a ratio. Autograph note on a fragment of paper (1945), for use in the revised preface to '*In Good King Charles's Golden Days*', published in the Standard Edition in 1947. Seventeen years after the enfranchisement of women, Shaw noted in the preface, 'the nation, consisting of men and women in virtually equal numbers, is misrepresented at Westminster by 24 women and 616 men.'

545 Written interview: replies to questions by Louise Morgan on old age. 3 pp., dated 1 May 1946. One of the questions asked is: 'Are women capable of learning to make the best of old age?' Shaw's response is terse. 'They are more capable than men. They live longer.'

ELLEN TERRY

Ellen Terry, leading lady to the tragedian Sir Henry Irving, entered into correspondence with Shaw over a professional matter in 1892. Soon they were writing with greater and greater frequency, until the correspondence blossomed into a full-fledged love affair, one of the most exquisite series of letters ever penned. 'Does H.I. really say that you are in love with me?', asked Shaw on 7 March 1897. 'For that be all his sins forgiven him! . . . I am also touched by his refusing to believe that we have never met. No man of feeling *could* believe such heartlessness.' Incredible as it may seem, Ellen and Shaw did not meet (Ellen was terrified that a meeting would destroy the beautiful relationship) until she agreed in 1906, at the age of 58, to appear as Lady Cicely in *Captain Brassbound's Conversion*, a play Shaw had written for her in 1898.

'Let those who may complain that it was all on paper', wrote Shaw a year after Ellen's death in 1928, in a preface to an intended edition of the correspondence, 'remember that only on paper has humanity yet achieved glory, beauty, truth, knowledge, virtue, and abiding love.'

546 To Ellen Terry. Autograph letter, 7 March 1897. Ellen has sent him a photograph of her granddaughter Rosemary (daughter of Gordon Craig).

> [T]o think that this fellow-infant of mine will never know me except as 'an old gentleman' named *Mister* Shaw! And will speak of you as 'Granny' to future generations! What tragic lines that pet impostor of yours, William Shakespere, could have written on this profoundly foolish theme!

547 To Ellen Terry. Autograph letter, 22 August 1899, in pencil, from Ruan Minor, Cornwall. Shaw teases Ellen for not revealing to Sir Henry Irving that the play *Captain Brassbound's Conversion*, which she has considered taking on a tour to America, was written by G.B.S.

548 Photograph of Ellen Terry in her late forties (ca. 1895–98).

549 To Edward Gordon Craig, theatrical designer, who was Ellen's son. Typewritten letter, 12 April 1929. Shaw gives all the logical arguments in favor of publication of the Terry-Shaw correspondence at the present time. At the end of the letter Craig indicates his attitude toward Shaw with the inscription 'The letter of a Cockatrice.'

550 *Preface to be attached to the Correspondence of Ellen Terry and Bernard Shaw should it ever be published* (12 copies privately printed by R. & R. Clark, Ltd., Edinburgh, September 1929). The Humanities Research Center possesses two copies, one of them extensively revised by Shaw, with a letter of instructions to the American printer on p. [2], in red ink, dated 5 November 1930.

551 *Ellen Terry and Bernard Shaw: A Correspondence.* Limited to 3000 copies. New York and London, 1931. Printed by D.B. Updike at the Merrymount Press, Boston, Massachusetts.

552 *The Terry Letters.* Typewritten manuscript, with revisions, dated November 1934. 2 pp. Draft of a note written by Shaw to be copied by hand into the bound volume of the surviving letters sent to him by Ellen Terry, for presentation to the British Museum.

My debt to that great institution, contracted in the early days when I read and worked daily for many years in its Reading Room, is inestimable, and gives it a right to anything of mine that is of sufficient public interest to be worthy of its acceptance.

MRS PATRICK CAMPBELL

'All sorts of things have been happening to me', Shaw informed his French translator Augustin Hamon in March 1913, including, he confessed, 'a grand passion. . . .' The woman was the actress Mrs Patrick Campbell. Shaw had written *Pygmalion* for her in 1912, but complicated managerial negotiations and Mrs Campbell's prior commitment to appear in a Barrie play delayed the production. In September Shaw returned from a holiday on the Continent to be greeted by headlines announcing 'Famous Actress is Dying' and reports that physicians 'tonight have very little hope of her recovery'. Although the newspaper stories proved to be somewhat exaggerated, Mrs Campbell's illness was a serious one, and she remained incapacitated in her bed, painfully, for several months. During this period Shaw, when in London, was a daily visitor. In her autobiography in 1924 Mrs Campbell noted: 'There was one who, perhaps through the intelligent grasp of his genius, understood a little the nerve rack of my illness. Himself living in dreams, he made a dream-world for me. Only those who can understand this can understand the friendship Bernard Shaw gave to me by my sickbed. . . . He revelled in the mischievous fun and in the smiles he brought to my face. He did not care a snap of the fingers at the moment what anyone else might say or think.'

As Mrs Campbell's health improved Shaw's ardors grew, and his epistolary blarneying rapidly metamorphosed into the 'grand passion' he eventually divulged to his friends. It was reciprocated, at least initially, by Mrs Campbell, who in her last will and testament defined the relationship as an *amitié amoureuse*. Shaw, intemperately throwing caution to the winds, pursued Mrs Campbell like a lovesick schoolboy, infuriating Charlotte Shaw, who not only overheard one of their telephone conversations but discovered in Shaw's appointments book a whole series of 'engagements' scrawled into it by her rival: '10 p.m. Stella', 'Stella matinee', 'Stella tea', 'Stella air', 'my dear beautiful

Stella to the theatre' etc. They used the home of his invalid sister as a trysting place, impelling Lucy in disgust to warn her brother: 'Stella is an obstreperous child. . . . Dont let her blight your young affections, she is transcendentally and hellishly and ravishingly fascinating and seductive.'

Mrs Campbell's ardors cooled more rapidly than Shaw's. In the midst of rehearsals of *Pygmalion* in April 1914 Shaw's 'Dearest Princess of the Sixteen Chins' suddenly reappeared after a few days' mysterious absence to announce to her chagrined 'Joey' that she had married George Cornwallis-West, Winston Churchill's erstwhile stepfather. Shaw, however, had the last word, in the epilogue to the published text of *Pygmalion* (1916): 'Galatea never does quite like Pygmalion: his relation to her is too godlike to be altogether agreeable.'

553 Photograph: Mrs Patrick Campbell in bed, 1912. Taken by Shaw during her long illness following a taxi collision.

554 *Another 'Shakespeare' Sonnet.* Shorthand draft of a sonnet written for Mrs Campbell on 22 April 1913. The ornately lettered transcription was made at the order of the London dealer who sold the manuscript to T.E. Hanley in the 1950s.

555 *Pygmalion.* Rehearsal notes, 50 pages, covering the period 3 February–10 April 1914 (with additional notes for rehearsals in the autumn of 1914 of the company embarking on the American tour). Shaw's sketch of Mrs Campbell appears at the end of his notes for the rehearsal of 2 April. At the end of the notes for the dress rehearsal, on 9 April, Mrs Campbell scrawled a message to the director: 'dear dear Joey   Message to Tree. "listen to your fellow artists more attentively— & dont ejaculate so much   it makes a mucky untidy effect".'

556 *The Doctor's Dilemma: Getting Married: The Shewing-up of Blanco Posnet* (1913: third impression). Inscribed on the halftitle: 'to Stella Beatrice Cornwallis West | from George Bernard Shaw, who was | himself shewn-up *to* himself | by her. 17th May 1914.' A rare instance of Shaw signing his name in full; he has done so here, obviously, to play up the coincidence of both men in her life at this moment being named George.

555

557 *Misalliance: The Dark Lady of the Sonnets: Fanny's First Play* (1914). Inscribed on the halftitle: 'from Bernard Shaw to | Beatrice Stella, the dark lady | of HIS sonnets. | 17th May 1914.'

558 *Plays Pleasant and Unpleasant* (1912: tenth printing). Inscribed on the halftitle of the first volume: 'to Beatrice Stella Cornwallis | West, from the author, whom | she despised in those days, | only to find twenty years later | that he was a | Great | & | Good | Man.   17th May 1914.'

559 To Mrs Patrick Campbell. Typewritten letter, 11 August 1937.

I find that I have done a very wicked thing: I have kept all your letters. . . . There is only one thing to be done—to send the letters back to you so that you may have the complete correspondence in your hands. This will add to its value if you have to sell it.

560 To Mrs Patrick Campbell. Autograph letter, 14 August 1937.

I have now, with infinite labor and a little heartbreak[,] packed all the letters. . . . There can be no question of publication in our case until Charlotte's ashes and mine are scattered. . . . After that, the correspondence will be a valuable literary property. . . .

561 *Dear Liar* (1960). A stage production, adapted by Jerome Kilty from the correspondence of Shaw and Mrs Patrick Campbell (which had been published in 1952), first performed by Katharine Cornell and Brian Aherne at the Billy Rose Theatre, New York, on 16 March 1960.

VERSES

Shaw inherited from his father a penchant for scribbling doggerel at the slightest provocation, for his own amusement and that of his friends. He published or distributed only a handful of these verses during his lifetime, but several dozen have survived, usually in shorthand drafts jotted in pocket notebooks or on the backs of flyers. The HRC possesses more than twenty of these poems.

562 *Ode to J.K.B.* Typewritten (carbon) transcription of a poem, 28 lines, celebrating the removal of Shaw's friend Dr J. Kingston Barton of St Bartholomew's Hospital from lodgings over a silver shop in the Gloucester Road to a house in Courtfield Road; undated (February 1882). 1 p. WITH: Typewritten (carbon) transcription of verses ('Farewell, farewell to Courtfield Road!'), 24 lines, dated 21 March 1887, written after spending a fortnight at Barton's when his mother moved to 29 Fitzroy Square. 1 p. The second typescript contains confused annotations by Shaw (ca. 1946–47); both have notes by Dr F.E. Loewenstein, who published the verses in the *Saint Bartholomew's Hospital Journal*, March 1947.

> The rising sun oer Fitzroy Square
>   A lonely man shall see,
> Mourning the fleeting fortnight's fare
>   He spunged from Kingston B.

563 *'For shame for shame'* Shorthand manuscript, with accompanying lists of rhymes, 12 lines, dated 30 August 1883, on a single leaf in a pocket notebook (1882–83) containing a considerable number of shorthand verses, plus notes for *The Voice* (see No. 11), a pencil sketch, music drawings, notes on Economics, etc. The poem was one of several written under en-

couragement from an acquaintance, Robert Ellice Mack, author and editor of children's books, whose brother was a publisher. Shaw provided a number of verses to fit engraved blocks owned by the publisher, and received a fee of fifteen shillings for his labors. It is not known whether any of the contributions actually were published.

> For shame for shame, you naughty dog
>   Youre putting out your tongue
> At that poor pelican whose heart
>   By your contempt is wrung
> It often gives its own heart's blood
>   To feed its thirsty young
>
> The alligators in their cage
>   Are going into fits
> Of laughter at your impudence
>   They think youve lost your wits.
> If they could catch you in their jaws
>   They'd chop you into bits

> sits spits knits
> pits quits tits
> wits
>
> bung sung
> flung hung
> among lung
> wrung
> sprung stung

564 *'Rain, rain, rain, rain | Damn the rain!'* Autograph manuscript, 77 lines; undated (27–29 August 1892), 4 pp. Written for Geraldine Spooner, a young Fabian for whom Shaw briefly felt a romantic attachment. 'Rather in love with Geraldine', he confided to his diary in 1890. She, however, was not to be trifled with by the philandering GBS. She set her sights for and married the philosopher Herbert Wildon Carr. Shaw casually 'dropped in' on the newly-married couple in August 1892. After supper Geraldine drove him to the train station by horse cart, in 'torrents of rain.' In the train he amused himself by versifying the experience in shorthand. Two days later he transcribed and finished the verses, and sent a copy to Geraldine.

> The Umbrella is mightier than the Pen
> Rug and macintosh are mightier than the Umbrella
>   No matter!
>   Mightier thou than all three
>   With thy might thou hast won me this drive
>   Without thee perchance I had walked

Whereas now in a chariot I ride
Ride through the rain with Geraldine
     Hurrah!
With Geraldine, Geraldine, Geraldine, Geraldine, Geraldine
My old love Geraldine.

565 *'If I could truly now declare | I love but you alone'* Shorthand manuscript (with autograph transcription on reverse), 12 lines, dated 30 August 1892, on a leaf with a drawing of two men and a Union Jack, and a deleted note concerning the 8-hours work bill and 'a universal day'. Two days after expressing his affection for Geraldine Carr, the fickle Shaw was busy scribbling verses to amuse Florence Farr.

Then grudge me not this overplus
    That elsewhere I let fall
For if you were ubiquitous
    You should, I swear, have all.

566 *Property and Rent: Fanny's First Poem.* Autograph manuscript, 89 lines, dated 25 June 1916. 4 pp. The poem, published in the *New Witness* four days later, was motivated by a statement by Hilaire Belloc in response to a Shaw letter on economics: 'If Mr. Shaw desires to discuss seriously the Law of Diminishing Returns and seriously to propose as a novel economic proposition that it is not true, I shall be happy to meet him. If, on the other hand, he is making jokes, I shall be happy to reply to him in comic verse—a department of literature in which I fancy myself not a little.'

Be it so, Belloc: let's rehearse
Our economic stunt in verse:
We'll in the style of Robert Burns
Discuss Diminishing Returns. . . .

As Wagner's Wotan says 'Nun droht
Der dritte Frage'. Kindly note
Hilaire believes that Schedule A
Is something that we cannot pay
Because the line of demarcation
That splits the landlord from the nation
Is but a figment of my mind.
Would the collector were so blind!

567 *'Weep not for old George Bernard'* Typewritten transcription of a poem for the sculptress Kathleen Lady Scott, 10 lines, undated, with corrections and a note by Shaw's secretary Blanche Patch. Presumably first drafted when Shaw was sitting to Lady Scott in August 1918. (He revised the text considerably for publication in *Sixteen Self Sketches*, 1949.)

Behold him from the life by Kathleen wrought
Until one day the Lord said "No, my lass,
Copy no more: just follow your own thought:
Carve him sub specie æternitas
Thus, though his works may soon forgotten be
Yet shall he share your immortality.

568 *'I went riding by the sea'* Shorthand manuscript, 15 lines, with typewritten transcription; undated (September 1921). 1 p. This lilting little piece commemorates a happy moment during a brief visit to the seaside.

I went riding by the sea
At Torquay
Through the wet wind
Olive Chetwynd
Rode with me
    Ah me!
And I cant go back to Devon
For with Olive it was heaven
But without her I should cry so
By the sea
    Salt sea
That my tears would raise its level
Fifty fathom; and the devil
Only knows what would become of poor Torquay
Where I rode with Olive Chetwynd by the sea.

569 *'Two ladies of Galway'* Shorthand manuscript, 23 lines (on the same leaf as No. 568), with typewritten transcription, 16 October 1921. These verses were written for 'The Misses Catherine and Anna Gregory', Lady Gregory's young granddaughters, who had sent him a gift basket of apples.

> Two ladies of Galway named Catherine and Anna
> Whom some called Acushla and some called Alannah,
> On finding the gate of the fruit garden undone
> Stole Grandmamma's apples and sent them to London. . . .

570 *'Justinian · in History's view'* Shorthand manuscript, 8 lines, dated 31 October 1922. 1 p. Written for the *British Legion Album* (1924), issued in aid of Field-Marshal Earl Haig's appeal for ex-servicemen of all ranks.

> Justinian · in History's view
>   Your fame is not worth half a snowball
> Because, ungrateful monarch, you
>   Grudged Belisarius his obol.

571 *'If you his temper would unhinge'* Autograph manuscript, 16 lines, written on a postcard to Archibald Henderson, 17 November 1924. Henderson had asked Shaw how to pronounce the name of Dr Ralph Inge, Dean of St Paul's.

> If you his temper would unhinge
> And his most sacred rights infringe,
> Or, excommunicated, singe
> Where fiends for ever writhe and cringe
> Imploring that a drop of ginge-
> R ale may on their tongues impinge
>   Address him then as Doctor Inje.

572 *MS of an Ayotian Poem for Ellen Terry.* Autograph note by Dr F.E. Loewenstein, dated 14 June 1945, with a note by Shaw: 'It is not a continuous poem but a set of separate verses for photographs of Ayot in a manuscript booklet' which he had sent to Ellen Terry after she passed through Ayot in 1916 without stopping to visit him. The album is now in the Ellen Terry Memorial Museum, Smallhythe. Although the verses were dated 23 August 1916, some had apparently been composed considerably earlier, as evidenced by a verse fragment in the British Library dated December 1897. When Dr Loewenstein unearthed the typescript carbon of the verses in the files at Ayot, he induced Shaw to have them published. WITH: Typewritten (carbon) manuscript, combining new verses with several of the originals, numbered by Shaw, with some corrections, ca. 1947. 3 pp.

573 *The Ayot St. Lawrence Guide Book* (1947). Trial title printed by the Leagrave Press, Luton, with autograph revisions by Shaw altering the title from the original *Ayot St. Lawrence: A strip of doggerel verses as written for Ellen Terry*, and corrected page proofs. 6 pp., with four photographs affixed to two additional pages. This setting later was scrapped by Shaw in favor of an expanded book for which he provided a whole new set of verses, illustrated by photographs from his own collection of prints and negatives. The result, complete with a new title, was *Bernard Shaw's Rhyming Picture Guide to Ayot Saint Lawrence*, issued both in cloth and in wrappers, published six weeks after Shaw's death in 1950.

574 *'Ann Bullen here'* Shorthand manuscript, 5 lines, undated. Apparently a trial verse for the *Rhyming Picture Guide*, with two alternative last lines. (On the same card is an unfinished fragment of verse concerning the local blacksmith.)

> Ann Bullen here before her marriage
> For some years lived and kept her carriage
> Without a thought that Harry's axe
> Would end their all too short lived pax   or
> Would strike her from the almanacs.

RELIGION

575 *The Adventures of the Black Girl in Her Search for God* (1932), illustrated with wood engravings by John Farleigh. In February 1932, en route from Capetown to Port Elizabeth, South Africa, Shaw lost control of the automobile, driving full throttle over a ditch and hedge, and through five lines of barbed wire and a bunker three feet deep, before coming to a halt. He was uninjured, but Charlotte was so badly bruised and shaken that she spent a month in bed. Shaw, with time to kill, commenced a tale that had been formulating in his mind for nearly four decades and which he had long ago described as 'a Gospel of Shawianity'. The *Black Girl* is a comic yet cosmic fable, blending artfulness and innocence in the manner of Lewis Carroll and Voltaire, in which Shaw ardently carries his curiosity into those areas of thought which deal with man's relation to God, the universe, and his fellow man, and in which the markedly feministic trend of Shaw's thought leads us at last to a concept of a female deity, 'the mother of us all'. The work created much controversy when it first appeared, and generated an extraordinary number of imitative rejoinders, including C.H. Maxwell's *Adventures of the White Girl in Her Search for God* (1933), Dr W.R. Matthews's *The Adventures of Gabriel in His Search for Mr. Shaw* (1933), and C. Payne's *Four Men Seek God* (1935). As recently as 1973 Brigit Brophy provided yet another reaction to Shaw's work in *The Adventures of God in His Search for the Black Girl*.

576 To R. & R. Clark, Ltd. Autograph postcard, 25 June 1933, citing mistakes in the text of the *Black Girl*. Throughout the years Shaw meticulously reported to the printers the anachronisms and other errors brought to his attention by alert correspondents for correction in the next printing.

577 John Farleigh: 8 wood engravings for the *Black Girl*, each identified as the second of nine pulls, signed 'JF' and dated '1932'. WITH: Trial engraving of a self-portrait to depict the Image Maker in the tale. Engraved in response to a request from Shaw, to whom Farleigh had been recommended by William Maxwell: 'Are you sufficiently young and unknown to read a story and make one trial engraving for me for five guineas? That is, if the job interests you.' This was the first book by Shaw ever to be illustrated. Farleigh later provided illustrations or designs for Shaw's *Short Stories, Scraps and Shavings* (1934), *Prefaces* (1934), *Back to Methuselah* (Limited Editions Club, 1938), and *Shaw Gives Himself Away* (1939) before he was succeeded as Shaw's illustrator by Feliks Topolski. See also L26–27.

578 To John Farleigh. Autograph letter, 8 August 1939. Farleigh had sent a cheque for £100 to Shaw to repay a debt. Shaw returned it.

> The division of the spoils between us has been glaringly unjust; and £100 conscience money would ease my mind about it. Accept your own cheque as a readjustment of the bargain.

579 *Modern Religion*. A lecture delivered at the New Reform Club. Published as a supplement to the *Christian Commonwealth*, 3 April 1912. Autograph inscription in red ink at top of p. 1, dated 25 August 1929.

> This tract was a provisional affair. In 1912 I had not written the prefaces to Androcles and Methuselah; and if I had died then at the age of 56 I should have left no record of the views of religion which I had been preaching at the City Temple . . . and elsewhere. Now that Methuselah is on record there is no further use for this hasty sketch.

580 *Bernard Shaw & Jesus the Christ*. Typewritten (carbon) letter with autograph additions, 20 October 1916, headed in roman majuscules, written in response to Frank Harris's criticism of Shaw's preface to *Androcles and the Lion*. 'This, as you may see, is a duplicate. I keep the original copy lest this should be torpedoed. . . .' Published by Harris in his *Pearson's Magazine*, New York, February 1917, and in a pamphlet *Stories of Jesus the Christ* (1919), displayed here.

> Almost everyone who is interested in Jesus has a pet conception of him, and protests against my preface for not reproducing it. But my preface has nothing to do with any modern conception of him. I go to the Bible and I find there four biographies of Jesus. Three of them are called synoptic because they agree roughly as to the course of events in his life; and two of them are at least not contradictory as to his character. The fourth describes a different career and a different man—so different that if he were not named and had not been crucified by Pontius Pilate . . . he might have been classed as an apostle or even as the leader of a great heresy. The world has mixed these three Jesuses into one Jesus. . . . The ideal Christs are of all sorts, from tailor's dummies to reincarnations and revelations; but when you come to the documents, you come back to my preface.

581 Written interview: replies to 13 questions for the London *Jewish Chronicle*. 7 pp., undated (but published on 28 December 1928).

> *Do you believe the Jews to be the chosen race?*
> Certainly not. It is this monstrous presumption that has always been their ruin; and the fact that it has also been their consolation in captivity and ostracism does not remove it from the category of dangerous paranoic delusions. The Jews are too prone to console themselves by lies: the Psalms are my witness to the truth of this.

582 Written interview: replies to questions by W.R. Titterton on God and religion. 1 p. (in pencil), 4 August 1931. WITH: Autograph note on small 'compliments' card, admonishing Titterton to 'remember that I am professionally Bernard Shaw in two words. I particularly dislike being Georged.'

> Creation is a miracle of daily occurrence. 'A miracle a minute' would not be a bad slogan for God.

583 Biographical questions by Hesketh Pearson, 7 October 1939, with Shaw's delayed responses, 14 March 1940. Pearson states that he has come upon a number of references to Mahomet in Shaw's work, from which he deduces that Shaw had at one time been enthusiastic to make him the subject of a play. Did he fall back on *Saint Joan*, Pearson inquires, because of British stage censorship?

> I certainly should like to write a play about him. But the censorship, and the risk of being killed by some Moslem fanatic in the east, are against it. When I introduced him in The Black Girl, and made him say that his wife Ayesha was a devil, I had to alter it.

584 *St. Martin's, Bernard Shaw and the Prayer Book.* Typewritten manuscript, with revisions. 5 pp. Published in *St. Martin's Review*, April 1940.

> When my mother died the question arose as to whether there should be a religious service at her cremation. She had amused herself with Spiritualism in her latter days; but she had not attended any place of worship for at least

thirty years, and was, from the specific Church of England point of view, a complete heathen. But when I looked at the scale of charges. . . . I saw that an optional one was the fee of the officiating Church of England clergyman. I knew how poor a clergyman may be; and the feeling of one professional man for another, together with some critical curiosity as to how the ceremony would affect me, decided me to try the experiment. My conclusion was that the service should be scrapped as altogether too macabre.

WITH: Drawing made by Shaw's mother on 20–21 June 1908, in the belief that her hand had been given spirit guidance. Identified in a pencilled note by Shaw on the green tissue wrapper in which three drawings were preserved.

585 Shorthand draft of an inscription in a Breeches Bible (Geneva version, 1560), which had belonged to Charlotte Shaw, and which Shaw sold at auction in 1947. It is written on the reverse side of a fragment of a printed film contract form, with a transcription by Blanche Patch. Although the manuscript is dated 'Sep 1947' by Shaw in red ink, the revised inscription in the Bible itself (Fales collection, New York University) is dated 28 August 1947.

> Except as a curiosity the book as a material object is most undesirable. The binding is heavy and graceless: the printing is of the worst period. To anyone who has seen a page printed by Jenson or William Morris it is hateful. I must get rid of it. I really cannot bear it in my house.

586 *The Life Force.* Typewritten (carbon) manuscript, undated. 2 pp. During the period 1946–50 Shaw was encouraged by his bibliographic assistant Dr F.E. Loewenstein to print postcard messages on such diverse subjects as temperance, capital punishment, vegetarianism, copyright, the Shaw Society (founded by Loewenstein in 1943), and the St Joan statue by Clare Winsten which Shaw had commissioned and which stood in his garden. The text on the Life Force, drafted by Shaw for the same purpose, was not printed.

BROADCASTING

587 To Cecil Lewis, play director for the British Broadcasting Corporation. Typewritten letter, 24 June 1924. Shaw advises Lewis to assemble 'a company of good dramatic readers, regardless of their age and ap-

592a

pearance and memory, but very particular as to their voices and powers of expression and characterisation. . . . Queen Victoria had a beautiful voice and first rate delivery at an age when she could not have played any part on the stage presentably except the nurse in Romeo and Juliet.' Shaw made his first radio appearance for the B.B.C. on 20 November 1924, reading his play *O'Flaherty V.C.*, during which performance he sang a stanza of 'Tipperary.'

588 Memorandum by Shaw on his participation in the work of the B.B.C.'s Advisory Committee on Spoken English, of which he was a member from 1926 and chairman from 1930 to 1937. Autograph notes on both sides of a correspondence card.

589 *Recent Problems in Pronunciation Raised by Announcers*. Typewritten list of problem words distributed to members of the B.B.C.'s Advisory Committee on Spoken English, with the addition of several words in Shaw's autograph.

590 Minutes of the B.B.C.'s General Advisory Council, 20 February 1935, listing Shaw as a council member in attendance.

591 *Democracy*. B.B.C. radio talk on 14 December 1929. Typewritten manuscript, 21 pp., revised, with inserted leaf of textual additions, in shorthand. WITH: *The Apple Cart* (1930), containing the text of the broadcast, incorporated in the preface.

592 Photographs: (a) Shaw broadcasting for the B.B.C.; undated. (b) Shaw broadcasting in the U.S.S.R., July 1931.

593 Address to America. Shortwave radio talk, 11 October 1931, for the Columbia Broadcasting System.

Typewritten manuscript, 14 pp., used by Shaw for the broadcast. (For published text, see No. 671.)

594 Radio talk on South Africa, prior to departure from Cape Town, on 6 February 1932. Autograph manuscript, 22 pencilled pages, with revisions.

595 *Are We Heading for War?* (1934). Text of B.B.C. radio talk, 'Whither Britain?', broadcast on 6 February 1934, issued as a pamphlet.

596 *Modern Education* (but popularly known as *School*). B.B.C. radio talk to sixth form students on 11 June 1937. Shorthand draft, with longhand additions, 6 pp., dated Sidmouth, 24 May 1937, accompanied by a typewritten manuscript, 7 pp., consisting of a shortened and revised final version. One of Shaw's most genial talks, this was a broadcast giving advice to young people along the lines of his long-ago *Practical System of Moral Education for Females* (see No. 24). Stephen Potter has described it as 'the Classic Broadcast'.

597 Written interview: replies to questions on broadcasting by the *Radio Times*. 2 pp., dated 23 October 1947. WITH: Typeset proof of the interview, signed 'OK GBS'.

IRELAND

598 Ten photographs by Shaw of Irish country scenes (1905, 1908, 1909).

599 *'What Irish Protestants Think'*. Broadside (ca. 1913), issued by the United Irish Counties Anti-Partition Committee, New York City. It reproduces Shaw's speech delivered at a Home Rule demonstration in the Memorial Hall, London, on 6 December 1912, and his resolution 'That this meeting expresses its strong desire to see the end of racial and religious feuds in Ireland, and Irishmen of all creeds and classes working together for the common good of their native country.'

> [T]he British electorate does not care a rap about Home Rule or Ireland. It is hard enough to induce them to take an interest in their own affairs. It is impossible to make them take an interest in ours. Why should they? They know too well that they do not govern us any more than they govern themselves. Ireland is not governed by Englishmen, but by a handful of Irishmen who exploit our country in the name of England as far as the Irish democracy will stand it.

600 *F. Sheehy-Skeffington's Speech from the Dock . . . with letter from George Bernard Shaw* (pamphlet, 1915). An Irish pacifist, Sheehy-Skeffington had been arrested and tried in the Dublin Police Court for speaking against conscription. His wife appealed to Shaw to speak out: his reply first appeared in the *Freeman's Journal*, Dublin, on 16 June 1915.

> Protests are quite useless. The Opposition in the House of Commons will not oppose. The Press will not defend public liberties. England is thoroughly intimidated by Germany so far as her civilians are concerned. . . . Something can be done with a tyrannical Government. Nothing can be done with a terrified Government and a cowed people. . . . I can fight stupidity; but nobody can fight cowardice.

601 *England's Interest in Ireland.* Typewritten manuscript, with revisions; undated (ca. 1915–16). An unfinished essay, presumably unpublished. 'The plain remedy', Shaw notes, 'is Home Rule for England.'

> I must now insist that Ireland, as the poorest member of the Empire, is therefore the most dangerous, just as the poorest man in England is the most dangerous, because he tends constantly to drag all the rest down to his level. In preventing Ireland from governing itself and developing itself, England has prevented herself from the same activities and finally lost the art of them.

602 *O'Flaherty V.C.* Typewritten manuscript (used by the printer for setting type), with revisions, dated Torquay, 14 September 1915. 36 pp. Bound in at the back is a 'Prefatory Note' of three typewritten (carbon) pages. The short play, subsequently subtitled 'A Recruiting Pamphlet', was written for the Abbey Theatre, but was withdrawn during rehearsals when Shaw's friends privately informed him they feared the play might cause riots in the theatre, which would give the authorities in Dublin Castle a legitimate excuse for closing down the theatre. WITH: One of the 50 Rough Proof copies printed in 1915 for rehearsal purposes: *O'Flaherty V.C. An Interlude in the Great War of 1914*. It contains corrections and revisions copied in by Shaw's secretary Ann M. Elder.

603 From Lady Gregory. Typewritten letter, 19 September 1915. A long screed (5 pp.), anticipatory to her departure for America. She is despondent over the fact that her son is 'carrying out his desire . . . in going to the war' (this is the Major Gregory of Yeats's famed poem, killed in action in 1918), and is further burdened by theatre and publishing problems, her battle to retain Sir Hugh Lane's pictures for Dublin (claimed by Britain after his death in the Lusitania), and two lectures she has to prepare for American delivery. What buoys her is the realization that she will soon have O'Flaherty—'I long to see him'—which will drive away the foul taste left by the thirty or forty bad plays she has read recently.

Unfortunately the printed text was not ready before her departure, and it was early November before the two copies which Shaw eventually posted reached her in Denver. By the time she returned to Dublin the play she had hoped would do big things for the Abbey Players at home and abroad had been withdrawn, though the manager of the theatre, St John Ervine, had tactfully announced that it had not been suppressed, but merely postponed due to difficulties related to rehearsals.

604 *A Discarded Defence of Roger Casement* (1922). No. 21 of 25 numbered copies privately printed and signed by Clement Shorter. Sir Roger Casement, an Irish patriot who had distinguished himself in the British Consular Service, earning a knighthood for his work, sought to gain Irish independence during World War I with the assistance of Germany. When a German U-boat deposited him in Ireland, he was captured by British troops and conveyed to London for trial on charges of high treason. Found guilty, he was executed on 3 August 1916. Shaw, in response to an impassioned appeal from one of Casement's relatives, had drawn up a scheme for his defence, urging him to claim 'to be treated at worst as a prisoner of war captured in the prosecution of a perfectly legitimate enterprise for the liberation of his country from a foreign yoke'. Casement declined to adopt Shaw's plan of defence.

605 *Draft Memorial: Casement-Asquith.* A petition to the British Prime Minister, H.H. Asquith, as revised by Shaw in 1916 from an earlier draft. Typewritten (carbon) manuscript; undated. 3 pp.

606 To Alfred G. Gardiner, Liberal editor of the *Daily News.* Typewritten letter, 13 July 1916. Gardi-

ner had suggested that Casement might be reprieved if it could be argued that he was actually attempting to spy *on Germany.*

> I am not sure that the reprieve will come off. The mere fact that hanging him is the wrong thing to do raises a strong presumption that it will be done. . . . As far as I can judge, England is in a nasty fit of temper about Casement, and will not be induced to let go her prey by any ordinary line of appeal.

607 *Shall Roger Casement Hang?* Typewritten (carbon) manuscript, with revisions; undated. 6 pp. This was addressed to the editor of the *Times,* who rejected it. The *Manchester Guardian* published it on 22 July 1916.

> In Ireland he will be regarded as a national hero if he is executed, and quite possibly as a spy if he is not. For that reason it may well be that he would object very strongly to my attempt to prevent his canonization. But Ireland has enough heroes and martyrs already, and if England has not by this time had enough of manufacturing them in fits of temper, experience is thrown away on her; and she will continue to be governed, as she is at present to so great an extent unconsciously, by Casement's countrymen.

608 To Sir Horace Plunkett, Irish statesman opposed to partition of Ireland. Shorthand draft of letter, 3 August 1917, subsequently captioned THE CONVENTION by Shaw in red ink on first page. Following the Easter rebellion of 1916 in Dublin, the British government of David Lloyd George sought to resolve the differences between Irish leaders of north and south by sponsoring a convention intended to bring together all Irish parties to effect a solution to Home Rule. Shaw, determined to be one of the fifteen eminent Irishmen from public life nominated by the government to the convention, sought the cooperation of R.H. Haldane (Secretary of State for War), and finally appealed direct to the prime minister. Failing to receive the nomination, he proceeded to Ireland on his own, where he manipulated proceedings from behind the scenes, advising and guiding the chairman of the convention, his friend Sir Horace Plunkett, to whom he already had presented his basic views in this lengthy letter from London.

> I approach the [Irish] question before the Convention with one considerable advantage. I am free from the indecision which is called an open mind. My mind is made up as to the only possible solution as firmly as a human mind can be; and if the Convention is to change it, it will have something definite to change: it will shift me from one clear position to

another, not from one quandary to another. I have the further advantage of not being paralyzed by the need for tact which preoccupies all those who are actually members of the Convention and wish to make it a success. The spectacle of a number of Ulster gentlemen trying to look as if they thought there is a great deal to be said for transsubstantiation, confronted by a row of Catholic prelates resolutely looking at the bright side of Martin Luther, may be full of hope for a charitable future for Ireland; but it does not clear the air.

609 To Mrs R.C. Phillimore. Autograph postcard, 18 July 1917. Shaw agrees that the failure to appoint any women to the Irish Convention is scandalous. As for his own efforts to be appointed there is no news yet, though he has written direct to the prime minister.

The HRC possesses 25 pieces of Shaw correspondence (1897–1947) to 'Lion' Phillimore.

610 To Ralph D. Blumenfeld, editor of the *Daily Express*. Typewritten letter, 3 November 1917. Blumenfeld had asked Shaw to go to Ireland to report on the work of the Irish Convention, unaware that he had just returned from there. When Shaw indicated in his reply that he 'knew how the Irish problem must be solved', he was invited to write his views for the *Express*. Shaw had long harbored a contemptuous opinion of the paper but, recognizing the editor's sincerity and the validity of the argument that he would be

preaching to a new audience and therefore doing missionary work, he produced a series of articles, published on 27–29 November 1917. These were issued immediately afterwards in pamphlet form as *How to Settle the Irish Question*.

611 *War Issues for Irishmen* (1918). Proofs (9 galleys, each consisting of 3 numbered pages of the pamphlet), with a few revisions, including change of title from *The Issue for Irishmen*. Written by Shaw, at the appeal of the writer Stephen Gwynn, to assist the lagging recruiting program of the Irish Recruiting Council, the pamphlet was printed just as the Armistice was declared and had to be scrapped. Approximately 20 copies are known to exist.

612 Typewritten transcript of a letter from Shaw to Sylvia Beach, proprietor of the Paris bookshop Shakespeare and Company, 11 November 1921, declining to order a copy of James Joyce's *Ulysses*, of which she was publisher. The transcription was submitted to Shaw by the B.B.C. for permission to quote in a broadcast tribute to Joyce. He approved its use, on 22 January 1950, with two minor amendments, and appended an autograph note correcting the misimpression that, due to him, Joyce's *Exiles* had been rejected by the Stage Society after it had initially accepted the play.

613 To Paul Shelving, scenic designer of the Birmingham Repertory Theatre, who had designed *Back to Methuselah* at Malvern in 1929. Autograph letter, in pencil, 28 July 1930, on reverse of a photograph by Shaw of an elderly man seated on a bollard on Burren pier, Galway Bay, ca. 1915. WITH: Reproduction of the photograph, which Shaw had sent to Shelving to suggest the origin of the scene in Part IV of *Back to Methuselah*.

614 From P.J. Hernon, City Manager and Town Clerk, conveying a resolution of the Dublin City Council inviting Shaw to become a Freeman of his native city. Typewritten letter, 7 February 1946. Shaw's affirmative reply, in shorthand, is affixed to the back of the letter. As Shaw was too old to travel to Ireland to receive the Freedom, the Lord Mayor of Dublin and the City Manager came to Ayot to confer it on him.

I shall be gratefully proud to become a freeman of my native city. I have hitherto refused public credentials from for-

that I am an elderly Irish gentleman; and that if you imagine that any Irishman, much less an elderly one, would pay 150 francs for a book you little know my countrymen."

(GEORGE) BERNARD SHAW

The above letter may be quoted in full (as corrected) in the forthcoming broadcast on James Joyce.

Joyce was misinformed about his early play Exiles. It was never "about to performed by the Stage Society". He sent it to the Society; and it was sent to me to read. I at once spotted a considerable youthful talent; but as it contained a few words that were then tabooed as unmentionable, and still are; and as it was necessary to combat the current notion that the Stage Society existed for the performance of indecent plays, I reported that the unmentionable passages must be blue pencilled. I never said that the whole play was obscene. Presumably he refused to allow the bowdlerization. Anyhow Exiles was not performed. Joyce and I never met in person. I have never had time to decipher Finnegan's Wake.

G. Bernard Shaw
22/1/1950

IRELAND
by CLIPPER

"There is no magic like that of Ireland,
There are no skies like Irish skies,
There is no air like Irish air.
The Irish climate will make the stiffest
and slowest mind flexible for life."

G. Bernard Shaw

PAN AMERICAN WORLD AIRWAYS

eign cities: Dublin alone has a right to affirm that in spite of my necessarily controversial past and present I have not wholly disgraced her.

615 Written interview: reply to a question by Louise Morgan (one of a series on old age), 1 May 1946. 'In a recent interview with an Irish journalist you used the phrase "After seventy years in a country so much less happy . . . than my own. . . ." Why have you not lived in the happier country?'

> I followed my market to the place where I was most needed. Why does not the entire English nation emigrate *en masse* to Ireland, a much pleasanter land, in which the rule is 'Heaven for holiness and hell for company.' Perhaps they will, someday. When they do now they seldom come back. Strongbow burnt his boats.

616 Photograph (by James A. Whelan) of Shaw making the formal presentation of the surviving manuscripts of four of his early novels and the fragment of a fifth novel (unpublished), to John Dulanty, High Commissioner for Ireland, at Ayot St Lawrence, July 1946. Shaw had arranged for the manuscripts to be repaired and bound at his expense by Douglas Cockerell, one of Britain's finest restorers and bookbinders.

617 To P.J.A. Scott-Maunsell, secretary of the London Area Council of the Anti-Partition of Ireland League. Autograph note, undated (19 September 1947). Maunsell had solicited Shaw's support for the League's efforts at propaganda.

> I take no sides in Irish party politics, and have repeatedly declared my conviction that Ulster Protestant Capitalism, which will never yield to Catholic Republican agitation, will undo Partition when it is outvoted by organized Labor, and can fortify itself against Socialism only by an alliance with the agricultural proprietors of Eire.

*618 *Ireland by Clipper*. Large travel poster issued by Pan American World Airways in 1947 with Shaw's portrait superimposed on a background of Irish motifs. Beneath is a statement contributed by Shaw, with his signature reproduced in facsimile. A smaller version of the poster was issued as a window display card, and reproduced as a magazine advertisement.

619 Press release drafted by Shaw to explain why he had appealed for Irish prayers instead of presents. Typewritten manuscript, with revisions; undated (ca. 1949). 1 p. (See also No. 750.)

QUESTIONNAIRES

Shaw's public utterances never failed to interest and entertain newspaper readers, and journalists clamored incessantly for interviews. As a protection against misquotation and usurpation of valuable working hours, Shaw adopted a policy early in his career of requiring journalists to submit written questions of topical interest which could be answered in his spare moments 'in twenty words or less'. An intriguing question, however, often evoked a more generous response, and interviewers soon took care to frame their questions provocatively and to leave plenty of blank space as encouragement for possible expansiveness. Between 1900 and 1950 Shaw responded to more than 5000 of these journalistic questionnaires.

620 Replies to questions on *Arms and the Man*, for the journal *To-Day*, consisting of 5 question slips, 11 autograph pages (torn from a pocket notebook), and 3 typewritten pages, revised, dated 14 April 1894, with an autograph letter to the interviewer, whose name has been deleted.

> [My play] was written without the slightest reference to Bulgaria. . . . My own historical information being rather confused, I asked Mr Sidney Webb to find out a good war for my purpose. He spent about two minutes in a rapid survey of every war that has ever been waged, and then told me that the Servo-Bulgarian was what I wanted. I then read the account of the war in the Annual Register, with a modern railway map of the Balkan Peninsula before me, and filled in my blanks. . . .

621 Replies to questions by Huntly Carter on racial degeneration. 1 p., 21 November 1910.

> As we do not know the goal of evolution it is quite impossible for us to distinguish growth from degeneration. . . . Horses probably argue that the motor car must inevitably succumb to its chronic alcoholism. All we can guess about the habits of the Superman is that they would be morally disgraceful and physically fatal to a respectable alderman of our day.

622 Reply to query on fiction, for J.Y. Chapter, news editor of the *Westminster Gazette*. Autograph statement written across Chapter's undated typewritten letter (ca. 1911).

> In my opinion fiction should be sold by the pound. . . . Books are like boots: if only they are readable and fit comfortably, those which last longest are the best.

623 Replies to questions on Charles Dickens for the Dickens Centenary number of the *Bookman* (London), written on the reverse of a letter from the editor dated 2 January 1911 [*sic*]. 1 p., 4 January 1912.

My works are all over Dickens; and nothing but the stupendous illiteracy of modern criticism could have missed this glaring feature of my methods—especially my continual exploitation of Dickens's demonstration that it is possible to combine a mirror like exactness of character drawing with the wildest extravagances of humorous expression and grotesque situation.

624 Three written interviews for the *New York American*:

(a) *George Bernard Shaw on the Pope.* 4 pp., undated (published 26 June 1915); incomplete.

(b) *What George Bernard Shaw says about the War Loan.* 11 pp., undated (published 15 August 1915).

(c) *Will Women Be Compelled to Marry & Work? Is Compulsory Polygamy Possible?* 15 pp., typewritten answers to questions by W. Orton Tewson; undated (published 9 April 1916).

I was not aware that there was any such clamor. If you want to hear a real clamor, just induce some responsible public man, if you can, to propose, not that polygamy shall be compulsory, but simply that it shall be permissible.

625 To Hugo Vallentin. Autograph letter, 9 January 1917, protesting against the interview questions submitted by Vallentin's unidentified friend.

He mustn't put general historical & social questions to me: he must put topical, concrete, immediate ones that can be answered in an epigram.

626 To George Sylvester Viereck, American journalist. Autograph letter, 15 April 1927, railing against bogus interviews.

I really must protest against these faked interviews which I am forced to rewrite to avoid a fresh addition to the mass of legends and misunderstandings under which my reputation groans.
How could you write such reckless muck about me?

627 To W.R. Titterton, journalist and press agent for the Old Vic. Autograph note, 15 August 1931, in response to Titterton's report that he is publishing a written questionnaire interview 'as it stands in the dialogue form, & stating that I got the interview by correspondence.'

Why bother the public with uninteresting details? It will spoil the interview to give it away as a correspondence. Surely you can invent a domestic visit. *I* have no objection.

628 Reply to a request by James Milne for a list of the twelve greatest novels in all literature. Autograph statement, 17 September 1932, on the reverse of Milne's letter of 13 September.

629 Replies to questions by P.D. Vernon on human sterilization. 1 p., 4 February 1934. Shaw is asked: 'Do you agree with sterilization as it is practised in Germany at the present time?'

Why Germany? America began it. I do not 'agree with' any practice of criminal law at present.

630 Replies to questions by Andrew E. Malone on current politics and Shaw's new play *On the Rocks*. 6 pp., 25 July 1934. Does Shaw think that Ireland is on the rocks?

> Yes: of course she is on the rocks, the same old rocks. And when a Catholic Irishman tries to get her off, a Protestant Irishman immediately tries to keep her on; and *vice versa*. Contrairyness is the curse of Ireland, as fatheaded snobbery is the curse of England.

631 Replies to questions by John Hockin on the Far East. 6 pp., 9 July 1936. Shaw is asked if he agrees with the argument that the East is more advanced than the West since the latter relies on rule by force.

> Asia is the land of great conquerors. Compared to their conquests the British conquest of India was a mere poacher's raid. And they certainly had no scruples about using force. The question suggests that you are getting badly infected with western hypocrisy—a British speciality.

632 To Louise Morgan. Autograph note on a printed postcard bearing a message to journalists, 28 December 1938.

> Your questionnaire would require half a dozen substantial middle articles to answer it; and it has no topical interest for me. It should therefore have been accompanied by a cheque for at least £1800.

633 To Dorothy Royal. Autograph letter, 16 July 1946, informing her that he cannot answer questions that are typed on 'blotting paper', and providing a statement on women in sports.

> Athletic exercises are as good (or bad) for women as for men, except that as the lives of women are more precious than those of men the exercises must not be dangerous nor incompatible with pregnancy. This excludes all fighting exercises except perhaps fencing. Boxing contests between men and women would be quite unbearable.

634 Reply to questions by the American correspondent F.V. Conolly on American politics. 5 pp., 2 January 1948. Shaw is asked if—were he an American Democrat—he would vote for Henry Wallace.

> Of course I should vote for him. I was the first to propose his candi[d]ature in the British press. . . . Mr. Wallace's mental capacity is that of a citizen of the world, not [like Truman's] that of an American ward boss.

635 To R.B. Marriott, a member of the staff of the *Stage*. Autograph note, unsigned, on an autograph letter of 2 February 1949, in which Marriott asks 'how one is to know which questions on interesting current news [he is quoting Shaw's printed postcard to journalists] can be answered in twenty words or less? It seems to me that . . . there is an element of luck.'

Mr. Bernard Shaw is obliged to remind correspondents who seek to interview him for publication that as he is himself a professional journalist, he naturally prefers to communicate with the public through the Press at first hand. He is willing, when time permits, to answer written questions when they happen to be interesting as current news and can be answered in twenty words or less; but he receives personal visits only on the understanding that his conversation is not to be reported.

The whole art of getting an interview out of me lies in observing these conditions.
Your questionnaire would require half a dozen substantial middle articles to answer it; and it has no topical interest for me. It should therefore have been accompanied by a cheque for at least £1800.
(4 Whitehall Court (130) London, S.W.1.)
28th Dec. 1938

Shaw's response contains a suggestion that this was a game that gave him vast entertainment. It helps to explain why his responses were always so exuberant and theatrical.

> It is for the journalist to devise topical questions answerable in 20 words. That is where his skill comes in. If he asks questions answerable only in 20 volumes he has mistaken his profession.

TRANSLATORS

The satisfaction of seeing eleven of his plays emerge from the presses between 1898 and 1901 was tempered for Shaw by an unexpected complication: the need for protection of his foreign copyrights. The international agreements protected published dramatic works only for ten years unless, within that period, they were published in each foreign nation in its own language. Thus Shaw was obliged to cope with the immediate problem of obtaining translators in all the principal countries of Europe, and of underwriting the costs of publication wherever commercial arrangements were unfeasible.

Since his own familiarity with languages was limited to little French and less German, he could be of small assistance to the translators he selected. And as he tended to choose them, not for their reputations as literary men (his German translator was the principal exception), but because of their Socialist allegiances, their relation to British colleagues, or their rhetorical persuasiveness, his plays often were denied any chance of success even before they could be tried out on an audience. In the Romance countries—France, Italy, and Spain—the productions of most of his plays were total disasters. His success in Germany and Austria, in Hungary, Poland, and Tsarist Russia may be considered a reflection of local audiences' acumen in recognizing Shaw's dramatic skills in spite of the frequent bumblings of his translators.

Ironically, foreign critics were more disposed to praise him, despite the faulty translations, than the English critics were after seeing the original productions. To prevent his continental productions from being negatively affected at the boxoffice by the carping criticism reported in foreign news dispatches by local correspondents, Shaw began to authorize foreign premières. Many of his most important plays not only received their first performances in cities far removed from Britain, but were published in translation two and three years prior to their appearance in American and British editions.

636 *What I Owe to German Culture*. Typewritten manuscript, with Shaw's revisions copied in by his secretary Georgina Gillmore, 21 December 1910. 23 pp. Also a shorthand draft (incomplete). 13 pp. This is a preface, hastily drafted a few days before Shaw's departure on a voyage to Jamaica, B.W.I., for Vol. I of his collected *Dramatische Werke*, translated by Siegfried Trebitsch and published in 1911 by S. Fischer Verlag, Berlin.

> As to my friend the translator, I can only offer him my sympathy. He has expiated the crime of having discovered my works and made them successful in Germany by suffering all the insults and misunderstandings which afflict an original author complicated by the disparagements which fall on the head of the translator. . . . [T]here is no man in Europe to whom I am more deeply indebted or with whom I feel happier in all our relations. . . . And I conclude this long preface by my best bow to the German nation, and a very cordial shake-hands with Siegfried Trebitsch.

637 *Jitta's Atonement*. A free translation by Shaw of Siegfried Trebitsch's play *Frau Gittas Sühne* (1920). Shorthand manuscript of Acts II (incomplete) and III, dated 27 October 1920 at the beginning of II and 6 August 1921 at the end of III. 38 pp. Bound with a typewritten (partially carbon) manuscript, with revisions, including a six-page Translator's Note, and an autograph title page. June 1922. 137 pp. WITH: Siegfried Trebitsch, *Frau Gittas Sühne* (Berlin: Fischer, 1920).

Shaw undertook the translation to assist the war-impoverished Trebitsch monetarily, in gratitude for the successes he had achieved for Shaw during the decade prior to the war. 'It is not for me to say how far English drama is indebted to Herr Trebitsch for its present prestige abroad', Shaw wrote in his prefatory note. 'It *is* for me to say that my personal debt to him is incalculable.' WITH: *Drei Dramen* (Stuttgart und Berlin: J.G. Cotta, 1903). This edition of Trebitsch's translations of *Candida*, *The Devil's Disciple*, and *Arms and the Man* was the first foreign book publication of Shaw.

638 From Siegfried Trebitsch. Autograph letter, 11 October 1921, from Vienna. He has just received a copy of the typewritten transcription of Shaw's shorthand (prior to revision). Although he praises the work (in faulty English) it is obvious that he has mixed emotions about the liberties Shaw has taken in adapting *Jitta*, notably in the alteration of the tragedy into a comedy.

> Your version is as much better than mine as you are the greater poet of us two. I was puzzeled very much reading your bold alterations. . . . The III. Akt is in your version almost a comedy! I would not dare this towards a german audience. . . . If this play, where I miss your name as the adapters one[,] will reach the English-American footlights I shall owe it to your genious.

639 To Siegfried Trebitsch. Typewritten letter, undated (ca. 1940). Trebitsch, having fled Vienna before the Nazi invasion and settled in Paris, where he applied for French citizenship, had asked Shaw to assist him by granting him French translation rights to some of the plays. Although Shaw was aware that the Hamons were bad translators, and that few of his plays had ever achieved successful production in Paris, his sense of loyalty forbade the desertion of his old Socialist comrade and his wife.

> Hamon, with three daughters, has always been desperately poor. Years ago I had to buy his house in Brittany for him. And within the last few years I have had to buy him an annuity for his own and his wife's life, of £12 a month. And this enables him to live comfortably according to his standard of comfort.

The HRC possesses 59 pieces of Shaw correspondence (1904–50) to Trebitsch.

640 From Comte A. Guilbert de Voisins. Autograph letter, 6 October 1898. De Voisins, son of the famed ballet dancer Maria Taglione, is the first man on record to have approached Shaw for translation rights to one of his plays. For unknown reasons Shaw declined to authorize the translation of *Arms and the Man* for the *Revue Blanche*.

641 From Augustin Hamon. Autograph postcard in French, 17 October 1907, from Penvénan, Côtes du Nord. Hamon, the French radical editor of *L'Humanité Nouvelle*, was appointed Shaw's French translator in 1903 despite the fact he knew little English. He and his wife Henriette, who was better versed in the language, produced stodgy, naïve translations of the plays, revised patiently by Shaw (with the aid of a Larousse dictionary) in a classic example of the halt leading the blind. The consequence of Shaw's stubbornness in seeking to force these inept versions of his plays on the Parisian public was a consistently antagonistic press. As Hamon reports in this postcard, Shaw and the Hamons had recently been castigated in the theatrical paper *Comœdia* ('Il y est paru une note méchante contre vous et nous'). Although the Hamons translated virtually all of Shaw's fifty plays, only about seven or eight attained production in Paris, and then only in the small *coterie* theatres rather than in the commercial *théâtres du boulevard*.

642 French translations of Shaw's plays by Augustin and Henriette Hamon, all containing revisions by Shaw in French or in English, with his queries and explanations.

(a) *Candida*. Typewritten manuscript, 86 pp. (1905)

(b) *L'Homme et le Soldat* (later retitled *Le Héros et le Soldat*). Typewritten manuscript. 115 pp. (1907)

(c) *Le Disciple du Diable*. Page proofs for a limited edition, the cost of which was underwritten by Shaw. (1910)

(d) *César et Cléopâtre*. Typewritten manuscript, undated (ca. 1910). 62 pp. With two inserts of added dialogue for the 1928 publication by Éditions Montaigne. The new passages were first published in English in the collected edition, 1930.

(e) *La Profession de Madame Warren*. Tearsheets of the 1908 limited edition (also paid for by Shaw), revised for the 1912 edition. 60 pp., incomplete.

(f) *Sainte Jeanne*. Typewritten (carbon) manuscript. 138 pp. (1925)

643 From Antonio Agresti. Typewritten letter, 3 December 1911. Agresti, a journalist, was Shaw's Italian translator until his death in 1926. *Candida* was produced in 1911 with the young Italian actress Emma Gramatica appearing as Marchbanks! In July 1915 Gramatica, in Venice, 'committed the gross blunder' of producing *The Man of Destiny* in wartime. 'It provoked a riot,' Shaw reported to Siegfried Trebitsch, 'though Napoleon's speech about the English was omitted.'

HAWKINS

Merci, M. Dudgeon... à votre bonne santé, monsieur.

RICHARD

A la vôtre, monsieur. (Au moment où le verre est presque à ses lèvres, il s'arrête, jette un regard incertain sur le vin, puis ajoute avec une violence singulière) Quelqu'un veut-il avoir l'obligeance de me donner un verre d'eau ?

(Essie, qui, avec la plus grande attention, a écouté chacune de ses paroles et suivi chacun de ses mouvements, se lève furtivement, se glisse derrière Mme Dudgeon, et disparaît par la chambre à coucher pour en revenir bientôt avec un pot à eau ; puis elle sort de la maison le plus doucement possible.)

HAWKINS

Le testament n'est pas fait exactemement avec toute la phraséologie légale.

RICHARD

Oui ; mon père est mort sans les consolations de la loi.

HAWKINS

Il est bon tout de même, M. Dudgeon, il est bon tout de même... (Se préparant à lire.) Voyons, monsieur, êtes-vous prêt ?

RICHARD

Prêt ?... oui, oui, je suis prêt... Pour ce que nous allons entendre, puisse le Seigneur nous faire vraiment reconnaissant... En avant !

HAWKINS, lisant

« Ceci sont les dernières volontés et le testament de moi, Timothée Dudgeon, sur mon lit de mort, à Nevinstown, sur la route de Sprigtown à Webster-

[Handwritten marginal notes:]

This is certainly wrong. I are in Scotland without a copy of the play to refer to; but "violence" is impossible. Probably it should be "with a wry face" = "grimace" = "en haussant ses narines" Why the deuce should he be violent?

grimace bizarre

n / triste patience / ? patience souffrante

Vous avez de l'esprit ... beaucoup d'esprit

Is this the usual beginning of a French will?

Here he burlesques the "grace before meat". "For what we are about to receive, may the Lord make us truly thankful". There must be a French equivalent used by the Huguenots.

This is wrong. When a man dies without a priest to absolve him he is said to die without the consolations of religion. Richard, by way of a sardonic jest, speaks of his father, who made his will without the aid of a lawyer, as having died without the consolations of the law. Hawkins, appreciating the joke & anxious to flatter his client, applauds his wit by saying "Good" or "Good again", meaning "A bon mot, Monsieur, Bravo!"?

644 *Pigmalione*. Italian translation by Antonio Agresti. Typewritten manuscript, with Agresti's autograph revisions, October 1914. 96 pp.

645 To Julio Broutá. Autograph letter, 30 August 1926. Broutá was Shaw's Spanish translator until his death in 1932. As Argentina did not recognize or respect Spanish copyright, Shaw eventually transferred his Spanish publishing interests to South America.

> The [Spanish] Society [of Authors] sent me this year an account of tantièmes [royalties] due to me since 1921 !!! This seemed to me to be carrying the national watchword 'Mañana' to an extreme.

646 To Floryan Sobieniowski. Autograph letter, 26 July 1929. Sobieniowski, a Polish literary critic and translator of Whitman, persuaded Shaw in 1912 to give him translation rights to *Pygmalion*. With the success of the production in Warsaw (a month before the London production in 1914) he became the authorized translator of Shaw's plays in Poland until the playwright's death in 1950. *The Apple Cart* had its world première at the Teatr Polski, Warsaw, on 14 June 1929, attended by the President of the Polish Republic. It was a stunning success, causing (as Shaw notes) 'some jealousy among the less favored nations.' WITH: *The Apple Cart* page proofs, datestamped 21 March 1929. Presentation inscription on the first page: 'to Floryan Sobieniowski for translation. I have added all the latest corrections.'

647 *The Six of Calais*. Gaelic translation. Typewritten manuscript. 20 pp. Accompanied by an autograph letter from A. Mac Fhionnlaoich, Dublin, 18 April 1940, to Shaw's secretary Blanche Patch, identifying the translator as Cú Uladh.

THE GREAT WAR

When war broke out in 1914 Shaw did not take a pacifist position. He recognized that winning the war was a practical necessity, and for this reason he supported it. Glorifying it, however, was quite a different matter. Unlike his jingoistic fellows who blatantly romanticized the conflict, Shaw insisted upon approaching it with the same clearheaded logic he applied to all political problems. The war, he insisted, had been avoidable; its existence was proof of the bankruptcy of the present political system. Determinedly he produced, in the early months of the war, a sober treatise, *Common Sense About the War*, which examined candidly and unsparingly the causes of the war on both sides, and which presented Shaw's blueprint for peace after an inevitable Allied victory. Branded a traitor by many of his peers, socially ostracized, his finances seriously depleted by his unpopularity, his utterances rejected or unreported in the press, Shaw continued unflinchingly throughout the war to proclaim truth as he saw it, determined that his sanity would eventually break through the pall of wartime madness that enveloped the nation. Before it did, however, death had touched the first born of nearly every home in Britain. As the news reached Shaw of the bereavements of one after another of his close friends and colleagues—William Archer, Lady Gregory, William Maxwell, Mrs Patrick Campbell—the agony became intolerable. 'I know you will be very sorry for me', wrote J.M. Barrie as he reported the loss of his adopted son George, the model for Peter Pan. Shaw uncharacteristically and unabashedly wept as he read the letter. 'Such waste', he muttered to Charlotte, 'such utterly damnable waste.'

648 Notes on German-British tension. Autograph manuscript, February-September 1905. 1 p. Disturbed by growing enmity between Britain and Germany, Shaw joined forces with Count Harry Kessler of Germany and other humanists of both countries to issue, in January 1906, friendly letters of mutual esteem. Shaw drafted the British letter but, when its sponsors deleted two controversial passages to avoid giving offence to some of the more conservative signatories, Shaw declined to sign the document and withdrew from the project.

649 To R.C. Phillimore, a Fabian who had served with Shaw on the St Pancras Borough Council. Typewritten letter, 12 January 1912. Shaw discusses the political situation as it presently involves Edward Grey, British Foreign Secretary, and questions whether it would benefit the Fabians to interfere.

> [W]hat has happened is that after about 40 years mortal funk, England and France have at last bucked one another up to the point of bullying Germany, and Germany has had to knuckle down. . . . [W]e can do nothing but clamor for an entente with Germany, and a revival of the great alliance of the Protestant North in defence of civilization.

650 To Clifford Sharp, editor of the *New Statesman*. Autograph letter, 21 October 1914, concerning the completion of the 36,000 word *Common Sense About the War*.

> The war article is a superb performance and will reflect eternal glory on your editorship; but whether the paper will survive it is another matter.

651 *Common Sense About the War*. Special War Supplement to the *New Statesman*, London, 14 November 1914. Although a large press run was ordered to meet an exceptional demand for the issue (normal sale was 4000 copies, including 2800 subscribers), all copies were sold on the first day. Four additional printings over the next six weeks, totalling 75,000 copies, also sold out. The *New York Times* paid $2000 for serial rights, publishing the text on three consecutive Sundays commencing 15 November.

> The time has now come to pluck up courage and begin to talk and write soberly about the war. . . . I do not hold my tongue easily; and my inborn dramatic faculty and professional habit as a playwright prevent me from taking a one-sided view even when the most probable result of taking a many-sided one is prompt lynching.

652 To Bertrand Russell. Printed correspondence card on *Common Sense About the War*, with autograph postscript, 2 February 1915. Shaw's polemic elicited so many hundreds of letters that he could not possibly deal personally with all of them. He therefore resorted to a printed message for the acknowledgment of friendly letters, while concentrating on individual replies to his critics.

653 To Siegfried Trebitsch. Autograph letter, 27 August 1915. The letter is written as much to the censor as to the addressee (whose name was obliterated, not by the censor, but by the individual who later sold the letter to an autograph dealer).

> I dont object to his returning a letter as inadvisable; but when he takes to blacking out sentences and sending you selected passages . . . I had rather not be made responsible for the effect they may produce on you, and, through you as an influential journalist, upon the Vienna press. . . .

> The Germans must put up as best they can with what you call my 'disdain.' The English complain of it far more bitterly. If the human race wishes me to respect it, it must behave very differently. The war leaves me exactly as the war against Philip II left Shakespear, and the war against Louis XIV left

Swift. It is so horribly mischievous, and yet so horribly childish. We all boast of it as a great war because it has shed more gallons of blood than any previous one. In reality, it is the most trivial folly in history. . . .

654 To Henry Arthur Jones. Autograph note, 29 October 1915, at the foot of a typewritten letter of 27 October from H.M. Paull, Secretary of the Dramatists' Club, stating the members had instructed him to request Shaw to 'absent himself for the present' due to his attitude toward the war.

> I hope *you* are not one of the 'several members', though in these raving mad times it is hard to know.
> Cheerful sort of club, isnt it?

655 To Henry Arthur Jones. Autograph letter, 2 November 1915. Jones had admitted that he 'strongly supported the proposal' of the Dramatists' Club. 'Whether you know it or not', he wrote, 'and whether you care or not, you are one of our country's worst enemies. And you are an enemy within our walls.' Shaw's response was good-tempered, placating, and reasonable, but Jones had been too deeply shocked by Shaw's wartime utterances to condone any part of them, and he spent the rest of his life indulging in splenetic derogation of his erstwhile friend.

656 *The American German Case Against Germany*. Typewritten (carbon) manuscript, with revisions; undated. 14 pp. Published (with 'American' deleted from the title) in the *New York Times*, 16 April 1916.

> It is only the Irishman whose enthusiasm for his birthplace increases as the square of his distance from it.

I have received so many letters upon Common Sense About The War that I have had to give up all hope of dealing with them separately. Even the very kind and entirely reassuring letters elicited by my protest in The Daily Citizen must go unanswered. Many branches of the Independent Labor Party and other Liberal and Socialist organizations have passed resolutions which have been of the timeliest service to me publicly, and which have given me sincere personal gratification. In the hope of being able to write a separate letter in every case I have deferred my acknowledgments until it has become plain that I must make them in this fashion or not at all. It is the best I can do; and I rely on the same kindness that prompted the letters and resolutions to accept my thanks in this indiscriminate but very earnest form. G. Bernard Shaw.

10 Adelphi Terrace, London, W.C.

657 *The Emperor and the Little Girl.* Shorthand manuscript, dated Birmingham, 18–19 September 1916. 25 pp. Written for a friend, Carmel Haden Guest, to publish in aid of a Belgian orphanage. WITH: Tearsheets of the fable as published in the *New York Tribune Magazine*, 22 October 1916. An imaginary scene on a battlefield in which the Kaiser and a war waif meet between the battle lines and converse, it is 'a parable of human vanity set over against human suffering,' wrote Archibald Henderson in his centenary biography of Shaw (1956), 'the revelation of the meaning of war to one of its makers who vainly seeks self-exculpation in the phrase: "Ich habe es nicht gewollt".'

658 *A Speculation on the Future of Anglo-American Diplomacy.* Typewritten manuscript, heavily revised; undated (October 1916). 6 pp.

> After the present convulsion I presume the United States will no longer neglect to equip themselves with war material enough to take the field as a first-rate power. . . . The world is growing smaller; and the saying that Great Britain is no longer an island will soon apply to the whole North American continent. . . . With Russia and the yellow world on one flank, America must be considering what she has on the other.

659 Statement on the war, contributed to a symposium conducted by Annie Nathan Meyer, the American educator, for a proposed book to benefit the War Library Fund. Autograph manuscript, 16 November 1917. 1 p.

> [P]ocket your silly spites and vanities, and fight like a man, respecting your enemy as you respect yourself. The Cause is bigger than America, or it would not have been worth fighting for.

660 To Alex. M. Thompson, journalist and co-editor of the *Clarion*, a Socialist paper. Typewritten letter, 22 December 1917. Shaw has been requested to address a meeting of workers disgruntled by seeing their patriotism 'impudently exploited by profiteers.'

> I have told the truth about the war, and stated the democratic case for it. Ever since the war began I have addressed large audiences about it. Nobody has reported my speeches. You have abused me for all you are worth. . . . What is the use of your asking me to go and speak to the disaffected workers, when the Clarion will assure them next week that I am a treacherous pro-German?

661 *Peace Conference Hints.* Corrected page proofs of the last quire, datestamped 19 February 1919, revised by Shaw. The remaining proofs are a duplicate set with corrections and revisions copied in by Charlotte Shaw. WITH: Copy of the published book (1919), a postwar *Common Sense*, advocating a League of Nations, which would not, however, be internationally comprehensive, but would be comprised of a 'carefully selected group of politically and psychologically homogeneous constituents.'

662 From John Bookbinder of the 28th Czechoslovak Regiment. Typewritten letter, dated Prague, 24 December 1920. New Year's greetings, from the soldiers of the regiment, to 'our great Irish teacher', whose work 'always has been the philosophical basement of life' [*sic*].

663 To Cecil Lewis. Autograph postcard, 7 February 1928. Shaw promises to attend a performance of Lewis's play *The Unknown Warrior* at the Arts Theatre Club, and suggests what the plot of the play would be were *he* to deal with the subject.

In *my* Unknown Warrior a desperate necessity arises in a future frightful war to consult a survivor of 1914–18. Not one can be found. The Dean [of St Paul's], the Prime Minister, & the Foreign Secretary resolve to raise the U.W. from the dead by black magic at night. They find Christ seated on his tomb. He offers to raise the U.W. for them, and does so. The U.W. asks what they want *in German*.

RUSSIA

To understand Shaw's apparent tolerance of Fascist dictators after the first world war and his proclaimed allegiance to Communism in the 1930s, it is necessary to remember that never at any time had democracy been congenial to him. Shaw was, as G.K. Chesterton recognized, 'a splendid republican', whose concern as a lifelong Socialist was for 'the Public Thing'. Government of the people and for the people won his approval, but government by the people—by the mass mind—was anathema. At the turn of the century, in his preface to *Three Plays for Puritans*, he predicted the debasement of the democratic attitude into a pathetic romantic illusion, at which point 'the brute force of the strong-minded Bismarckian man of action, impatient of humbug, will combine with the subtlety and spiritual energy of the man of thought whom shams cannot illude or interest.' If the judgment echoed the views of Carlyle and Nietzsche, the image Shaw conjured up was quintessentially a neo-Platonic concept of the philosopher-king, one which he would a few years later seek to inculcate in the minds of his audience through the arguments of his play *Major Barbara*. All of his stage rulers, from Cæsar to Magnus and Good King Charles, would posit an identical formula for kingcraft: a powerful, intelligent, charismatic ruler, autocratic but not despotic, dedicated to the public weal yet independent of the caprices of the masses.

Convinced after the Great War that nineteenth-century liberalism was played out and that capitalism was bankrupt, Shaw spent the years between the two wars exhorting the British government to take stock and to recognize its incompetence. There was, he insisted, a vital lesson to be learned from the dictatorships, and the great danger for Britain lay in the government's refusal to recognize and confront political realities. Although Shaw initially paid respect to the efficiency of the Fascist leaders, he quickly rejected the dictators as the evidence of their excesses, their regressions, and especially their denial of individual responsibility became manifest.

The Soviet experiment, however, won Shaw's complete admiration, and it astonished him that its detractors should speak of the Revolution as if it were 'a transient riot headed by a couple of rascals.' It was futile, he rejoindered, to deny the 'monumental triumph of the Bolshevik Revolution. You might as well argue with an earthquake.' From stage and platform for half a century Shaw had preached that only by economic salvation does one free the mind and the spirit, and it was his firm conviction that Communism alone could eventually accomplish this. Yet he did not blindly give blanket endorsement to its tenets and its methods: he was never a doctrinaire communist, and never became a member of the Communist Party.

He shared the Soviet principle of social justice and economic equality: a classless society; he rejected Marxist determinism and the principle of historical necessity. The errors of the Soviet government he criticized as bluntly as he did those of the British government. He looked upon Communism, however, as the greatest political experiment in all modern history and, as he iterated in his famous 'Tovarischi' address to his Russian hosts in Moscow on his 75th birthday in 1931, he firmly believed that 'when you bring your experiment to its final triumphant conclusion—and I know that you *will* do it—we in the West who still only play with Socialism, we, whether we like it or not, will have to follow in your footsteps.'

664 From Sasha Kropotkin Lebedeff. Autograph letters, 22 July and 4 August 1913. Mrs Boris Lebedeff was the daughter of the great Russian revolutionist and social philosopher Prince Peter Kropotkin, whom Shaw had known well during his years in exile in England. The Lebedeffs served for several years as Shaw's translators and agents in pre-revolutionary Russia, where his plays had been performed since 1904, the most popular successes being *Arms and the Man*, *Mrs Warren's Profession*, and *Pygmalion*, and where a 'Complete Edition' of his plays was published as early as 1910. Mrs Lebedeff informs Shaw that, far from being shocked, as he fears, by 'swear-words' in *Pygmalion*, she may without boasting assert that 'I have, on occasion, shocked far less proper people than yourself with my fluency, both in Russian & English.'

665 *What We Expect from Russia.* In: *Twentieth Century Russia and Anglo-Russian Review*, July 1917. A contribution to a symposium.

> What I expect from New Russia ... is a vigorous prosecution of the War, as I unfortunately know no other method of binding a nation into a politically conscious and strenuously coherent whole after the dissolution of its traditional constitution except a war which threatens its existence as an independent State.

666 *Who Jailed the Twelve?* Shorthand manuscript, undated. 2 pp. A rebuke to Moscow 'Reds' concerning the trial of twelve Communists convicted in London for 'seditious conspiracy.' It was written for *Pravda*, which did not publish it. Shaw released the text to the press on 4 December 1925. It was published in the *New Leader* (London) under the original title. The *New York American* recaptioned it *Shaw Insists Russia Disavow Menace of Third Internationale.*

> I do not suggest that the Soviet Government should drop the Third International through a hole in the ice into the Neva, though it has done more harm to Russia and to Communism than ever Rasputin did. What I ask the Soviet to do is to disband it, and find employment for its members as writers of cinema scenarios and stories for boys under fourteen years of age. I feel sure that in this I have the hearty support of Mr Chicherin, Mr Krassin, Mr Rakovsky, and every really useful and able servant of Russia who has ever had to do a day's genuine and effective diplomatic work for her. . . . Here is my last word on the subject to Russia. The Third International means isolation; and isolation means encirclement.

667 Photographs of Shaw's visit to the U.S.S.R., 20–31 July 1931. On the reverse of each photograph is a pencilled note by Shaw identifying the people accompanying him and the places visited.

(a) With Maksim Litvinov, people's commissar for foreign affairs, and Nancy Lady Astor at a settlement for youthful convicts.

(b) With 'children stunting on the Collective Farm'.

(c) With 'A Collective Farm director, formerly of Massachusetts, [who] explains that he came back to Russia because there was no freedom of speech in America.'

(d) With Anatoli Lunacharsky, former commissar for education, and Konstantin Stanislavski, co-founder and director of the Moscow Art Theatre, at the Villa Troubetskoy, near Moscow, 'now a rest house for the Intellectual Proletariat'.

668 *Lenin Extempore.* In: *Left Review*, December 1934. An extemporaneous speech for a motion picture, delivered in Leningrad, 25 July 1931. The circumstances were recounted in a letter to Charlotte Shaw that evening, in which Shaw informed her that one of his hosts, Lunacharsky, had taken him to a film studio to see the shooting of 'a great Lenin talkie'. There Shaw was easily encouraged to 'stage-manage' and improvise 'quite a good little interlude'. He could not, he confessed to Charlotte, 'resist shewing off before the awestruck Russian talkie experts.' (British Library.)

669 Photograph (by Unionbild G.m.b.H.) of Shaw in Leningrad (24–25 July 1931).

670 Charlotte Shaw to Margaret Lady Rhondda. Autograph letter, 4 October 1931. Charlotte warns Lady Rhondda, who has invited them to dinner shortly after Shaw's return from his Russian visit: 'You will have to control G.B.S. severely about Russia! When he is started it is almost impossible to stop him!'

671 *'Look, you boob . . . !' What Bernard Shaw told the Americans about Russia!* Text of Shaw's radio broadcast *A Little Talk on America*, delivered by shortwave to the United States on 11 October 1931, and photographed simultaneously by Movietone News. (See also No. 593.)

672 *Reborn Russia in Pictures.* Autograph manuscript (incomplete); undated. 13 pp. Written in South Africa, March 1932, for a special Russian Supplement in the *Cape Times.*

> [W]e should be most perdurably foolish if we let the lessons of the Russian Revolution be lost on us. For, so far, it works. We protested that it wouldn't, that it couldn't, that it shouldn't; but it does. It is our plan that is breaking down: it is the Russian plan that is building up.

673 Statement on Marxism. Autograph manuscript, undated. 6 pp. Presumably an undelivered reply to a New Zealand journalist's written question, ca. March–April 1934.

> I wrote a Marxist novel 45 years ago, and felt about bourgeois civilization exactly as Lenin did when he discovered Marx 14 years later. . . . Consequently the Russian Revolution produced no bouleversement in my ideas nor change in

my outlook. I understood perfectly, and rejoiced in its success. And its mistakes—for it made many mistakes—were mistakes which I had foreseen and warned my fellow Socialists against. I knew that the hard facts of life would force the Soviet Government to remedy them. I knew that they could be remedied. . . . If Lenin had only read me as he read Marx there would have been none of the chaos which led to the N.E.P. [New Economic Policy] and no premature expulsion of the Kulaks from their farms.

674 Written interview: replies to questions by an unidentified journalist on the U.S.S.R. 1 p., 24 September 1934. Asked what the U.S.S.R. has contributed towards the progress of mankind, Shaw answers: 'Its leadership in the greatest social experiment ever consciously made in human history.'

675 *Stalin-Wells Talk* (1934). The *New Statesman* in October 1934 published a verbatim record of the conversation between H.G. Wells and Joseph Stalin during Wells's recent visit to Moscow, which contained a clash of views on a number of subjects. The questions raised in the dialogue were debated in the Letters to the Editor column in successive weeks by Shaw, the economist J.M. Keynes, the German playwright-in-exile Ernst Toller, and others. At Wells's urgence, and with the consent of the others, the *New Statesman* collected the materials in a pamphlet, with a cover design and caricatures by the popular political cartoonist Sidney Low.

> Stalin has exiled Trotsky and become the Pontifex Maximus of the New Russo-Catholic Church of Communism on two grounds. First, he is a practical Nationalist statesman recognising that Russia is a big enough handful for mortal rulers to tackle without taking on the rest of the world as well. . . . Second, Stalin, inflexible as to his final aim, is a complete opportunist as to the means. . . . It is evident that Stalin is a man who will get things done, including, if necessary, the removal of Trotsky and the World Revolution from the business of the day. [From 'Mr. Shaw's comment', first published 3 November 1934.]

676 *Britain and the Soviets: The Congress of Peace and Friendship with the U.S.S.R.* (1936). Shaw, who was one of the original supporters of the Congress, was called upon during the opening session, 7 December 1935, to make a few extemporaneous remarks.

> Things are going Russia's way; and there is every evidence that things are not going our old way. Even the strongest Conservative cannot possibly be satisfied with the general trend of events in the stage Capitalism has reached in this country. Apparently, Providence is getting sick of Capitalism. . . . If it knew as much as we know about it, it would have got sick a hundred years ago. . . . There are these two great balancing forces [the U.S.S.R. and the U.S.A.] and we must not forget that unless Russia and America are at the back of [the League of Nations], Geneva will count for nothing in diplomacy.

677 To Clarence H. Norman. Autograph postcard, 22 April 1940. Shaw replies to a comment about the war with Germany. 'Yes; but what about America? It was the U.S.A. that won the last rubber. Neither they nor the U.S.S.R. may be able to keep out of it this time either.' Two months later, in a prepared but undelivered B.B.C. talk on the war ('The Unavoidable Subject'), banned by the censor, Shaw concluded: 'Russia and America may soon have the fate of the world in their hands; that is why I am always so civil to Russia.'

678 Written interview: replies to questions by W.R. Titterton on Russia, Poland, and Finland. 3 pp. (two of them are fragments); undated (May 1941).

"*Look, you boob . . . !*"

William Gropper in "New Masses," N.Y.

What BERNARD SHAW told the Americans about RUSSIA!

HIS FAMOUS BROADCAST

PRICE **3d.**

[W]e can find nothing kinder to say about [Stalin] than to call him a bloodstained monster and then complain that he has no confidence in our good intentions! The sooner we do something to deserve it, the better. If he were not so able we should have driven him into Adolf's arms long ago. Happily Uncle Joe knows what puerile fools we are politically, and is goodnatured enough to laugh at us. Remember: I have seen the man and talked to him. Nobody could have been pleasanter with us or treated us better; BUT—he laughed at us. We amused him.

679 *Surprises from Russia.* Shorthand draft, 30 November 1945. 6 pp. Typewritten manuscript insert, corrected. 2 pp. Galley proofs. 3 pp. Published in the *Sunday Express*, London, 30 December 1945.

> Stalin declared for collective farming and Socialism in a single country to begin with, and at once became, without knowing it, the Arch-Fabian of Europe. Trotsky, catastrophist world revolutionist ... vanished and perished in spite of his great and well-earned prestige. And the only groups in Europe which could say 'We told you so' were and are the English Fabians, who had never used a scrap of foreign material in their propaganda. ...

680 U.S.S.R. commemorative stamp honoring the centenary of Shaw's birth, 26 July 1956. Shaw was honored postally by Rumania in the same year and by Czechoslovakia in 1969. ('A prophet is not without honor. . . .')

FASCISM AND WORLD WAR II

681 *To the Editor of The Nation: Mr Shaw Replies.* Autograph manuscript, 7 November 1927. 5 pp. The Italian historian Gaetano Salvemini, an anti-fascist living in exile in London, attacked Shaw's political leanings in a vitriolic letter in the *Manchester Guardian* on 19 October 1927. Shaw, he said, 'after having,

680

with pitiless satire, tilted at the social, political, and religious institutions, the intellectual and moral standards of our time, has at last discovered embodied in Fascism his ideal of civil life. In Mussolini he has found the man before whom his rebel spirit surrenders arms. Kate has at long last met her Petruchio.' This set off a controversy that boiled for two months, eventually spilling over into the pages of the *Nation*. Late in the year a number of the letters of Salvemini, Shaw, and others were published in an unauthorized pamphlet *Bernard Shaw & Fascism*. It reprinted the Shaw reply of 7 November.

> Are we to recognize the Government of Signor Mussolini as for the time being the constitutional Government of Italy, as Queen Victoria's Governments accepted that of Napoleon III in France, or are we to treat him as Mr. Winston Churchill treated Lenin, and receive every diplomatic communication from Italy with a shout, diplomatic and journalistic, of 'Tyrant! Usurper! Abominable Ogre! Murderer of Matteotti! Slayer of Liberty! Do not dare to address England until you have signed your own death warrant and given Italy a British and soi-disant democratic Constitution' [?] ... [T]he Government of Signor Mussolini, and not the grievances of our friends the refugees, is the Government of Italy; and the policy of spitting in its face ... is not a possible policy for us. ... Besides, we are afraid of Mussolini. I do not know why we should be; but we certainly are; and since Corfu he has known it. That is the most dangerous point in the Anglo-Italian situation.

682 Written interview for Raymond Savage Ltd., a literary agency: replies by Shaw to his own questions, on armament. 6 pp., dated 12 March 1935. Typewritten manuscript, on six small slips, each initialed, with the last slip signed in full beneath the word 'Authorized'. Shaw lists the principal world powers.

> I have left out not only Japan but China; and China, especially Communist China, the existence of which our statesmen have either not yet discovered or are trying to ignore like ostriches, is a very important factor in the future of the world.

683 Written interview: replies to questions by W.R. Titterton on dictators. 4 pp., dated 4 July 1938. Typewritten replies, with autograph revisions and additions. Published in the *Sunday Chronicle*, London, on 10 July under the misleading caption 'Dictators: Give Us Some More!'

> Dictators are always necessary. Every employer is a dictator. Every sergeant is a dictator. Every ship captain is a dictator. Every policeman at the street crossing is a dictator.

The difficulty is always to find enough capable dictators to make the best of our resources. People want to be dictated to: it saves them the trouble of thinking for themselves. We are all in favor of government of the people, for the people, by the people. And when we get it the universal cry is 'Tell us what to do, governor.' . . . No system can safeguard peace where pugnacity is esteemed the noblest virtue. The most effective check on it at present is poison gas; but the cure is viler than the disease.

684 *Uncommon Sense About the War. New States-man,* 7 October 1939. This inevitable sequel by Shaw to his controversial utterance at the outbreak of the first World War received front page attention by the press throughout the world. Syndicated in America by Hearst, it was considered significant enough to be run simultaneously in both the morning and afternoon newspapers. Representative John E. Rankin of Mississippi caused it to be published in its entirety in the Congressional Record.

[H.G. Wells] warns us that we are risking not merely a military defeat, but the existence of civilisation and even of the human race. Dear H.G., let us not flatter ourselves. The utmost we can do is to kill, say, twenty-five millions of one another, and make ruins of all our great cities show places for Maori tourists.

Well, let us. In a few months we shall matter no more than last summer's flies. As two of the flies, we naturally deprecate such an event; but the world will get on without us; and the world will have had an immense gratification of the primitive instinct that is at the bottom of all this mischief and that we never mention: to wit pugnacity, sheer pugnacity for its own sake, that much admired quality of which an example has just been so strikingly set us by the Irish Republican Army.

685 Photograph (by *Illustrated Magazine*) of Shaw with his war helmet. In November 1939 Shaw ordered a white bakelite-lined helmet for protection against shrapnel, as the government issue was uncomfortably heavy for him. At the same time he acquired a white coat and a white walking stick as a warning to motorists on dark days.

686 Written interview: replies to questions by W.R. Titterton on the Lease-and-Lend Act. 2 pp., dated 17 March 1941. Shaw's responses are partially typewritten.

Declarations of war are out of fashion. . . . Nowadays you just go for your enemy and leave him to infer your intentions. The U.S.A. is quite openly at war with Germany; but

there has been no formal declaration. In his last broadcast the President [Franklin D. Roosevelt] said 'General Chiang Kai Shek needs our help. He shall have it.' That means that the U.S.A. is at war with Japan. It was the spear point of his speech; and yet the papers and even Adolf Hitler himself twaddled about the speech next day without noticing it. Amazing stupidity!

687 Written interview: replies (mostly typewritten) to questions by Dorothy Royal on postwar capitalism and politics. 5 pp., dated 27 September 1944. Does Shaw agree that, after her defeat, Germany will have to be governed by the Allies for half a century before it will be safe to let her again govern herself?

All this talk of governing Germany when we cannot even govern ourselves is childish nonsense. Leave Germany to itself, and there will be a reaction against Hitlerism as surely as there was a reaction after Cromwell's major generals. When a horse is down you may have to sit on his head for a minute or two before helping him up; but you cannot sit on his head for fifty years. Both horse and man must get on their own legs again pretty quickly if they are to survive.

688 *The Ideal of Citizenship*: *Being the Speech of Pericles over those fallen in the war.* Translated from the Greek of Thucydides by A.E. Zimmern (London: Medici Society, 1916). The inscription by Shaw is his last pronouncement on war and demagoguery. It is dated 23 February 1950, which was General Election day in Britain.

—Moral—
Keep your feet hard on the ground; and your fingers in your ears when eloquent phrasemongers mount the rostrum, or your empires will fall as that of Pericles did.

THE BEERBOHM DRAWINGS

Bernard Shaw was one of Max Beerbohm's favorite subjects. Sir Rupert Hart-Davis records more than sixty cartoons of Shaw in his definitive catalog of Beerbohm caricatures. The HRC possesses eight Beerbohm cartoons of Shaw, in addition to a large mural group in which he figures, and half a dozen leaves of drawing paper with unfinished drawings or sketches of Shaw's head.

689 *Light-headed from want of food. From a photograph—showing how cruelly they wrong him.* Caricature of a shabby Shaw, signed 'Max to A.B.W[alkley].' 1901. Unpublished. Pen and ink, wash, and crayon, 12½" by 7¾".

*690 *Popular notion of Bernard Shaw since marriage*, signed 'Max to A.B.W[alkley].' 1900. The cartoon of Shaw as a fat plutocrat was displayed in Beerbohm's one man show in the Carfax Galleries, London, December 1901. The Shaws visited the galleries two days after the opening, and Charlotte, as Shaw reported to Beerbohm, had to be restrained from 'buying the capitalist G.B.S., with the object of concealing or destroying it as a libel on her husband's charms.' Unpublished. Watercolor, ink, and crayon, 12¼" by 7¾".

*691 *Historic scene at 10 Adelphi Terrace*. Unsigned. 10 December 1903. Shaw had just announced his candidacy for a South St Pancras seat on the London County Council and called on local public-spirited friends to canvass for him. One of these was James Timewell, a master tailor and founder of the Police and Public Vigilance Society, who was in process of interviewing Shaw on his position concerning municipal issues when Beerbohm arrived for lunch. In the cartoon the diminutive tailor, the air around him dotted with interrogation and exclamation marks, gazes up at a stiffly-seated Shaw and announces: 'But here I stay till I find something that he *is* sound on!' Pen and ink, 10" by 8".

*692 *To G.B.S. from Max*, beneath a musical stave dotted with notes. 14 January 1905. In late December 1904 Beerbohm published in the *Saturday Review* a notice of the Stage Society production of Tolstoy's *The Power of Darkness* in which he was severely critical of the translators, Louise and Aylmer Maude. The latter responded on 7 January; a week later there was a letter from Shaw lauding Aylmer Maude's work and endorsing the views expressed in the Maude rebuttal. Max's drawing, on the same day that Shaw's letter was published, was a latter-day version of the fight scene in Act IV of Gounod's opera *Faust*. A frightened 'Marguerite Tolstoi' (pigtails sticking out stiffly like banderillas), in the background, looks on while 'Valentine Max, angry brother of Marguerite Tolstoi' dauntlessly attacks the startled 'Aylmer Faust, betrayer of Marguerite Tolstoi' as 'Mephisto Bernard, influential friend

of Aylmer Faust' intercepts Max's thrust with a sword whose point crackles with electrical charges. Ink and watercolor, 18" by 12".

*693 [Arthur W. Pinero and Shaw], signed 'Bilbo.' A fashionplate Pinero, with top hat, frock coat, and cane, strolls past Shaw, clad in a sagging widebrim hat, unpressed jacket with too-short sleeves, and clinging trousers on pipestem legs. Pinero says: 'Though it is an arguable point whether I be, as I was once reputed, and as I still venture to deem myself, the most intellectual, I remain, beyond dispute, the dressiest, of contemporary British dramatists.' Published as a *Vanity Fair* cartoon supplement on 1 February 1906, with Pinero's statement altered to the third person. Pencil and watercolor, 13" by 9".

694

*694 [Shaw as General John Burgoyne], signed 'Max'. Affixed to the drawing is a cutting from A.B. Walkley's criticism of *The Devil's Disciple* in the *Times* of 15 October 1907: 'Mr. Shaw found it amusing to work up this sketch of himself disguised in a wig and an old-world courtliness of manner, and that settled it.' The Vedrenne-Barker production of the play—its first in the West End—had opened at the Savoy Theatre the previous evening. Hitherto unpublished. Pen and ink, 12¼″ by 7⅞″.

*695 *After the Publication*, signed 'Max'. 1911 (ca. May). Beerbohm was fond of contrasted 'Before' and 'After' cartoons. The first drawing of this pair, which apparently has not survived, presumably shewed Shaw lavishing attention and information on his authorized biographer Archibald Henderson. After the monumental work appeared in 1911 Shaw wrote to the press (see No. 703) complaining of its inaccuracies. Beerbohm's second drawing shews Shaw nonchalantly addressing an openmouthed little man with an umbrella: 'What name? . . . Ah, to be sure; and let me tell you, Mr Henderson, I've just been writing to the press to point out some of your inaccuracies, and to say I can't wade through your pages, and have no further use for you.' Unpublished. Pencil, 16″ by 12½″.

*696 [Untitled, unsigned fresco of heads and shoulders of 21 prominent men.] ca. 1922. Tempera on gesso, 40¾″ by 47¼″.

*697 *'Mr Shaw's apotheosis is one of the wonders of the age'*, signed 'Max'. The quotation is from A.B. Walkley's column in the *Times*, 9 July 1924. The drawing is a large profile of Shaw's head and torso. He is stretched out on the ground looking down, like Gulliver, on a group of five effete Lilliputian worshippers ritualistically swinging censers, from which the incense floats upward to Shaw's nostrils. 'A.B.W.', in evening attire, says in an aside: 'And calls himself a non-smoker!' Pencil and wash, 12½″ by 16″.

*698 [Self-portrait of Max Beerbohm], signed 'Max'. Undated. Ink and wash, 12″ by 6½″.

*699 [William Archer and Harley Granville Barker.] Unsigned, ca. 1908. Rough sketch for a drawing of Archer, whose head is filled with the dream of a National Theatre (shown in a balloon), holding the tail of the coat of Granville Barker, who, suitcase in hand, is off to America. Unpublished. Pencil, 17″ by 15″.

*700 *Frank Harris presenting 'The Man Shakespeare'*. Unsigned, ca. 1910. Rough sketch for a drawing of a suggested frontispiece for Harris's recently published biography of Shakespear, shewing footlights and the audience's heads in the foreground. Unpublished. Pencil and ink, 15″ by 18″.

BIOGRAPHY AND AUTOBIOGRAPHY

The terms 'biography' and 'autobiography', in Shaw's case, are virtually synonymous. With the sole exception of G.K. Chesterton, every serious biographer of Shaw from Holbrook Jackson in 1907 to Stephen Winsten in 1949 suffered some portion, at least, of his work to undergo Shaw's 'revisionist' surgery. It was the fee he exacted for his cooperation. Those who preferred to pursue an independent course learned, to their grief, how difficult it is to persuade a publisher to contract for a work whose subject publicly threatens legal action. It wasnt, as some have insisted, that Shaw had any skeletons rattling in his closet which he was determined to hide. It was, rather, in his nature as a longtime practising journalist to be skeptical of the accuracy of reporters. 'Every statement published about me', he asserted, 'is inaccurate', and at every opportunity he sought to expunge the errors and resolve the misconceptions. Eventually this became a compulsion. As the burglar says in *Too True to be Good*, in what must surely be one of Shaw's most autobiographic utterances in his plays, 'I can explain anything to anybody, and I love doing it.'

As he himself, however, was the first to admit, Shaw had spent much of his life deliberately creating a persona—'G.B.S.'—who 'is not a real person', but 'a legend created by myself'. Eventually it became impossible to separate fiction from fact. 'My memory', Shaw told Sydney Cockerell, 'is excessively theatrical. It arranges everything for the stage. This is artistically a great improvement; but as police evidence it is worthless.' Ironically, those Shaw biographies written during his lifetime which are least trustworthy are those which most fully benefitted from his fosterage.

701 H.L. Mencken, *George Bernard Shaw: His Plays* (Boston, 1905). The first book written on Shaw, containing a presentation inscription headed 'Peccavi' (Latin: 'I have sinned'): To George Bernard Shaw who, if the very sincere admiration of a young man is worth anything to him, has that of Henry Louis Mencken', dated Baltimore, Md., 2 December 1905. Accompanying this is a typewritten letter of 3 December from Mencken: '[A]s the title indicates, it is an attempt to get between covers some sort of connected review of your dramas. . . . In case you come to the United States shortly I shall give myself the pleasure of calling upon you—to make my apologies.'

702 To Archibald Henderson, Professor of Mathematics at the University of North Carolina. Autograph letter, 5 September 1905. Shaw spent a large portion of the year 1905 drafting answers to the questions posed by his first biographer. One letter, in January, ran to 54 autograph pages. By September Shaw had reached 'Question 22, about Nietzsche.'

> The truth is I am rather an imposter as a pundit in the philosophy of Schopenhauer & Nietzsche. . . . I have often referred to them to remind my readers that what they called my individual eccentricities are part of the common European stock.

703 Archibald Henderson, *George Bernard Shaw: His Life and Works* (London, 1911). WITH: Press cuttings of letters in the *Morning Post* on 2 May 1911, from Shaw criticizing the accuracy of the biography, and on 26 May, from Henderson defending his work. (See Beerbohm drawing, No. 695.) As was to be his custom for the remainder of his life, Shaw plied his biographer with a plethora of materials (some of them inconsistent and contradictory), made extended alterations in the manuscript and in the proofs—and then denounced the work as inaccurate! Henderson, stung by Shaw's chiding disclaimers, responded forcefully:

> Mr. Shaw is a dialectician, which means that, if necessary, the same words can mean to him two different things; whereas I am a mathematician, which means that they can mean only one. I do not, of course, intend to imply that Mr. Shaw is not perfectly sincere in repudiating the implication about Henley. Quite conceivably he did not mean

what he said, or his casual remark may have acquired an unexpected significance in print. But he is a man of many words, and he is unaccustomed to being confronted with them. When he is, his invariable and quite natural impulse is to 'repudiate' them.

704 To Archibald Henderson. Autograph letter, 16 November 1917. Shaw compiles for students a list of outstanding plays under the headings of Comedies and Tragedies, noting that Henderson's third category, Serious Plays, is an absurd one. 'All plays are serious.'

> Of course the classifications are not absolute: Faust is a tragedy as well as a comedy in spite of the happy ending, and Hamlet & Troilus & Cressida are comedies as well as tragedies, in spite of the general slaughter at the end; but you will see the congruity of it all the same[.]

705 Augustin Hamon, *Le Molière du XXe Siècle* (Paris, 1913). Page proofs of the first quire ('Épitre [*sic*] dédicatoire'), 16 pp., and tearsheets of pp. 33–38, all revised by Shaw. WITH: Copy No. 2 of the limited edition of 20 numbered copies on 'papier du Japon', inscribed 'Pour George Bernard Shaw | le Molière contemporain | bien amicalement | AHamon | 20 sept 1912'.

> Do not force the note about my plays being comic. You may leave that to the enemy. Your struggle will be to resist the notion that I am a mere farceur, and to convince people that I am serious.

706 To Thomas Demetrius O'Bolger. Typewritten (carbon) letter, revised, dated at end February 1916. 29 pp. One of the most candid and detailed autobiographical letters ever written by Shaw, concerning his mother's relations with her singing teacher, George John Lee, who shared a home with Shaw's parents. O'Bolger, a professor of English at the University of Pennsylvania, wrote a Ph.D. thesis, *The Real Shaw*, in 1913, for which he solicited and obtained the assistance of his subject. As publication of the thesis was mandatory, O'Bolger sought to attract a publisher by expanding the manuscript into a significant study of Shaw's formative years. In this endeavor he received from Shaw extravagant courtesies, letters of encouragement, and an enthusiastic deluge of volunteered information. When, however, O'Bolger began to submit portions of his manuscript to Shaw, the dramatist grew testy, charging that the biographer was distorting the facts and aspersing his mother. He com-

1. COMEDIES.

The medieval "bible mysteries" in which Cain, the Bethlehem shepherds, Judas &c, are presented as comic characters.

The Falstaff plays of Shakespear

Don Quixote (not written for the stage, but historically a comedy).

Tirso da Molina's Burlador of Seville, and the cycle of Don Juan plays founded on it, including Molière's Festin de Pierre, Mozart's Don Giovanni, Byron's Poem, and Man & Superman.

Beaumarchais' Figaro plays.

Goethe's Faust.

Ibsen's Peer Gynt, Wild Duck, & John Gabriel Borkman.

Strindberg's Spook Sonata.

Finally

The Comedies of Aristophanes.

Incidentally

(The Don Cæsar de Bazan plays.
(The Harlequinades
(Robert Macaire, both in the old crude version and Stevenson's.
((These should be taken as an appendix to Molière and Beaumarchais)
(Punch & Judy.

2. TRAGEDIES.

3. SERIOUS DRAMAS.

This heading is absurd. All plays are serious. You can distinguish Comedy & Tragedy as Plays of the serious end of the Picture. You can better Tragi-comedy, & even Melodrama; but Serious Drama is nonsense.

The Medieval Passion Plays.

Shakespear's Hamlet, Lear, Macbeth, with history & Shakespear, Measure for Measure & Troilus &c.

~~...~~

Richard Wagner's Nibelung's Ring.

Ibsen's Brand, Rosmersholm, Master Builder, & When We Dead Awaken.

Masefield's tragedies   } to illustrate the rebirth of tragedy in England
The Doctor's Dilemma.   } after 3 centuries.

Finally

The Greek tragedies.

---

10 Adelphi Terrace. London W.C.2.
16th Nov. 1917

My dear Henderson

I amuse myself by scrawling the attached suggestions for your amusement.

The notion is not "This is a very jolly play: you really ought to read it", but to provide a good strong culture skeleton on which the student can afterwards put as much flesh (fat or lean) as he pleases.

Of course the classifications are not absolute: Faust is a tragedy as well as a comedy in spite of the happy ending, and Hamlet & Troilus & Cressida are comedies as well as tragedies, in spite of the general slaughter at the end; but you will see the congruity of it all the same

ever
G. Bernard Shaw.

704

menced now to throw monkey wrenches into the machinery. Though O'Bolger attempted to placate him, Shaw resorted to a series of cat and mouse tactics which drove the scholar frantic. He died in 1923 of pernicious anæmia, frustrated and bitter after spending the last decade of his life rewriting his manuscript five times, while Shaw, perversely deaf to entreaties, continued to the end to discourage interested publishers.

707 From Thomas D. O'Bolger. Typewritten letter, 9 February 1922. Shaw had accused O'Bolger of borrowing techniques from his father, a police inspector. In *Sixteen Self Sketches* (1949) Shaw commented: 'Though Professor O'Bolger adopted literature as his profession he inherited his father's police attitude and technique, always testing the statements and the evidence of accused or suspected persons with a view to their prosecution for breaches of law. . . .' O'Bolger, for his own part, insisted his interpretation of Shaw was the most levelheaded by any of Shaw's biographers.

You have yourself lived in a cloud regarding yourself—you have boasted the unreality of the fantasma G.B.S.: you have been petted and humored in England and it has brought you up with a jolt to find that I am unable to enter into the fantastic view of you to the detriment or discredit of the real view of you.

I have written you up as a biologic instance of a literary man's genesis in so far as I could get at it. I could no more write the splashy generalities of Chesterton than I could the humdrum of Henderson. I took your autobiographical notes *by their logic*, not by their sentimental coloration.

708 *The Late Professor O'Bolger.* Typewritten manuscript fragment, written for the section in *Sixteen Self Sketches* (1949) captioned 'Biographers' Blunders Corrected'. 4 pp. Shaw here defends his actions in a rather superficial and distorted statement of the facts.

. . . I wrote him many letters in answer to his appeals for information. But when the biography was written and offered to an American publisher, it contained statements so defamatory that the publisher, though accepting it on its literary merits, demanded a certificate of my confirmation and approval. How impossible it was for me to give such a certificate will be made clear by what follows.

Here follows a letter to O'Bolger of 7 August 1919, abridged and reframed—like all of Shaw's autobiographical writings when published at a time subsequent to their original composition or publication.

709 To Frank Harris. Autograph statement in pencil, 24 June 1930. 3 pp. In response to Harris's entreaties Shaw supplies him with information concerning his sexual experiences. This appeared in Harris's posthumously published biography of Shaw in 1931. Shaw revised the statement significantly when he 'reprinted' it in *Sixteen Self Sketches*, 1949.

First, O Biographer, get it clear in your mind that you can learn nothing about your sitter (or Biograph*ee*) from a mere record of his copulations. . . . If you have any doubts as to my normal virility, dismiss them from your mind. I was not impotent; I was not sterile; I was not homosexual; and I was extremely, though not promiscuously susceptible.

The HRC possesses 48 pieces of Shaw correspondence (1908–30) to Harris.

710 To Frank Harris. Autograph letter, 21 April 1931. Harris had sent transcriptions of Shaw's letters to him for approval for publication. Shaw touched these up. When Harris protested against Shaw's substitution of the euphemism 'gallantries' for 'copulations' and 'mistress' for 'whore', Shaw firmly rebuffed him.

I tell you, if there is one expression in this book of yours that cannot be read aloud at a confirmation class, you are lost for ever. Your life and loves are just being forgotten. . . . This book is your chance of recovering your tall hat; and you want to throw it away for the sake of being in the fashion of O'Neill, Joyce, and George Moore. And even George does not imagine that force in literature is attained by calling a spade a f———g shovel. Even if it were, that sort of thing does not belong to your generation or mine, which could say all that it wanted to say without lessons from the forecastle and the barrack guard room.

711 Frank Harris, *Bernard Shaw* (1931). *Postscript by the Subject of this Memoir.* Shorthand manuscript, dated 5 October 1931. 5 pp. Typewritten transcription, with Shaw's revisions. 9 pp. There are presentation inscriptions on the last page of each of these, dated 28 October 1931. The inscription on the typescript reads in part: 'All the galley proofs on which I made my corrections of Frank Harris's text have been destroyed; and this, with the original shorthand, which I now give to Mrs Harris, is all that remains of the materials used in the work done by me.' Shaw had taken the proof sheets in hand after Harris's death: when he discovered that the work was riddled with error, he supplied or corrected the facts, he claimed, piously preserving 'all the criticisms, jibes, explosions [shorthand notation] Bastilles, ... 3 chateaux, ...

(End of chapter)

(Beginning of chapter)

BLOODY SUNDAY IN TRAFALGAR SQUARE

There was a trade-depression in the years 1886-7 and the unemployed got out of hand. The Democratic Federation made the most of their opportunity and on a February day in '86 marched with the workless from Trafalgar Square to Hyde Park, passing through Pall Mall, *whilst the police, through a mistake which cost their chief his place, were waiting for them in the Mall. The* rich men gathered in their club windows to ~~come~~ see the fun. ~~exposition remarks~~ The unemployed, *fancying* that ~~clubmen and~~ they were *being mocked,* ~~been created for a amusement~~ broke the ~~in~~ club windows, *and went on to the park where they held their meeting. Some of the stragglers* ~~of a chieftain, startled by the realization that they had been~~ ~~ride one use, retreated to the rear of their premises, protecting~~ ~~friends. The crowd collapsed and~~ looted a shop or two, *and captured* the carriage of *a* ~~~~ lady by the Achilles Statue. ~~Buthall~~ ~~one the railings of Hyde Park and held their meeting~~ Hyndman, John Burns and two others were arrested *and tried* as ringleaders; *but by good luck the foreman of the jury was an imposing Christian Socialist in whose hands the rest were sheep; and the four were* ~~after~~ acquitted. *If* ~~There, as so often happens among men~~ *This beginning of insurrection grew until it centred on the supposed right to hold meetings in* ~~other for the common good, Hyndman Burns and~~ *Trafalgar Square. The cry of Free Speech rallied all the workers to the Socialists, and a grand mass meeting* ~~there~~ ~~democrats squabbled and separated, the unemployed being~~ *was announced for* ~~left to look after themselves~~ ~~grew, fostered by~~ ~~arrests also of the Pall Mall Gazette, and on~~ the 13th November 1887, *thereafter to be* ~~also~~ known as "Bloody Sunday." *The police prohibited it under an Act which empowered them* ~~thousands of the workless and a few~~

(Pages 1, 2, 3 & 4 follow)

of passing ill humor, and condemnations'. Shaw's decision to destroy the manuscript is explained in a statement made ten years later to Hesketh Pearson: 'Since you must consider the copyright question as between your executors and mine, I strongly advise you to do what I did in the Harris case. When the book is safely in print, take the copy and burn every scrap of it. It will then be forever impossible for either of us to lay a finger on any page or passage and say "This is Pearson's copyright, and this is Shaw's." It will be all yours without any possible question. . . .'

712 To Hesketh Pearson. Autograph letter, 2 December 1938, in which Shaw gives Pearson his approval of a biography: '[Y]ou may go ahead with my blessing.' Eventually Shaw's cooperation developed to a point where he became, as Pearson later phrased it, 'my uninvited collaborator', expending more than a full year's labor in writing long autobiographical letters, reading and revising two complete drafts of every chapter, providing entire chapters of his own composition, and then revising or expanding even these.

713 To Hesketh Pearson. Typewritten letter, 15 March 1939, and autograph postcard, 23 September 1939. The biographee provides information concerning a boyhood escapade in Dalkey at the age of twelve, his relations with Jane Patterson, and his near-drowning at Llanbedr in 1907.

714 Hesketh Pearson, *Bernard Shaw: His Life and Personality* (1942). Typewritten and autograph manuscript (incomplete), with an amplitude of autograph revisions, deletions, and additions (many of them on affixed slips of diverse sizes and shapes) by Shaw. 780 pp. (partially carbon copies). The HRC also possesses a number of draft texts and revisions by Shaw, including the chapter 'Bloody Sunday in Trafalgar Square' (5 pp., on 3 leaves, shorthand and an extensively revised fragment of typescript), as well as autograph notes of criticism of portions of Pearson's text, including an attack on the argument that all Shaw's characters are representations of Shaw.

> Nobody could mistake a picture by Michael Angelo for a picture by Rembrandt: all the M.A. pictures proclaim the hand and character of M.A., and all the Rembrandt pictures those of Rembrandt. But who would be so absurd as to say that all the figures in the Sistine Chapel are self-portraits of M.A. or all in The Night Watch of Rembrandt? Jaques, Hamlet, Macbeth, Timon and Coriolanus are all 'Shakespeares'. . . . They speak the same unmistakable language and have the same brain at the back of them. . . . So have Broadbent and Larry Doyle, Dick Dudgeon and Blanco Posnet. All my characters are 'Shaws.' But to say that they are all self-portraits is silly. It is what every bad critic said 40 years ago. You must not let yourself be overwhelmed by my style.

715 Hesketh Pearson: Obituary of Shaw prepared prematurely for the B.B.C. Typewritten manuscript, revised by Shaw; undated (1946). Labelled 'Private and Confidential' by Pearson at the top of the first page. Shaw, apparently unaware at first that he was reading his obituary, altered the first line from 'The great career which has just come to a close' to '. . . which has just entered its ninth decade', scribbling above it in red ink a vexed note: 'Damn it, I'm not dead yet.'

716 *Shaw Gives Himself Away.* Privately printed at the Gregynog Press, Newtown, Montgomeryshire, August 1939. Frontispiece illustration by John Farleigh. One of 275 copies bound in black-green oasis morocco, decorated with inlaid design in orange leather. The binding was designed by Paul Nash. The contents consist of previously published autobiographical prefaces and articles, revised throughout by Shaw, with an added preface. This copy is a presentation to Sidney and Beatrice Webb, dated 16 December 1939.

717 *Scraps and Shavings of Autobiography.* Typewritten manuscript, revised, consisting of portions of Chapters 4 and 14; undated. 25 pp. WITH: 35 galley proofs (including the text of an autobiographic letter to Frank Harris, 5 June 1930, which was later deleted), undated; and first page proofs, datestamped 26 April 1948. The work was originally intended to be a slightly enlarged version of *Shaw Gives Himself Away* for popular consumption in Shaw's Standard Edition. Along the way the concept altered, and the revamped book, containing mostly new or extensively revised material, emerged as *Sixteen Self Sketches.*

718 *Sixteen Self Sketches* (1949). Frontispiece from a wood engraving by M. Pikov, with verses by Shaw on facing page. Contains a presentation inscription, dated 4 March 1949: 'Dear Hesketh Pearson | More Biography'.

719 Cinematograph Terms. 'Told me by Sidney Paxton.' Autograph memorandum, 25 May 1912. 1 p. Actors' salaries, Shaw notes, range from four shillings a day to two guineas. 'Films can be made with 3 days work or thereabouts. The actors improvise the dialogue. Profession getting overcrowded'.

720 *The Cinema as a Moral Leveller*. Typewritten manuscript, revised. 5 pp. A contribution to the *New Statesman* 'Special Supplement on the Modern Theatre', 27 June 1914. The cinema, Shaw proclaims, is an invention more significant than printing ever was, for it tells its story to the illiterate as much as to the literate, 'and it keeps its victim . . . not only awake but fascinated as if by a serpent's eye. And that is why the cinema is going to produce effects that all the cheap books in the world could never produce.' He calls for endowment of 'a cinema theatre devoted wholly to the castigation by ridicule of current morality.'

> Otherwise the next generation of Englishmen will no longer be English: they will represent a world-average of character and conduct, which means that they will have rather less virtue than is needed to run Lapland.

721 To Arthur W. Pinero. Autograph letter, 22 September 1915. Shaw reports that he has had an offer, from America, of £1000 each for film rights to *John Bull's Other Island* and *You Never Can Tell*.

> Is this a good offer or not? Patriotism calls for an energetic exploitation of America at the present rate of exchange.

722 Photograph of Shaw: blown up from a frame of the Movietone newsreel in which he made his talking picture début in June 1927.

723 From Mary Pickford. Cablegram, 6 February 1930. Having just made a talking picture of Shakespear's *The Taming of the Shrew* with her husband Douglas Fairbanks, Miss Pickford was now ready to take on *Cæsar and Cleopatra*. 'I could do it very well', she cabled, 'especially if you approved scenario. . . .' Shaw's drafted response ('Reply cheaply') on the cablegram reads: 'Temptress why a scenario? is the play not good enough? I am waiting until the talkies are through with scenarios and ready for me just as I am without one plea'.

*724 Large photograph of Shaw signing a contract for the filming of *How He Lied to Her Husband* (1930). Looking on is John Maxwell, chairman of British International Pictures. Both men's signatures are inscribed on the photograph.

725 *Bernard Shaw on his first talkie*. Typewritten manuscript, revised, for the Malvern Festival souvenir book, 1931. 3 pp. Shaw explains why he has refused to do business with Hollywood and has produced his film in London. His argument indicates that he does not agree with the axiom that one picture is worth a thousand words.

> My plays do not consist of occasional remarks to illustrate pictures, but of verbal fencing matches between protagonists and antagonists whose thrusts and ripostes, parries and parades, follow one another much more closely than thunder follows lightning. The first rule for their producers is that there must never be a moment of silence from the rise of the curtain to its fall. Hollywood would not hear of such a condition: it was, they said, impossible. To cut out half my dialogue, in order to insert dozens of changing pictures between the lines of what was left, seemed to them quite indispensable. So we parted. . . .

726 To Blanche Patch. Autograph letter, 29 March 1935, aboard the Llangibby Castle on a tour round Africa. Shaw instructs Miss Patch that Dr Paul Koretz is to inform Louis B. Mayer that he has never considered an outright sale of *Pygmalion* (his usual arrangement was for a five year licence in each language).

> . . . I should not pay any attention unless the bidding began at a million dollars. But I am negotiating with Universal Films for the English language rights in the scenario. . . .

727 To Blanche Patch. Autograph letter, 20 March 1936. At San Simeon in 1933, when the Shaws were overnight guests of William Randolph Hearst, Shaw had blarneyingly encouraged Marion Davies to believe that, in the event he authorized a film version of *Pygmalion*, she would be an ideal Eliza Doolittle. When the news was released in 1936 that Shaw had granted the screen rights to Gabriel Pascal, Miss Davies wrote to remind him of his promise. From the Gulf of Panama, aboard the Arandora Star, Shaw instructed Blanche Patch to forward the letter to Pascal, adding tactfully: 'Marion is by far the most attractive of the stars who are not really eighteen.' WITH: Photograph (by World Wide) of Shaw on his visit to the Metro-Goldwyn-Mayer studios in 1933, seated at lunch with Charles Chaplin, Marion Davies, Louis B. Mayer, Clark Gable, and George Hearst, son of the publisher.

728 Scenario for *Saint Joan*. Autograph manuscript (in pencil) of brief scenes and passages, interspersed with cross references, in red ink, to the text of the published play, dated 15 October 1934. 32 pp. The leaves, most of which are cracked or torn, have been repaired, mounted on board, and bound in blue morocco with gilt dentelles (by Birdsall of Northampton). Inserted at the front is the bookplate of Harold White,

whose Leagrave Press in 1950 published Shaw's last work, the *Rhyming Picture Guide to Ayot Saint Lawrence*.

729 From Gabriel Pascal. Typewritten letter, 18 June 1937, addressed to 'My dear master'. (Pascal's deferential use of this flattering salutation was soon emulated by Dr Loewenstein and other sycophants who surrounded Shaw in his last years.) Although Pascal had not yet completed negotiations for the release of *Pygmalion*, and not a foot of film had ground through the camera, he was pressuring Shaw to reserve film rights for him for *The Millionairess* or *Candida* and for *The Devil's Disciple*. He eventually produced only four Shaw plays (*Pygmalion, Major Barbara, Cæsar and Cleopatra*, and *Androcles and the Lion*) on the screen before his death in 1954, although he had held widely-publicized options on a number of others.

*730 Large photograph of Shaw and Gabriel Pascal (ca. 1939), inscribed by Shaw at lower left: 'THE OLD IDIOT & HIS KEEPER Excellent portrait of the keeper. G. Bernard Shaw O.I.' Presentation inscription at lower right by Pascal to Roy Limbert, 9 August 1939.

731 *Pygmalion: A Scenario*. Typewritten manuscript, with minor revisions. 141 pp. Presentation inscription on the title page, dated 1 March 1938: 'to Floryan Sobieniowski for translation into Polish.' Above this is a typewritten warning.

> *NOTE*: This scenario is not technically complete; but it indicates exactly what the producer has to work on in the studio, with all the omissions from and additions to the text of the original play. These are so extensive that the printed play should be carefully kept out of the studio, as it can only confuse and mislead the producer and the performers.

*732 Large poster for the Gabriel Pascal film version of *Pygmalion* (1938). WITH: Four theatre lobby display cards for the film.

733 Revisions for a 'film version' of *Pygmalion* by Penguin Books, 1941. Typewritten and autograph revisions pasted into a 1939 acting edition of the play, with revisions, corrections, and instructions to the printer, to whom it was sent on 5 November 1939. There are 17 inserted pages and innumerable slips.

Inserted at the front is an autograph postcard to the printer William Maxwell, 9 November 1939: 'I have sent a fearful job to Brandon St: a new edition of Pygmalion with several screen scenes interpolated. It will keep the comp[ositor]s busy for part of the duration. . . . The occasion of it is a proposal to Penguinize Pyg.' As Shaw's postcard indicates, this was not to be a publication of the film's complete screenplay, but a reprint of the play, illustrated by Feliks Topolski, with 'some screen stuff' thrown in.

734 Reconciliation statement between Shaw and Pascal Film Productions, Ltd., on *Pygmalion* film grosses and royalties, 16 December 1939. The statement shews that Shaw had earned royalties of over $200,000 (£41,592) during the first twelve months the film was in release. At the foot is a memorandum by Shaw: 'The understanding arrived at on the 14 Dec. . . . in conversation with Pascal and Davenport is that they may use this money [an outstanding Pascal liability to Shaw of £12,774] plus £12000 of their own until they begin "shooting" Major Barbara in January, when they will receive £60,000 from G.F.D. [General Film Distributors], out of which I can be repaid.'

735 From H.G. Wells. Autograph letter, 16 April 1941. He has just seen the 'delightful' film version of *Major Barbara* and assures Shaw he has given the play 'fresh definition'.

> The house was packed . . . and you could not have had a more responsive audience. They laughed at all the right places. Mostly young people in uniform they were. . . . I firmly believe that we are getting the young. We shall rise again sooner than Marx did and for a better reason.

WITH: Photograph of Robert Newton as Bill Walker, Wendy Hiller as Barbara, Robert Morley as Andrew Undershaft, Rex Harrison as Cusins, and Emlyn Williams as Snobby Price, in the Salvation Army shelter in West Ham.

736 From Gilbert Murray. Typewritten letter, initialled, 26 July 1941. (Shaw has drafted a shorthand reply on the reverse side.) Murray and Lady Mary, his wife, were 'completely bowled over' by the main part of the *Major Barbara* film, though they had serious reservations about its ending. He was 'moved and thrilled', he indicates, up to the tragic scene on the wharf, lit up by the Bodgers' Whiskey sign, when Barbara casts her bonnet into the water.

737 To Gabriel Pascal. Autograph letter, 15 March 1944, and autograph replies to Pascal's questions, on a postcard, 4 May 1944. Pascal had begun work on his third Shaw film, *Cæsar and Cleopatra*. It took more than two years to complete, costing over six and a half million dollars. In war-ravaged, austerity-conscious Britain Pascal's extravagances and delays were deemed so outrageous that, in 1946, he was 'severely censured' by the Association of Cine Technicians, which effectually barred him from further film production in England.

As usual, Shaw mingled a floodtide of cautions and queries with his pontifications.

> Has Cæsar got the smile? . . . It is extremely important that Cleopatra's charm shall be that of a beautiful child, *not of sex*. The whole play would be disgusting if Cæsar were an old man seducing a child.

> [On the pronunciation of Cleopatra] The Italian long 'ah' of course. To call her Cleopaytra would stamp the film as American. In America they call a tomato a tomayter.

738 *Cæsar and Cleopatra* shooting script (ca. 1945). Although Shaw received sole credit for the screenplay, much of it was written or revised by Pascal and his scriptwriter Marjorie Deans. WITH: Photograph (by Wilfred Newton) of Stewart Granger as Apollodorus, Vivien Leigh as Cleopatra, Basil Sydney as Rufio, and Claude Rains as Cæsar.

LATE YEARS

739 To the Permanent Secretary of the Royal Swedish Academy. Shorthand draft of a letter, 18 November 1926, delivered through the Swedish Minister in London, Baron Palmstierna. WITH: Photostat of the letter in the archive of the Swedish Academy. Shaw expresses his pleasure at having won the 1925 Nobel Prize for Literature, but requests that the money ('a lifebelt thrown to a swimmer who has already reached the shore in safety') be used for the translation into English of Swedish books 'of which we in Britain are deplorably ignorant.' The funds were applied to the creation of the Anglo-Swedish Foundation, whose second annual report (1929) is displayed.

*740 Edward Elgar, '*The Severn Suite*' *for Brass Band*, Op. 87 (1930). Printed above the title is the

dedication 'To my friend G. Bernard Shaw.' To the left of the title Elgar has inserted the inscription: 'To dear G.B.S. (& Charlotte) from their affectionate Edward Elgar 24th Feb. 1930'. Bound in orange-brown limp morocco by Bumpus. This was another of the volumes Shaw inscribed in 1949 and sent to Sotheby's for auction. Despite Shaw's two flyleaf pages of autograph reminiscences, it brought only £28.

741   Photographs of Shaw on his travels:

(a)   At Nice, 1928. Inscribed 'to Frank Harris from G. Bernard Shaw' on the reverse.

(b)   At the Parthenon, Greece, 1932, on the Empress of Britain world cruise.

(c)   With Gov. Theodore Roosevelt in Manila, 1933, on the same cruise.

742   *'G.B.S.' in the air.* Press cutting from the *Cape Times*, South Africa, 25 January 1932, reporting that the Shaws had flown in a Union Airways mail service Junker monoplane over the Cape peninsula. Although it was Charlotte's initial flight, Shaw had taken his first plane ride as far back as 1916, in a Grahame-White two-seater biplane, from the Hendon Aerodrome in London. WITH: Photograph of Shaw standing before the biplane, and Passenger Flight Certificate of 20 May 1916, signed by Bernard F. Hale, Pilot-Aviator. The man who actually piloted Shaw's flight, however, was H.C. Biard, who recalled in his book *Wings* (1934):

> I took him up to about a thousand feet, circled over the flying-ground, did a few minor stunts, opened the throttle full out to show him a turn of speed, and came down again. He stood the display without turning a hair. He seemed chiefly interested in the fact that, when one is flying upside-down in the loop, there is no particular sensation of invertedness. Mr. Shaw commented on this as he climbed out of his seat. 'The world is like that, young man!' he remarked gravely.

743 To Emery Walker. Autograph letter, 25 January 1932, from Cape Town. Shaw reports on social conditions in South Africa.

> This place is full of sunshine, long days, and darkies to do all the work. The gardens and old Dutch Peter de Hooghe interiors are enchanting; but the social problems—poor whites competing for unskilled labor jobs with a black proletariat which can live on next to nothing, with no pensions nor unemployment insurance, and race war between Dutch and English—are insoluble. . . .

744 *What I said in N.Z.* (1934). A compilation of Shaw's newspaper utterances and reports of his lecture talks during his visit to New Zealand, 15 March–14 April 1934.

745 To Blanche Patch. Autograph letter, 16 May 1934, written aboard R.M.S. Rangitane approaching Plymouth on its return from New Zealand. Shaw, who as usual has been busily at work on the journey, encloses shorthand drafts of the last portion of a play *The Simpleton*, 'the final title of which will probably be The Unexpected Isles or something like that', a second play in three acts *The Millionairess*, and the complete draft of 'a scene' called *The Burgesses of Calais* (later retitled *The Six of Calais*). Work was the only way Shaw could survive the boredom of the several long ocean journeys (two of them completely round the world) that Charlotte insisted on his taking with her between 1932 and 1936.

746 Photographs of Shaw at Ayot St Lawrence:

(a) At his desk, 1937 (by Studio Lisa).

(b) At the Bechstein piano, 1932 (by Alfred Eisenstaedt).

(c) At the gate of Shaw's Corner, 1948 (by Mirror Features). On the reverse is a presentation inscription, dated 25 October 1949, to the Rev. E.H.I. Campbell.

(d) In the garden with his housekeeper's ginger cat Bunch, ca. 1948–50 (from a color transparency by Felix H. Man).

747 Standing in the doorway of his workshop (photograph by Studio Lisa, 1937). This curious edifice, variously known as the 'shelter' and the 'hut', built out in the garden a distance from the house, was originally intended for Charlotte's use, but was soon appropriated by G.B.S. It revolved on a pivot to catch the sun at all hours of the day. In cold weather Shaw donned fingerless gloves for typing. The pair on display, much worn (and scorched from having been carelessly deposited atop a heater), were sent to his secretary Blanche Patch on 8 September 1947 with an appeal: 'Repair Urgent'. Miss Patch knitted him a new pair instead. (See also L38–39.)

748 *Everybody's Political What's What?* (1944). This was Shaw's last major work, the final distillation of sixty years of political experience. It was, however, the work of an aged man, whose memory frequently lapsed or played tricks with him. And as he forwarded each chapter to be typeset as soon as it was written, all through 1942 and into 1943, the result was a text crammed with repetitions, divagations, and errors. Fortunately for Shaw the book was taken in hand by a young Scottish disciple, John Wardrop, who patiently and diligently combed through the galleys for several months. The page proofs, datestamped 1 June to 8 December 1943, were corrected and revised by Shaw, again with Wardrop's invaluable assistance. Two trial title pages contain a subtitle 'Machiavelli Modernized' which was discarded before publication.

749 Review of Field-Marshal Viscount Montgomery's published lecture *Military Leadership*. Galley proof, with a few revisions. Published in *Reynolds News*, 19 May 1946 ('We asked Bernard Shaw, the world's most biting commentator on soldiers and politicians, to write this review').

> Lord Montgomery . . . goes so far as to declare that the idolatry of the glory merchant is mostly sheer illusion. As a matter of fact ambitious conquerors do not last as long as fundamentally pacifist ones, who with thrones within their

reach, throw away the sword and end as political duffers and constitutional reactionaries.

750 *A Catalogue of an Exhibition celebrating the Ninetieth Birthday of Bernard Shaw*. National Book League, London, 1946. WITH: Season ticket to the exhibition. Shaw's ninetieth birthday on 26 July 1946 drew unprecedented attention in the world press, which filled its columns with editorials, middle articles, photographs, and bogus interviews concocted by reporters who had descended in swarms upon Ayot and quizzed all the locals. The post brought a deluge of letters and telegrams containing birthday messages—hundreds a day until well into August—most of which were opened and destroyed at Shaw's request ('F.E.L. Throw away all the birthday ones. They make me sick.') by Dr Loewenstein and Shaw's neighbor Stephen Winsten. Cakes arrived from Canada and Australia, grain cereals and molasses from American vegetarian wellwishers, and sweets from neighboring schoolgirls. The B.B.C. transported a camera crew to Shaw's Corner to record for television Shaw's 'final message' to the world. One of the few events on his birthday which genuinely delighted him was the receipt of a golden shamrock sent by a Dublin dustman on behalf of the Bernard Shaw branch of the Irish Labour Party, which he instantly attached to his watch chain and wore until his death. Most of the attention, however, appalled him, and he defensively composed a message for yet another form postcard, one printed so hastily that his surname was omitted. Shaw resorted to this message card for the four birthdays remaining to him. One was posted to L.J. Johnston, 21 June 1950, acknowledging a portrait drawing that Johnston had sent to him. The printed text read:

Mr. Bernard implores his friends and readers not to celebrate his birthdays nor even to mention them to him. It is easy to write one letter or send one birthday cake; but the arrival of hundreds of them together is a calamity that is not the less dreaded because it occurs only once a year.

F.E.L.
Throw away all the birthday ones.
They make me sick.

751 To Winston Churchill, former Prime Minister of Great Britain. Shorthand draft (ca. August 1946), acknowledging Churchill's 'friendly birthday message' (a telegram) on his ninetieth birthday, which had especially pleased him 'as the only other message I had from anyone of your political eminence was from Eamon de Valera!'

No man of action has any chance of being British Prime Minister until a war frightens the electorate out of its chronic dread of Government interference and preference for guaranteed fanéants like Ramsay [MacDonald] and [Stanley] Baldwin and their like. But the worst of military glory is that the electorate, understanding only the glory and the fear of defeat, forces their leader either to keep feeding them with it and go from Austerlitz to Moscow, Leipsic, Waterloo and St. Helena, or, like the first Churchill and Wellington, chuck soldiering and become political nobodies like Lloyd George. The alternative is to keep the electorate excited about programmes so popular that the Blimps and reactionaries in general cannot withstand them. In short, Disraeli's invention and your father's creed: Tory Democracy. . . .

752 *Fabian Essays in Socialism: Jubilee Edition* (1948). This was the fifth edition of the work, first edited by Shaw in 1889. It contained a new preface by Shaw, 'Sixty Years After'. Page proofs, corrected and revised, April 1947, on lightweight porous paper, with an autograph note on the halftitle: 'The revise must be on proper paper. This proof is a disgrace to the printer and an insult to me. The corrections shew through it.'

753 Membership application for the British Interplanetary Society (1947), completed by Shaw, who became its oldest member. For personal reference he listed the space enthusiast and science fiction writer Arthur C. Clarke. To the request for category of membership, the 93 year old Shaw replied 'Life'.

SHAW SOCIETIES

754 To Dr F.E. Loewenstein. Autograph letter, 14 November 1941. Loewenstein, a Jewish refugee from Germany then resident in London, who had been compiling a Shaw bibliography since 1936, sought permission to found a Shaw Society. Shaw recalls that the Browning Society was 'a terror to Browning.' Literary societies, however, have their use by providing 'a rallying point for the co-operation and education of kindred spirits and a forum for their irreconcilable controversies.' Loewenstein has permission to proceed with his Society—'but dont bother me about it.'

The HRC possesses 80 pieces of Shaw correspondence (1936–50) to Loewenstein, plus several dozen undated notes and memoranda. There also are a number of Loewenstein's manuscripts corrected and revised by Shaw.

755 Printed postcard message to correspondents, referring them to the 'Founder of the Shaw Society', Dr F.E. Loewenstein, 'who is better informed on many points than Mr. Shaw himself'.

756 Cuttings of Shaw's beard (10 October 1945) and hair (16 February 1950). Loewenstein wrote to Shaw on 24 July 1944, in a letter signed 'Delilah', to ask for a lock of hair for 'the Shaw Museum.' 'You idiot', Shaw scrawled across it in a note of disgust, 'my hair is white, like any other old man's hair. Cut a wisp off the nearest white dog: it will do just as well.' (Parke-Bernet auction catalogue, 24 March 1970: reproduced in facsimile on the cover.) Loewenstein stubbornly awaited his opportunity to acquire the coveted relics on later occasions.

757 The Shaw Society (London) published fifty numbers of the *Shaw Society Bulletin* (which commenced as a wartime newsletter in November 1943); in December 1953 this was expanded into the *Shavian,* published at intervals ever since. It flourished under its principal editor Eric J. Batson, and under his successors Barbara Smoker and T.F. Evans, but now appears only sporadically in a typewriter-offset format. The Society itself is virtually moribund at present.

758 *The Shavian,* No. 1 (Spring 1946). Published by the Shaw Society of Ireland. Joint editors: F.E. Loewenstein (London) and Felix Grendon (Dublin). This was the only publication of the Society, which ceased operation after Grendon came to America.

759 Shaw Society Tract No. 1. H.C. Duffin, *Creative Evolution* (1950). Revised by Shaw. Shavian Tract No. 2. Irving Fiske, *Bernard Shaw's Debt to Blake*

(1951). Foreword and Notes by G.B.S. A total of six tracts were issued, the most recent in 1958. The last four were reprints of inaccessible Shaviana.

760 *The Shaw Bulletin,* No. 2 (Autumn 1951). Published by the Shaw Society of America, founded in 1950. It later became *The Shaw Review* under the able and resourceful direction of its longtime editor Stanley Weintraub. The Society disbanded in 1965, at which time the journal was taken over by the Pennsylvania State University Press, which had been co-publisher for several years. The journal remains, as ever, indispensable to scholars.

761 *The Independent Shavian,* Vol. XIV, No. 3 (Spring 1976). This is the publication of the New York Shavians, first organized in 1952 as the New York Regional Group of the Shaw Society, London, by the indefatigable Vera Scriabine, who has been its dynamo for a quarter of a century. The publication began as the *Regional* in March 1957; its title was changed in 1962 when the group seceded from London and incorporated as an independent society. This very readable journal complements the more scholarly *Shaw Review* with reprints of buried Shavian treasure and reports of worldwide activities pertaining to Shaw.

762 *The California Shavian*, Vol. III, No. 5 (September–October 1962). The Shaw Society of California was founded in 1956, supported enthusiastically by Eddy D. Feldman, who was editor of the journal from its inception in 1960 until its most recent issue in 1966. The Society still exists, but is generally inactive.

763 *Bernard Shaw Day in Chicago*. Souvenir of a centenary celebration in Chicago on 26 July 1956, the date marking the formation of the Shaw Society of Chicago. The sponsors announced that Shaw, who never visited the city, had once proclaimed that Chicago was 'America with the lid off' (the source for the statement being Hesketh Pearson). Under energetic leadership, headed by Lois Solomon and abetted by Elmer Gertz, the Society issued a *Newsletter* for several years, and sponsored and participated in many significant Shavian activities. It still functions, but no longer publishes.

764 *GBS*, Nos. 1–5 (1972–76). The annual bulletin of the Shaw Society of Japan, founded in 1971 by Professor Matahiko Ichikawa, scholar and translator, who, emulating Shaw, is still active in his nineties. The Society meets twice yearly.

Other Shaw societies include the Shaw Society of India, founded in 1950 in Vijayawada, whose president is the scholar and translator P. Sundaro Rao, and the Shaw Society of Canada, established in Toronto in 1974 by K.H. Reid (there was a shortlived predecessor in 1946 founded by a Canadian bookseller Lee Pritzker). Canada has also had, since 1962, an annual Shaw Festival at Niagara-on-the-Lake, for which a magnificent new theatre was built in 1973, with Queen Elizabeth II and Prince Philip participating in the opening ceremonies at a performance, appropriately, of *You Never Can Tell*.

No.......................

The British Interplanetary Society

(LIMITED BY GUARANTEE)

Registered Offices :—
ALBEMARLE HOUSE, 1, ALBEMARLE STREET, PICCADILLY, LONDON, W.1

APPLICATION FOR ADMISSION TO MEMBERSHIP

Surname SHAW   Christian Names *George Bernard*
(IN BLOCK LETTERS)

Permanent Address *Ayot Saint Lawrence, Welwyn, Herts.*

Date of Birth *26th July 1856* Nationality *Irish British subject.*

Degrees and Certificates held *None of an academic character.*

Names of other Societies with which you are connected :

NAME........................   MEMBERSHIP GRADE *Life*

„ *Royal Astronomical*   „ „

„   „ „

Present Occupation *Author & Playwright.*

Name and Address of Employers........................
(OPTIONAL)

Personal References :

1. Name and Address *Arthur C. Clarke Esq.*
   157 Friary Road, London S.E. 15

2. Name and Address........................

(THE NAMES OF TWO PERSONS WHO HAVE KNOWN YOU FOR SOME TIME SHOULD BE GIVEN,
UNLESS THE APPLICATION IS PROPOSED BY A MEMBER OF THE SOCIETY.)

[P.T.O.

746c

THE END

765 Death Mask of Shaw. Plaster cast, from the original mould by Charles Smith, prepared by the staff of the British Museum. At the instigation of Lady Astor, and after consultation with the noted artist Sir Gerald Kelly, the Public Trustee as Shaw's executor quietly arranged for a death mask to be made on 3 November 1950. In deference, however, to the feelings of Shaw's surviving relatives and friends, he declined to permit the mask to be displayed. In 1976 the representatives of the Shaw Estate generously arranged to have a plaster cast made from the original mould, to be presented as a gift to the Humanities Research Center in recognition of the assistance given by the Center to Shavian scholarship. The mask is here exhibited publicly for the first time.

Also displayed is a selection of newspaper obituaries of Shaw as published, in innumerable languages, in November 1950.

Art Works

Displayed in the Leeds Gallery are the following paintings, drawings, sculptures, and photographs not recorded elsewhere in the exhibit catalog.

L 1. Jacob Epstein: Shaw. Bronze, height 17½″. Signed 'Epstein.' Undated (1934).

L 2. Feliks Topolski: Shaw. Oil on canvas, 84″ by 41″. Signed and dated 'Feliks Topolski | 43.'

L 3. Erich Kahn: Shaw. Oil on canvas, 17½″ by 13½″. Signed 'E K'. Undated (1948).

L 4. Ivan Opffer: Shaw. Conté crayon and wash, 13¾″ by 12″. Signed 'Ivan Opffer Whitehall Ct 1927.'

L 5. Frederick H. Evans: Photograph of Shaw, 8¾″ by 5⅝″. Signed and dated 'by Frederick H. Evans 1900'. Affixed to multiple mounts, creating a series of borders, with the photographer's blindstamped monogram at the foot of each mount.

L 6. Frederick H. Evans: Photograph of Shaw, 9⅛″ by 6¾″. Signed and dated 'Frederick H. Evans. 1901.'

L 7. Frederick H. Evans: Photograph of Shaw in full-length view, 9⅜″ by 4⅜″. Signed and dated 'by Frederick H. Evans | 1902'.

L 8. George Bernard Shaw: Four photographic self-portraits. Overall: 9⅜″ by 22½″. Inscribed by Evans 'George Bernard Shaw taken by himself: printed in platinotype by Frederick H. Evans | (circa 1903)'.

L 9. George Bernard Shaw: Photographic self-portrait, 7⅝″ by 6⅜″. On reverse: lengthy inscription to Olga James, signed and dated 'G. Bernard Shaw | 17 January 1905.'

L 10. Official Press Bureau: Photograph of Shaw, 8¼″ by 6″. Undated.

L 11. Harley Granville Barker: Photograph of Shaw sunbathing near Studland Bay, Dorset, 13″ by 10″. Dated '1901'.

L 12. Lena Connell: Photograph of Shaw, 7½″ by 5¾″. Inscribed 'to Hugo Vallentin from G. Bernard Shaw. | 20th April 1911.'

L 13. Jacob Epstein: Shaw. Bronze, height 25″. Signed 'Epstein'. Undated (1934).

L 14. William Rothenstein: Shaw. Charcoal, 11¾″ by 8½″. Signed and dated 'Rothenstein 97'.

L 15. Attributed to William Rothenstein: Shaw. Oil on canvas, mounted on panel, 17¾″ by 13½″. Unsigned and undated.

L 16. William Rothenstein: Shaw. Sanguine crayon, 11″ by 8¾″. Signed and dated 'W.R. | 1928'. Inscribed 'I dedicate myself to Lillah [McCarthy], who has bought me from Rothenstein | G. Bernard Shaw | 12th Dec. 1929.'

L 17. Feliks Topolski: Shaw. Sketch in sepia ink, 19″ by 12½″, for the Watergate Theatre program of *Far-fetched Fables* (see No. 512). Signed 'FT.' Undated (1950).

L 18. Bernard Partridge: 'Ahenobarbus | at Rehearsal.' | 'Geo. Bernard Shaw 1894'. Charcoal pencil, ink, and watercolor wash, 17½″ by 11¾″. Signed with the artist's initials in a palette design. The drawing depicts Shaw directing a rehearsal of *Arms and the Man* (April 1894), in which the artist performed under the stage name of Bernard Gould.

L 19. Percy Home: Four pencil and watercolor sketches drawn during an early performance of the London production of *Saint Joan*, designed by Charles Ricketts; each 15″ by 10½″. Unsigned and undated (March 1924).

L 20. Walter Tittle: Shaw. Oil on canvas, 24¼″ by 20¼″. Signed and dated 'Walter Tittle | London, 1924'.

L 21. Jo Davidson: Shaw. Bronze, height 18″. Signed 'Jo Davidson.' Undated (1929).

L 22. George Frederick Watts: Ellen Terry portrait, captioned 'Watchman, what of the night?'. Oil on canvas, 25¾″ by 20¾″. Signed and dated 'G.F. Watts | 1880.'

L 23. Walter Tittle: Shaw. Etching, 11¾″ by 6⅞″. Signed 'Walter Tittle'. Undated.

L 24. Edmund J. Sullivan: Shaw. Etching, 9¾″ by 7⅞″. Signed 'Edmund J. Sullivan'. Dated '1929'.

L 25. Yousuf Karsh: Photographic study of Shaw (reproduction), 13½″ by 9″. Undated (1939).

L 26. John Farleigh: Design for dustwrapper of *The Adventures of the Black Girl in Her Search for God*. Wood engraving: proof, second of nine pulls, 8¾″ by 11¾″. Signed and dated 'John Farleigh 1932'.

L 27. John Farleigh: Design for endpapers of *The Adventures of the Black Girl in Her Search for God*. Wood engraving: proof, second of nine pulls, 8¼″ by 5½″. Signed and dated 'John Farleigh 1932'.

L 28. British Information Services: Set of eight photographs of Shaw issued by the Central Office of Information following his death in November 1950. Each 12″ by 15″.

L 29. Feliks Topolski: Shaw. Sketch in sepia ink, 11″ by 7½″, designed as a frontispiece for *In Good King Charles's Golden Days*. Unsigned and undated (1939).

L 30. Feliks Topolski: 'Portrait of Shaw with Cane and Hat'. Ink and wash, 11¾″ by 8⅛″. Signed 'Feliks Topolski'. Undated (ca. 1938–39).

L 31. Tom Hutt: Shaw. Charcoal, ink and chalk, 12¼″ by 7″. Signed and dated 'Tom | Hutt | 1912'. Inscribed 'Am I like that? | Great heavens! | G. Bernard Shaw | 21st March 1912.' | 'These are patent leather shoes. | I never wore a pair in my life.'

L 32. Ernest Marriott: Shaw. Pen and ink, 8″ by 5½″. Signed 'Ernest | Marriott'. Undated (1890).

L 33. Miguel Covarrubias: 'G.B. Shaw | the Omnipotent'. Pen and ink, 9¾″ by 7¾″. Signed 'Covarrubias'. Undated.

L 34. Claud Lovat Fraser: 'G.B.S. | St. James's Theatre. | 10.xii '13'. Lithograph, 11¾″ by 8″. Signed 'Lovat Fraser.' Printed in 1930. The occasion was a performance of John Masefield's *The Witch* in the Barker-McCarthy season at the St James's.

L 35. Francis Carruthers Gould: 'Bernardo de Shaw'. Watercolor, 6⅛″ by 4⅝″. Signed 'F C G'. Undated. An illustration of Shaw as a Canterbury pilgrim for *Froissart's Modern Chronicles, 1903–06* (1908).

L 36. Eric H. Kennington: Col. T.E. Lawrence. Bronze, height 16″. Signed 'T.E.L.–E.H.K. I.'. Undated (1926).

L 37. Sir John Lavery: Shaw. Oil on canvas, 19⅜″ by 15½″. Signed 'J. Lavery'. Undated (1925).

L 38. Clare Winsten: Shaw in the Shelter. Oil on canvas, 20″ by 12″. Unsigned and undated (ca. 1945).

L 39. George Bernard Shaw: The Shelter. Watercolor, 12″ by 9⅜″. Unsigned and undated (ca. 1945).

L 40. George Bernard Shaw: Design for a water tower, planned for Ayot St Lawrence. Watercolor and collage, 10⅞″ by 8¼″. Unsigned and undated (1948). Stephen Winsten, in *Shaw's Corner* (1952): 'He designed a water tower by sticking coloured paper to a cardboard base, more like a Moorish temple. There he sat on his couch by the window, panama on head to protect him from the sun, cutting his strips of paper and enjoying it like a child.'

L 41. Clare Winsten: Shaw. Sketch in brown pastel crayon, 12″ by 9¾″. Signed 'C Winsten'. Undated (ca. 1948–49).

L 42. Feliks Topolski: Shaw, rear view. Charcoal, 14½″ by 9″. Signed 'Feliks Topolski 43'.

L 43. Clare Winsten: Shaw. Bronze, height 17″. Signed and dated 'Winsten 1946 | 1/6'.

Shaw was unquestionably the most extensively limned personage of the twentieth century, as hundreds of paintings, sculptures, drawings, and cartoons will attest. Moreover, the photogenic, ubiquitous G.B.S. cooperatively posed for tens of thousands of camera studies and snapshots by photographers on every continent in the world. A generous sampling of these photographs, spanning three-quarters of a century, is displayed in montage in the Josey Room.

Acknowledgments

The Shaw materials in this exhibit are drawn primarily from the T.E. Hanley Collection, the Hoblitzelle Theatre Arts Collection, the Gernsheim Photographic Collection, and the Iconography Collection, all within the Humanities Research Center, The University of Texas at Austin. Significant items are represented from the libraries of such noted bibliophiles as Sir Sydney Cockerell, Robert Downing, Robert Hoe, Louis H. Silver, Sir Emery Walker, and Gabriel Wells.

I am most grateful to the Shaw Estate and the Society of Authors for permission to quote from Shaw's published and unpublished writings, and to reproduce a number of his manuscripts and drawings photographically. For permission to reproduce copyrighted materials I am also indebted to Dr Claudius Beatty, John Houseman, Eva Reichmann, the late Col. William S. Sharpe, the British Library of Political and Economic Science, and the trustees of the estates of Hilaire Belloc, Florence Farr, John Galsworthy, Harley Granville Barker, H.L. Mencken, Gilbert Murray, Charles Ricketts, William Rothenstein, Charlotte F. Shaw, Ellen Terry, Sir Herbert Beerbohm Tree, and H.G. Wells. In the preparation of the catalog I have received valuable assistance from Sir Rupert Hart-Davis (as always), Professor Masahiko Masumoto, Paul Myers, and Barbara Smoker.

Although Lois B. Garcia and I receive nominal credit for the preparation of the Shaw exhibit and the compilation of its catalog, every major exhibit sponsored by the Humanities Research Center is in reality a collaboration encompassing all departments. During the twelve months that I labored on the project I encountered a spirit and degree of cooperation I have never before experienced anywhere, ranging from the Director, Dr Warren Roberts, down to part-time secretaries and stack assistants. To all of the staff, but especially to the following, I tender my warm thanks: James E. Bagg, Robert Bass, Hiram Butler, Charlotte Carl-Mitchell, Dortha Collins, Joe Coltharp, Jane Combs, Dr W.H. Crain, Ellen Dunlap, Dr David Farmer, Roy Flukinger, Kathleen Gee, William R. Holman, John Kirkpatrick, Sally Leach, May Ellen MacNamara, and Betsy Williams.

And a special salute—an *enormous* one—to Lois B. Garcia, most exemplary of collaborators, whose friendship alone has been worth all the effort of this undertaking.

D.H.L.

Selective Index

The index is keyed to the display numbers in the exhibit. Square brackets signify that the reference appears in the sectional introduction immediately preceding the bracketed display number.

"The Spellbinder in a
Characteristic Pose"
by J.H. Dowd.

A Note on the Author

Dan H. Laurence's career has included work as a professional actor, director, college professor, writer, lecturer, and bibliographer. He has been awarded a Guggenheim Memorial Fellowship on three occasions and has edited Bernard Shaw's collected letters, collected plays, and uncollected writings. He has just completed a comprehensive two-volume bibliography of Shaw which has occupied him for more than twenty years.

COLOPHON

This catalog has been set in Linotype
Caledonia with the headings set in Palatino.
The calligraphy was done by Robert Boyajian.
Typography by William R. Holman.